Introductory Calculus

Taken from:

Technical Calculus, Fifth Edition
by Dale Ewen, Joan S. Gary, and James E. Trefzger

Taken from:

Technical Calculus, Fifth Edition
by Dale Ewen, Joan S. Gary, and James E. Trefzger
Copyright © 2005, 2002, 1998, 1986, 1977 by Pearson Education, Inc.
Published by Prentice Hall
Upper Saddle River, New Jersey 07458

This special edition published in cooperation with Pearson Custom Publishing.

Printed in the United States of America

10 9 8 7

ISBN 0-536-91233-5

2005360046

AG

Please visit our web site at *www.pearsoncustom.com*

PEARSON CUSTOM PUBLISHING
75 Arlington Street, Suite 300, Boston, MA 02116
A Pearson Education Company

Contents

4 Derivatives of Transcendental Functions   181

5 The Integral   237

6 Applications of Integration   261

1

Analytic Geometry

INTRODUCTION

Analytic geometry is the study of the relationships between algebra and geometry. We will study equations with a dependent and an independent variable and sketch a corresponding figure in two dimensions. We begin with linear equations (straight lines) and then study the conic sections, that is, parabolas, circles, ellipses, and hyperbolas. These curves occur often in nature and play an important role in applied mathematics.

For example, the existence of the focus of a parabola is what makes flashlights, microphones, and satellite dishes work. Planets orbit the sun in elliptical paths, and circular wheels and gears help to keep us mobile. Analytic geometry, which we use to study these curves, evolved from the work of René Descartes, a French mathematician in the seventeenth century.

Objectives

- Determine if a relation is a function.
- Use functional notation.
- Graph equations.
- Find the slope of a line.
- Write the equation of a line given defining properties.
- Determine if lines are parallel, perpendicular, or neither.
- Use the distance formula.
- Use the midpoint formula.
- Graph circles, ellipses, parabolas, and hyperbolas.
- Find the center and radius of a circle.
- Find the vertex, directrix, and focus of a parabola.
- Find the vertices, foci, and lengths of the major and minor axes of an ellipse.
- Find the vertices, foci, and lengths of the transverse and conjugate axes of a hyperbola.
- Use translation of axes in sketching graphs and identifying key features.
- Solve systems of quadratic equations.
- Graph using polar coordinates.
- Convert between polar and rectangular coordinates.

1

The **positive integers** are the counting numbers; that is, 1, 2, 3, ... Note that the positive integers form an infinite set. The **negative integers** may be defined as the set of opposites of the positive integers; that is, $-1, -2, -3, \ldots$. **Zero** is the dividing point between the positive integers and the negative integers and is neither positive nor negative. The set of **integers** consists of the positive integers, the negative integers, and zero. The set may be represented on a number line as in Fig. 1.1.

Figure 1.1   Number line.

The **rational numbers** are those numbers that can be represented as the ratio of two integers, such as $\dfrac{3}{4}, \dfrac{-7}{5}$, and $\dfrac{5}{1}$. The **irrational numbers** are those numbers that cannot be represented as the ratio of two integers, such as $\sqrt{3}, \sqrt[3]{16}$, and π.

The set of **real numbers** is the set consisting of the rational numbers and the irrational numbers. With respect to the number line, we say there is a one-to-one correspondence between the real numbers and the points on the number line; that is, for each real number there is a corresponding point on the number line, and for each point on the number line there is a corresponding real number. As a result, we say the number line is dense, or "filled."

Inequalities are statements involving less than or greater than and may be used to describe various intervals on the number line, as follows:

Type of interval	Symbols	Meaning	Number line graph
Open	$x > a$	x is greater than a	
	$x < b$	x is less than b	
	$a < x < b$	x is between a and b	
Half-open	$x \geq a$	x is greater than or equal to a	
	$x \leq b$	x is less than or equal to b	
	$a < x \leq b$	x is between a and b, including b but excluding a	
	$a \leq x < b$	x is between a and b, including a but excluding b	
Closed	$a \leq x \leq b$	x is between a and b, including both a and b	

Analytic geometry is the study of the relationships between algebra and geometry. The concepts of analytic geometry provide us with ways of algebraically analyzing a geometrical problem. Likewise, with these concepts we can often solve an algebraic problem by viewing it geometrically. We will develop several basic relations between equations and their graphs.

In common usage, a relation means that two or more things have something in common. We say that a brother and a sister are related because they have the same parents or that a person's career potential is related to his or her education and work experience. In mathematics a **relation** is defined as a set of ordered pairs of numbers in the form (x, y). Sometimes an equation, a rule, a data chart, or some other type of description is given that states the relationship between x and y. In an ordered pair the first element or variable, called the **independent variable,** may be represented by any letter, but x is normally used. The second element or variable is normally represented by the letter y and is called the **dependent variable** because its value depends on the particular choice of the independent variable.

All of the numbers that can be used as the first element of an ordered pair or as replacements for the independent variable of a given relation form a set of numbers called the **domain.** The domain is often referred to as the set of all x's. We can think of these x-values as "inputs." The **range** of a relation is the set of numbers that can be used as the second element of an ordered pair or as replacements for the dependent variable. The range is often referred to as the set of all y's. We can think of these y-values as "outputs."

EXAMPLE 1

Given the relation described in ordered pair form $A = \{(1, 2), (3, 5), (7, 9), (6, 3)\}$, find its domain and its range.

The domain is the set of first elements: $\{1, 3, 6, 7\}$. The range is the set of second elements: $\{2, 3, 5, 9\}$.

Note: Braces $\{\ \}$ are normally used to group elements of sets.

EXAMPLE 2

Given the relation in equation form $y = x^2$, find its domain and its range.

The domain is the set of possible replacements for the independent variable x. Note that there are no restrictions on the numbers that you may substitute for x. That is, we may replace x by any real number. We say that the domain is the set of real numbers.

After each replacement of x, there is no possible way that we can obtain a negative value for y because the square of any real number is always positive or zero. Thus, the range is the set of nonnegative real numbers, or $y \geq 0$.

EXAMPLE 3

Find the domain and the range of the relation $y = \sqrt{x - 4}$.

Note that no value of x less than 4 may be used because the square root of any negative number is not a real number. Thus, the domain is the set of real numbers greater than or equal to 4, or $x \geq 4$.

After each possible x-replacement, the square root of the resulting value is never negative, so the range is $y \geq 0$.

FUNCTION

A **function** is a special relation: a set of ordered pairs in which no two distinct ordered pairs have the same first element.

In equation form, a relation is a function when for each possible value of the first or independent variable, there is only one corresponding value of the second or dependent variable. In brief, for a relation to be a function, each value of x must correspond to one, and only one, value of y.

EXAMPLE 4

Is the relation $B = \{(3, 2), (6, 7), (5, 3), (1, 1), (3, 7)\}$ a function? Find its domain and its range.

B is not a function because it contains two different ordered pairs that have the same first element: $(3, 2)$ and $(3, 7)$. In other words, the fact that both 2 and 7 correspond to 3 causes the relation B not to be a function. The domain of B is $\{1, 3, 5, 6\}$. The range of B is $\{1, 2, 3, 7\}$.

Does the set $A = \{(1, 2), (3, 5), (7, 9), (6, 3)\}$ from Example 1 describe a function? Yes, because no two ordered pairs have the same first element.

EXAMPLE 5

Is the relation $x = y^2$ a function? Find its domain and its range.

Can we find two ordered pairs that have the same first element? Yes, for example, $[(9, 3)$ and $(9, -3)$ as well as $(16, 4)$ and $(16, -4)]$ and many others. Therefore, $x = y^2$ is not a function because for at least one x-value, there corresponds more than one y-value.

To find the domain, note that each x-value is the square of a real number and can never be negative. Thus, the domain is $x \geq 0$.

There are no restrictions on replacements for y; therefore, the range is the set of all real numbers.

Consider the relations in Examples 2 and 3. Are they functions? Note that in the relation $y = x^2$, for each value of x there is only one corresponding value of y. For example, $(2, 4)$, $(-2, 4)$, $(3, 9)$, $(-3, 9)$, $(4, 16)$, $(-4, 16)$, and so forth. Therefore, $y = x^2$ is a function.

Example 3 was the relation $y = \sqrt{x - 4}$. Here we find that for each x-value there corresponds only one y-value, for example, $(5, 1)$, $(8, 2)$, $(10, \sqrt{6})$, ... Therefore, $y = \sqrt{x - 4}$ is a function.

In summary, a function is a relationship between two sets of numbers, the domain and the range, that relates each number, x, in the domain to one and only one number, y, in the range.

Next let's consider the following, more intuitive function: On a summer vacation trip, you are driving 65 mi/h using cruise control on an interstate highway. You want to relate the distance and the time you are traveling. First, we know that distance equals rate times time, or $d = rt$. Also, since $r = 65$, we have the relation $d = 65t$. As you drive along, you begin to think how far you can drive in 1 h:

$$d = 65t = 65(1) = 65 \text{ mi}$$

How far can you drive in 3 h?

$$d = 65t = 65(3) = 195 \text{ mi}$$

Is this relation a function? Yes, because for each value of t, there is one and only one value of d; that is, during each driving time period, there is one and only one distance traveled. What are the domain and the range? First, note that $t \geq 0$ and $d \geq 0$. While there are no theoretical upper limits on t and d, the practical limits depend on the amount of time and the distance that you want to travel.

Functional Notation

To say that y is a function of x means that for each value of x from the domain of the function, we can find exactly one value of y from the range. This statement is said so often that we have developed the following notation, called **functional notation,** to write that y is a function of x:

$$y = f(x)$$

with $f(x)$ read "f of x." *Note:* $f(x)$ does **not** mean f times x.

In each of the following equations, y can be replaced by $f(x)$, and the resulting equation is written in functional notation:

Equation	Functional notation form
$y = 3x - 4$	$f(x) = 3x - 4$
$y = 5x^2 - 8x + 7$	$f(x) = 5x^2 - 8x + 7$
$y = \sqrt{6 - 2x}$	$f(x) = \sqrt{6 - 2x}$

Functional notation can be used to simplify statements. For example, find the value of $y = 3x^2 + 5x - 6$ for $x = 2$. Using substitution, we replace x with 2 as follows:

$$y = 3x^2 + 5x - 6$$
$$y = 3(2)^2 + 5(2) - 6 = 16$$

The statement "Find the value of $y = 3x^2 + 5x - 6$ for $x = 2$" may be abbreviated using functional notation as follows:

$$\text{given } f(x) = 3x^2 + 5x - 6, \text{ find } f(2)$$

EXAMPLE 6

Given the function $f(x) = 5x - 4$, find each of the following:
(a) $f(0)$
  Replace x with 0 as follows:

$$f(0) = 5(0) - 4 = 0 - 4 = -4$$

(b) $f(7)$
  Replace x with 7 as follows:

$$f(7) = 5(7) - 4 = 35 - 4 = 31$$

A function is usually named by a specific letter, such as $f(x)$, where f names the function. Other letters, such as g in $g(x)$ and h in $h(x)$, are also often used to represent or name functions.

EXAMPLE 7

Given the function $g(x) = \sqrt{x + 4} + 3x^2$, find each of the following:
(a) $g(5)$
  Replace x with 5 as follows:

$$g(5) = \sqrt{5 + 4} + 3(5)^2 = 3 + 75 = 78$$

(b) $g(-3)$
  Replace x with -3 as follows:

$$g(-3) = \sqrt{-3 + 4} + 3(-3)^2 = 1 + 27 = 28$$

(c) $g(-10)$
  Replace x with -10 as follows:

$$g(-10) = \sqrt{-10 + 4} + 3(-10)^2 = \sqrt{-6} + 300$$

which is not a real number because $\sqrt{-6}$ is not a real number. Another way of responding to part (c) is to say, "Since -10 is not in the domain of $g(x)$, $g(-10)$ has no real value."

Letters may also be used with functional notation, as illustrated by the following example.

EXAMPLE 8

Given the function $f(x) = x^2 - 4x$, find each of the following:

(a) $f(a)$

Replace x with a as follows:

$$f(a) = a^2 - 4a$$

(b) $f(3c^2)$

Replace x with $3c^2$ as follows:

$$f(3c^2) = (3c^2)^2 - 4(3c^2) = 9c^4 - 12c^2$$

(c) $f(a + 5)$

Replace x with $a + 5$ as follows:

$$f(a + 5) = (a + 5)^2 - 4(a + 5)$$
$$= a^2 + 10a + 25 - 4a - 20$$
$$= a^2 + 6a + 5$$

Using a calculator, we have

2nd CUSTOM   F2   6   **x^2-4x ENTER**   (**2nd CUSTOM** restores standard menus.)

  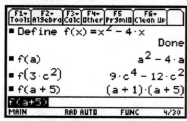

Note that the last answer is factored.
Use **expand** to multiply if you wish.

Other letters, such as t in $f(t)$ and r in $f(r)$, are used in applications to name independent variables.

EXAMPLE 9

Given the function $f(t) = 0.50t + 5.4$, find each of the following:

(a) $f(3.2)$

Replace t with 3.2 as follows:

$$f(t) = 0.50t + 5.4$$
$$f(3.2) = 0.50(3.2) + 5.4$$
$$= 1.6 + 5.4$$
$$= 7.0$$

(b) $f(t_0)$

Replace t with t_0 as follows:

$$f(t) = 0.50t + 5.4$$
$$f(t_0) = 0.50t_0 + 5.4$$

Exercises 1.1

Determine whether or not each relation is a function. Write its domain and its range.

1. $A = \{(2, 4), (3, 7), (9, 2)\}$
2. $B = \{(5, 2), (3, 3), (1, 2)\}$
3. $C = \{(2, 5), (7, 3), (2, 1), (1, 3)\}$
4. $D = \{(0, 2), (5, -1), (2, 7), (5, 1)\}$
5. $E = \{(3, 2), (5, 2), (2, 2), (-2, 2)\}$
6. $F = \{(3, 4), (3, -4), (-3, -4), (-3, 4)\}$
7. $y = 2x + 5$
8. $y = -3x$
9. $y = x^2 + 1$
10. $y = 2x^2 - 3$
11. $x = y^2 - 2$
12. $x = 3y^2 + 4$
13. $y = \sqrt{x + 3}$
14. $y = \sqrt{3 - 6x}$
15. $y = 6 + \sqrt{2x - 8}$
16. $y = 16 - \sqrt{x + 5}$

17. Given the function $f(x) = 8x - 12$, find
    (a) $f(4)$ **(b)** $f(0)$ **(c)** $f(-2)$

18. Given the function $g(x) = 20 - 4x$, find
    (a) $g(6)$ **(b)** $g(0)$ **(c)** $g(-3)$

19. Given $g(x) = 10x + 15$, find
    (a) $g(2)$ **(b)** $g(0)$ **(c)** $g(-4)$

20. Given $f(x) = x^2 - 4$, find
    (a) $f(6)$ **(b)** $f(0)$ **(c)** $f(-6)$

21. Given $h(x) = 3x^2 + 4x$, find
    (a) $h(5)$ **(b)** $h(0)$ **(c)** $h(-2)$

22. Given $f(x) = -2x^2 + 6x - 7$, find
    (a) $f(3)$ **(b)** $f(0)$ **(c)** $f(-1)$

23. Given $f(t) = \dfrac{5 - t^2}{2t}$, find
    (a) $f(1)$ **(b)** $f(-3)$ **(c)** $f(0)$

24. Given $g(t) = \sqrt{21 - 5t}$, find
    (a) $g(1)$ **(b)** $g(-3)$ **(c)** $g(2)$ **(d)** $g(8)$

25. Given $f(x) = 6x + 8$, find
    (a) $f(a)$ **(b)** $f(4a)$ **(c)** $f(c^2)$

26. Given $g(x) = 8x^2 - 7x$, find
    (a) $g(z)$ **(b)** $g(2y)$ **(c)** $g(3t^2)$

27. Given $h(x) = 4x^2 - 12x$, find
    (a) $h(x + 2)$ **(b)** $h(x - 3)$ **(c)** $h(2x + 1)$

28. Given $f(y) = y^2 - 3y + 6$, find
    (a) $f(y - 1)$ **(b)** $f(y^2 + 1)$ **(c)** $f(1 - 4y)$

29. Given $f(x) = 3x - 1$ and $g(x) = x^2 - 6x + 1$, find
    (a) $f(x) + g(x)$ **(b)** $f(x) - g(x)$ **(c)** $[f(x)][g(x)]$ **(d)** $f(x + h)$

30. Given $f(t) = 5 - 2t + t^2$ and $g(t) = t^2 - 4t + 4$, find
    (a) $f(t) + g(t)$ **(b)** $g(t) - f(t)$ **(c)** $[f(t)][g(t)]$ **(d)** $g(t + h)$

Find the domain of each function.

31. $f(x) = \dfrac{3x + 4}{x - 2}$

32. $f(t) = \dfrac{8}{6t + 3}$

33. $g(t) = \dfrac{2t + 4t^2}{(t - 6)(t + 3)}$

34. $g(x) = \dfrac{3x - 10}{x^2 + 4}$

35. $f(x) = \dfrac{12}{\sqrt{15 - 3x}}$

36. $g(t) = \dfrac{9}{\sqrt{5t + 20}}$

1.2 GRAPHING EQUATIONS

Consider a plane in which two number lines intersect at right angles. Let the point of intersection be the zero point of each line and call it the **origin.** Each line is called an **axis.** The horizontal number line is usually called the **x-axis** and the vertical line is usually called the **y-axis.** On each axis the same scale (unit length) is preferred but not always possible in all applications. Such a system is called the **rectangular coordinate system,** or the **Cartesian coordinate system.** (The name *Cartesian* is after Descartes, the seventeenth-century French mathematician who first conceived this idea of combining algebra and geometry together in such a way that each could aid the study of the other.) The plane is divided by the axes into four regions called **quadrants.** The quadrants are numbered as shown in Fig. 1.2.

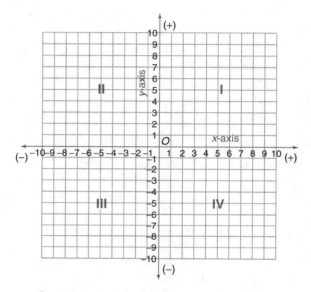

Figure 1.2   The rectangular coordinate system.

In the plane there is a point that corresponds to each ordered pair of real numbers (x, y). Likewise, there is an ordered pair (x, y) that corresponds to each point in the plane. Together x and y are called the **coordinates** of the point; x is called the **abscissa** and y is called the **ordinate.** This relationship is called a **one-to-one correspondence.** The location, or position, of a point in the plane corresponding to a given ordered pair is found by first counting right or left from O (origin) the number of units along the x-axis indicated by the first number of the ordered pair (right if positive, left if negative). Then from this point reached on the x-axis, count up or down the number of units indicated by the second number of the ordered pair (up if positive, down if negative).

EXAMPLE 1

Plot the point corresponding to each ordered pair in the number plane:

$A(3, 1)$ $B(2, -3)$ $C(-4, -2)$ $D(-3, 0)$ $E(-6, 2)$ $F(0, 2)$ (See Fig. 1.3.)

To graph equations we plot a sample of ordered pairs and connect them with a smooth curve. To obtain the sample, we need to generate ordered pairs from a given equation. One way to generate these ordered pairs is by randomly choosing a value for x, replacing this value for x in the equation, and solving for y.

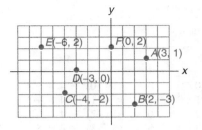

Figure 1.3

EXAMPLE 2

Graph $y = 2x - 3$.

x	y
1	-1
3	3
-2	-7
0	-3

$y = 2x - 3$ or $f(x) = 2x - 3$

$y = 2(1) - 3 = -1$
$y = 2(3) - 3 = 3$
$y = 2(-2) - 3 = -7$
$y = 2(0) - 3 = -3$

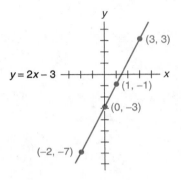

Figure 1.4

Plot the ordered pairs and connect them with a smooth line as in Fig. 1.4.

A **linear equation** with two unknowns is an equation of degree one in the form $ax + by = c$ with a and b not both 0. Its graph is always a straight line. Therefore, two ordered pairs are sufficient to graph a linear function, since two points determine a straight line. However, finding a third point provides good insurance against a careless error.

EXAMPLE 3

Graph $y = -3x + 5$.

x	y
0	5
2	-1
-1	8

$y = -3x + 5$ or $g(x) = -3x + 5$

$y = -3(0) + 5 = 5$
$y = -3(2) + 5 = -1$
$y = -3(-1) + 5 = 8$

See Fig. 1.5.

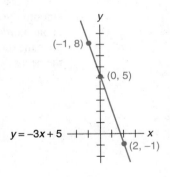

Figure 1.5

The graph of an equation that is not linear is usually a curve of some kind and hence several points are required to sketch a smooth curve.

EXAMPLE 4

Graph $y = x^2 - 4$.

x	y	$y = x^2 - 4$
0	-4	$y = (0)^2 - 4 = -4$
1	-3	$y = (1)^2 - 4 = -3$
2	0	$y = (2)^2 - 4 = 0$
3	5	$y = (3)^2 - 4 = 5$
-1	-3	$y = (-1)^2 - 4 = -3$
-2	0	$y = (-2)^2 - 4 = 0$
-3	5	$y = (-3)^2 - 4 = 5$

See Fig. 1.6.

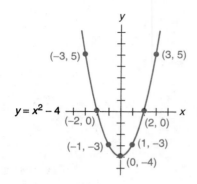

Figure 1.6

EXAMPLE 5

Graph $y = 2x^2 + x - 5$.

x	y	$y = 2x^2 + x - 5$
0	-5	$y = 2(0)^2 + (0) - 5 = -5$
1	-2	$y = 2(1)^2 + (1) - 5 = -2$
2	5	$y = 2(2)^2 + (2) - 5 = 5$
-1	-4	$y = 2(-1)^2 + (-1) - 5 = -4$
-2	1	$y = 2(-2)^2 + (-2) - 5 = 1$
-3	10	$y = 2(-3)^2 + (-3) - 5 = 10$

See Fig. 1.7.

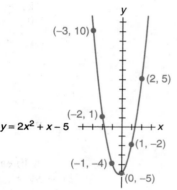

Figure 1.7

For a more complicated function, more ordered pairs are usually required to obtain a smooth curve. It may also be necessary to change the scale of the graph in order to plot enough ordered pairs to obtain a smooth curve. To change the scale means to enlarge or reduce the unit length on the axes according to a specified ratio. This ratio is chosen such that the necessary values can be fit in the space allowed for the graph.

EXAMPLE 6

Graph $y = x^3 + 4x^2 - x - 4$.

x	y	$y = x^3 + 4x^2 - x - 4$
0	−4	$y = (0)^3 + 4(0)^2 - (0) - 4 = -4$
1	0	$y = (1)^3 + 4(1)^2 - (1) - 4 = 0$
2	18	$y = (2)^3 + 4(2)^2 - (2) - 4 = 18$
3	56	$y = (3)^3 + 4(3)^2 - (3) - 4 = 56$
−1	0	$y = (-1)^3 + 4(-1)^2 - (-1) - 4 = 0$
−2	6	$y = (-2)^3 + 4(-2)^2 - (-2) - 4 = 6$
−3	8	$y = (-3)^3 + 4(-3)^2 - (-3) - 4 = 8$
−4	0	$y = (-4)^3 + 4(-4)^2 - (-4) - 4 = 0$
−5	−24	$y = (-5)^3 + 4(-5)^2 - (-5) - 4 = -24$

See Fig. 1.8.

$y = x^3 + 4x^2 - x - 4$

Figure 1.8

EXAMPLE 7

Graph $y = \sqrt{2x - 6}$.

x	y	$y = \sqrt{2x - 6}$	
3	0	$y = \sqrt{2(3) - 6} = \sqrt{0} = 0$	
5	2	$y = \sqrt{2(5) - 6} = \sqrt{4} = 2$	
7	2.8	$y = \sqrt{2(7) - 6} = \sqrt{8} = 2.8$	(approx.)
8	3.2	$y = \sqrt{2(8) - 6} = \sqrt{10} = 3.2$	(approx.)
11	4	$y = \sqrt{2(11) - 6} = \sqrt{16} = 4$	
13	4.5	$y = \sqrt{2(13) - 6} = \sqrt{20} = 4.5$	(approx.)

$y = \sqrt{2x - 6}$

Figure 1.9

See Fig. 1.9.

Using a graphing calculator, we have

green diamond Y =   green diamond   TblSet   3 down arrow 2 ENTER ENTER   green diamond TABLE

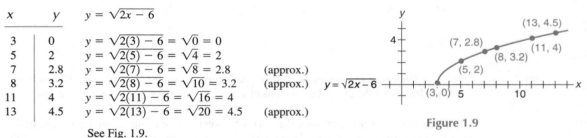

green diamond WINDOW   green diamond GRAPH   F3 (Trace)   8   ENTER

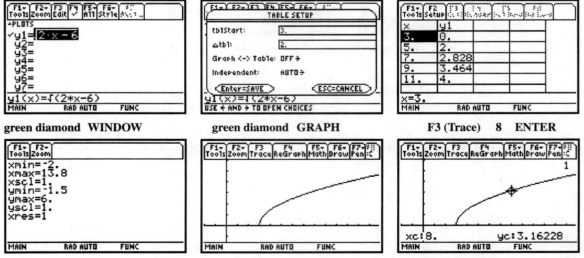

Specific function values can be calculated on the **Trace** screen.

Solving Equations by Graphing

Equations may be solved graphically. This method is particularly useful when an algebraic method is very cumbersome, cannot be recalled, or does not exist; it is especially useful in technical applications.

Solving for y = 0   To solve the equation $y = x^2 - x - 6$ for $y = 0$ graphically means to find the point or points, if any, where the graph crosses the line $y = 0$ (the x-axis).

EXAMPLE 8

Solve $y = x^2 - x - 6$ for $y = 0$ graphically.
  First, graph the equation $y = x^2 - x - 6$ (see Fig. 1.10).

x	y
1	-6
2	-4
3	0
4	6
0	-6
-1	-4
-2	0
-3	6

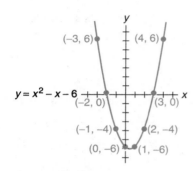

Figure 1.10

Then note the values of x where the curve crosses the x-axis: $x = -2$ and $x = 3$.
Therefore, from the graph the solutions of $y = x^2 - x - 6$ for $y = 0$ are $x = -2$ and $x = 3$.

Sometimes the curve crosses the x-axis between the unit marks on the x-axis. In this case we must estimate as closely as possible the point of intersection of the curve and the x-axis. If a particular problem requires greater accuracy, we can scale the graph to allow a more accurate estimation.

EXAMPLE 9

Solve $y = x^2 + 2x - 4$ for $y = 0$ graphically.
  First, graph the equation $y = x^2 + 2x - 4$ (see Fig. 1.11).

x	y
0	-4
1	-1
2	4
-1	-5
-2	-4
-3	-1
-4	4

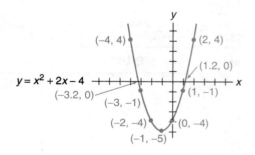

Figure 1.11

The values of x where the curve crosses the x-axis are approximately 1.2 and -3.2.
Therefore, the approximate solutions of $y = x^2 + 2x - 4$ for $y = 0$ are $x = 1.2$ and $x = -3.2$.

Solving for y = k

EXAMPLE 10

Solve the equation from Example 9, which was $y = x^2 + 2x - 4$, for $y = 4$ and $y = -3$.

First, find the values of x where the curve crosses the line $y = 4$. From the graph in Fig. 1.12, the x-values are 2 and -4. Therefore, solving for $y = 4$, we find that the solutions of $y = x^2 + 2x - 4$ are $x = 2$ and $x = -4$.

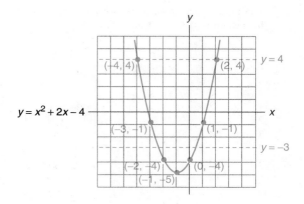

Figure 1.12

Next, find the values of x where the curve crosses the line $y = -3$. From the graph in Fig. 1.12, the approximate x-values are 0.4 and -2.4. That is, for $y = -3$, the solutions of $y = x^2 + 2x - 4$ are approximately $x = 0.4$ and $x = -2.4$.

Note that $y = x^2 + 2x - 4$ has no solutions for $y = -7$.

EXAMPLE 11

The voltage V in volts (V) in a given circuit varies with time t in milliseconds (ms) according to the equation $V = 6t^2 + t$. Solve for t when $V = 0$, 70, and 120.

t	V
0	0
1	7
2	26
3	57
4	100
5	155

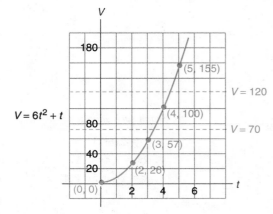

Figure 1.13

In Fig. 1.13, we used the scales

$$t: \quad 1 \text{ square} = 1 \text{ ms}$$
$$V: \quad 1 \text{ square} = 20 \text{ V}$$

From the graph,

$$\text{at} \quad V = 0 \text{ V}, \qquad t = 0 \text{ ms}$$
$$\text{at} \quad V = 70 \text{ V}, \qquad t = 3.3 \text{ ms}$$
$$\text{at} \quad V = 120 \text{ V}, \qquad t = 4.4 \text{ ms}$$

Negative values of time, t, are not meaningful in this example.

EXAMPLE 12

The work w done in a circuit varies with time t according to the equation $w = 8t^2 + 4t$. Solve for t when $w = 60$, 120, and 250.

t	w
0	0
1	12
2	40
3	84
4	144
5	220
6	312

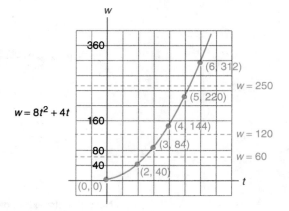

Figure 1.14

In Fig. 1.14, we used the scales

$$t: \quad 1 \text{ square} = 1 \text{ unit}$$
$$w: \quad 1 \text{ square} = 40 \text{ units}$$

From the graph,

$$\text{at} \quad w = 60, \qquad t = 2.5$$
$$\text{at} \quad w = 120, \qquad t = 3.6$$
$$\text{at} \quad w = 250, \qquad t = 5.4$$

Exercises 1.2

Graph each equation.

1. $y = 2x + 1$ **2.** $y = 3x - 4$ **3.** $-2x - 3y = 6$

4. $2y = -4x - 3$ **5.** $y = x^2 - 9$ **6.** $y = x^2 + x - 6$

7. $y = x^2 - 5x + 4$ **8.** $y = x^2 + 3$ **9.** $y = 2x^2 + 3x - 2$

10. $y = -x^2 + 2x + 4$ **11.** $y = x^2 + 2x$ **12.** $y = x^2 - 4x$

13. $y = -2x^2 + 4x$ **14.** $y = -\frac{1}{4}x^2 - \frac{3}{2}x + 2$ **15.** $y = x^3 - x^2 - 10x + 8$

16. $y = x^3 - 4x^2 + x + 6$ **17.** $y = x^3 + 2x^2 - 7x + 4$ **18.** $y = x^3 - 8x - 3$

19. $y = \sqrt{x + 4}$ **20.** $y = \sqrt{3x - 12}$ **21.** $y = \sqrt{12 - 6x}$

22. $y = \sqrt{3 - x}$

Solve each equation graphically for the given values.

23. Exercise 5 for $y = 0, -5$, and 2.
24. Exercise 6 for $y = 0, 6$, and -3.
25. Exercise 7 for $y = 0, 2$, and -4.
26. Exercise 8 for $y = 0, 4$, and 6.
27. Exercise 9 for $y = 0, 3$, and 5.
28. Exercise 10 for $y = 0, 4$, and -2.
29. Exercise 11 for $y = 0, 3$, and 6.
30. Exercise 12 for $y = 0, -2$, and 3.
31. Exercise 13 for $y = 0, 5, -4$, and $-1\frac{1}{2}$.
32. Exercise 14 for $y = 0, -1$, and 1.5.
33. Exercise 15 for $y = 0, 2$, and -2.
34. Exercise 16 for $y = 0, 2$, and 8.
35. Exercise 17 for $y = 0, 4$, and 8.
36. Exercise 18 for $y = 0, 2$, and -3.

Solve each equation graphically for the given values.

37. $y = x^2 + 3x - 4$ for $y = 0, 6$, and -2.
38. $y = 2x^2 - 5x - 3$ for $y = 2, 0$, and -3.
39. $y = -\frac{1}{2}x^2 + 2$ for $y = 0, 4$, and -4.
40. $y = -\frac{1}{4}x^2 + x$ for $y = 0, \frac{1}{2}$, and -4.
41. $y = x^3 - 3x^2 + 1$ for $y = 0, -2$, and -0.5.
42. $y = -x^3 + 3x + 2$ for $y = 2, 0$, and 3.

43. The resistance r in ohms (Ω) of a resistor in a circuit of constant current varies with time, t in milliseconds (ms) according to the equation
$$r = 10t^2 + 20$$
Solve for t when $r = 90\ \Omega$, $180\ \Omega$, and $320\ \Omega$.

44. An object dropped from an airplane 2500 m above the ground falls according to the equation $h = 2500 - 4.95t^2$, where h is the height in metres above the ground and t is the time in seconds. Find the times for the object to fall to a height of 2000 m, 1200 m, and 600 m above the ground. Also find the time it takes to hit the ground.

45. The energy dissipated (work lost) w by a resistor varies with the time t in ms, according to the equation $w = 5t^2 + 6t$. Solve for t when $w = 2, 4$, and 10.

46. The resistance, r, in a given circuit varies with time t in milliseconds, according to the equation $r = 10 + \sqrt{t}$. Find t when $r = 14.1\ \Omega$, $14.3\ \Omega$, and $14.7\ \Omega$. (*Hint:* Choose a suitable scale for the graph and graph only the part you need.)

47. A given inductor carries a current expressed by the equation $i = t^3 - 15$, where i is the current in amperes (A) and t is the time in seconds. Find t when i is 5 A and 15 A.

48. The charge q in coulombs (C) flowing in a given circuit varies with the time t in microseconds (μs), according to the equation $q = t^2 - \dfrac{t^3}{3}$. Find t when q is 5 C and 10 C.

49. A machinist needs to drill four holes 2.00 in. apart in a straight line in a metal plate as shown in Fig. 1.15. The first hole is placed at the origin, and the line forms an angle of 36.0° with the vertical axis. Find the coordinates of the other three holes.

50. A machinist often uses a coordinate system to drill holes by placing the origin at the most convenient location. A bolt circle is the circle formed by completing an arc through the centers of the bolt holes in a piece of metal. Find the coordinates of the centers of eight equally spaced, $\frac{1}{4}$-in. holes on a bolt circle of radius 4.00 in. as shown in Fig. 1.16.

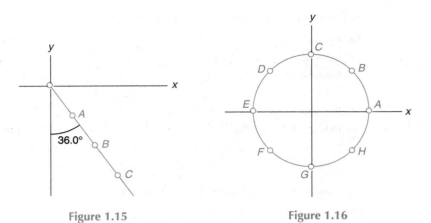

Figure 1.15   Figure 1.16

1.3   THE STRAIGHT LINE

The **slope** of a nonvertical line is the ratio of the difference of the *y*-coordinates of any two points on the line to the difference of their *x*-coordinates when the differences are taken in the same order (see Fig. 1.17).

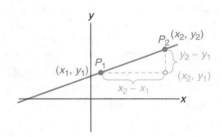

Figure 1.17   Slope of line through P_1 and P_2.

SLOPE OF A LINE

If $P_1(x_1, y_1)$ and $P_2(x_2, y_2)$ represent any two points on a straight line, then the slope m of the line is

$$m = \frac{y_2 - y_1}{x_2 - x_1}$$

EXAMPLE 1

Find the slope of the line passing through $(-2, 1)$ and $(3, 5)$.

    If we let $x_1 = -2$, $y_1 = 1$, $x_2 = 3$, and $y_2 = 5$ as in Fig. 1.18, then

$$m = \frac{y_2 - y_1}{x_2 - x_1} = \frac{5 - 1}{3 - (-2)} = \frac{4}{5}$$

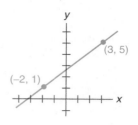

Figure 1.18

Note that if we reverse the order of taking the differences of the coordinates, the result is the same.

$$\frac{y_1 - y_2}{x_1 - x_2} = \frac{1 - 5}{-2 - 3} = \frac{-4}{-5} = \frac{4}{5} = m$$

EXAMPLE 2

Find the slope of the line passing through $(-2, 4)$ and $(6, -6)$.
    If we let $x_1 = -2$, $y_1 = 4$, $x_2 = 6$, and $y_2 = -6$ as in Fig. 1.19, then

$$m = \frac{y_2 - y_1}{x_2 - x_1} = \frac{-6 - 4}{6 - (-2)} = \frac{-10}{8} = -\frac{5}{4}$$

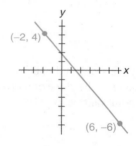

Figure 1.19

Note that in Example 1, the line slopes upward from left to right, while in Example 2, the line slopes downward. In general, we have the following:

1. If a line has positive slope, then the line slopes upward from left to right ("rises").
2. If a line has negative slope, then the line slopes downward from left to right ("falls").
3. If the line has zero slope, then the line is horizontal ("flat").
4. If the line is vertical, then the line has undefined slope, because $x_1 = x_2$, or $x_2 - x_1 = 0$. In this case, the ratio $\dfrac{y_2 - y_1}{x_2 - x_1}$ is undefined because division by zero is undefined.

We can use these facts to assist us in graphing a line if we know the slope of the line and one point P on the line. The line can be sketched by drawing a line through the given point P and a point Q which is plotted by moving one unit to the right of P, then moving vertically m units. That is, a point moving along a line will move vertically an amount equal to m, the slope, for every unit move to the right as in Fig. 1.20.

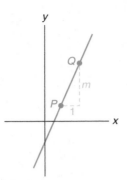

Figure 1.20   The slope m corresponds to the
vertical change for each horizontal change of 1.

EXAMPLE 3

Graph a line with slope -2 that passes through the point $(1, 3)$.

    Since the slope is -2, points on the line drop 2 units for every unit move to the right. The line passes through $(1, 3)$ and $(2, 1)$ as in Fig. 1.21.

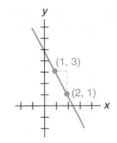

Figure 1.21

    Knowing the slope and one point on the line will also determine the equation of the straight line. Let m be the slope of a given nonvertical straight line, and let (x_1, y_1) be the coordinates of a point on this line. If (x, y) is any other point on the line as in Fig. 1.22, then we have

$$\frac{y - y_1}{x - x_1} = m$$

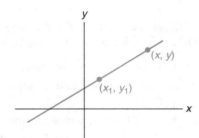

Figure 1.22

By multiplying each side of the equation by $(x - x_1)$, we obtain the following.

POINT-SLOPE FORM OF A STRAIGHT LINE

If m is the slope and (x_1, y_1) is any point on a nonvertical straight line, its equation is

$$y - y_1 = m(x - x_1)$$

EXAMPLE 4

Find the equation of the line with slope 3 that passes through the point $(-1, 2)$.

Here $m = 3$, $x_1 = -1$, and $y_1 = 2$. Using the point-slope form, we have the equation

$$y - y_1 = m(x - x_1)$$
$$y - 2 = 3[x - (-1)]$$

Simplifying, we have

$$y - 2 = 3x + 3$$
$$y = 3x + 5$$

The point-slope form can also be used to find the equation of a straight line that passes through two points.

EXAMPLE 5

Find the equation of the line passing through the points $(2, -3)$ and $(-2, 5)$.

First, find the slope.

$$m = \frac{y_2 - y_1}{x_2 - x_1} = \frac{5 - (-3)}{-2 - 2} = \frac{5 + 3}{-4} = \frac{8}{-4} = -2$$

Substitute $m = -2$ and the point $(2, -3)$ in the point-slope form.

$$y - y_1 = m(x - x_1)$$
$$y - (-3) = -2(x - 2)$$
$$y + 3 = -2x + 4$$
$$2x + y - 1 = 0$$

Note: We could have used the other point $(-2, 5)$ in the point-slope form to obtain the equation

$$y - 5 = -2[x - (-2)]$$

which also simplifies to

$$2x + y - 1 = 0$$

A nonvertical line will intersect the y-axis at some point in the form $(0, b)$ as in Fig. 1.23. This point $(0, b)$ is called the **y-intercept** of the line. If the slope of the line is m, then

$$y - y_1 = m(x - x_1)$$
$$y - b = m(x - 0)$$
$$y - b = mx$$
$$y = mx + b$$

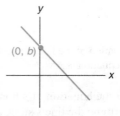

Figure 1.23 b is the y-coordinate of the point where the line crosses the y-axis.

If m is the slope and $(0, b)$ is the y-intercept of a nonvertical straight line, its equation is

$$y = mx + b$$

EXAMPLE 6

Find the equation of the line with slope $\frac{1}{2}$ that crosses the y-axis at $b = -3$.

Using the slope-intercept form, we have

$$y = mx + b$$
$$y = \frac{1}{2}x + (-3)$$
$$y = \frac{1}{2}x - 3$$

or

$$x - 2y - 6 = 0$$

A line parallel to the x-axis has slope $m = 0$ (see Fig. 1.24). Its equation is

$$y = mx + b$$
$$y = (0)x + b$$
$$y = b$$

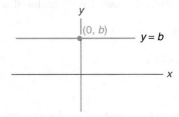

Figure 1.24   Horizontal line.

EQUATION OF A HORIZONTAL LINE

If a horizontal line passes through the point (a, b), its equation is

$$y = b$$

EXAMPLE 7

Find the equation of the line parallel to and 3 units above the x-axis.

The equation is $y = 3$.

By writing the equation of a nonvertical straight line in the slope-intercept form, we can quickly determine the line's slope and a point on the line (the point where it crosses the y-axis).

EXAMPLE 8

Find the slope and the y-intercept of $3y - x + 6 = 0$. Graph the line.
Write the equation in slope-intercept form; that is, solve for y.

$$3y - x + 6 = 0$$
$$3y = x - 6$$
$$y = \frac{x}{3} - 2$$
$$y = \left(\frac{1}{3}\right)x + (-2)$$

So $m = \frac{1}{3}$ and $b = -2$ (see Fig. 1.25).

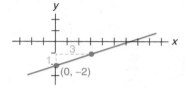

Figure 1.25

EXAMPLE 9

Describe and graph the line whose equation is $y = -5$.
This is a line parallel to and 5 units below the x-axis (see Fig. 1.26).

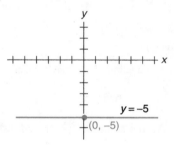

Figure 1.26

If a line is vertical, then we cannot use any of these equations since the line has undefined slope. However, note that in this case, as shown in Fig. 1.27, the line crosses the x-axis at some point in the form $(a, 0)$. All points on the line have the same abscissa as the point $(a, 0)$. This characterizes the line, giving us the following equation:

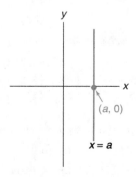

Figure 1.27   Vertical line.

EXAMPLE 10

Describe and graph the line whose equation is $x = 2$.

This is a line perpendicular to the x-axis that crosses the x-axis at the point $(2, 0)$ (see Fig. 1.28).

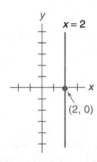

Figure 1.28

EXAMPLE 11

Write the equation of the line perpendicular to the x-axis that crosses the x-axis at the point $(-3, 0)$.

The equation is $x = -3$.

Note: All the equations presented in this section can be put in the form

$$Ax + By + C = 0 \quad \text{with } A \text{ and } B \text{ not both } 0.$$

This is known as the **general form** of the equation of the line and agrees with our definition of a linear equation.

Exercises 1.3

Find the slope of each line passing through the given points.

1. $(4, 2), (3, 1)$ **2.** $(-3, 2), (-1, -2)$ **3.** $(4, -5), (2, 3)$

4. $(-6, -4), (5, -3)$ **5.** $(-3, 2), (6, 2)$ **6.** $(4, -7), (4, 3)$

7. $(5, 7), (-3, 2)$ **8.** $(-3, 6), (-1, 3)$

Graph each line passing through the given point with the given slope.

9. $(2, -1), m = 2$ **10.** $(0, 1), m = -3$ **11.** $(-3, -2), m = \frac{1}{2}$

12. $(4, 4), m = -\frac{1}{3}$ **13.** $(4, 0), m = -2$ **14.** $(-3, 1), m = 4$

15. $(0, -3), m = -\frac{3}{4}$ **16.** $(5, -2), m = \frac{3}{2}$

Find the equation of the line with the given properties.

17. Passes through $(-2, 8)$ with slope -3.

18. Passes through $(3, -5)$ with slope 2.

19. Passes through $(-3, -4)$ with slope $\frac{1}{2}$.

20. Passes through $(6, -7)$ with slope $-\frac{3}{4}$.

21. Passes through $(-2, 7)$ and $(1, 4)$.

22. Passes through $(1, 6)$ and $(4, -3)$.

23. Passes through $(6, -8)$ and $(-4, -3)$.

24. Passes through $(-2, 2)$ and $(7, -1)$.

25. Crosses the y-axis at -2 with slope -5.

26. Crosses the y-axis at 8 with slope $\frac{1}{3}$.

27. Has y-intercept 7 and slope 2.

28. Has y-intercept -4 and slope $-\frac{3}{4}$.

29. Parallel to and 5 units above the x-axis.

30. Parallel to and 2 units below the x-axis.

31. Perpendicular to the x-axis and crosses the x-axis at $(-2, 0)$.

32. Perpendicular to the x-axis and crosses the x-axis at $(5, 0)$.

33. Parallel to the x-axis containing the point $(2, -3)$.

34. Parallel to the y-axis containing the point $(-5, -4)$.

35. Perpendicular to the x-axis containing the point $(-7, 9)$.

36. Perpendicular to the y-axis containing the point $(4, 6)$.

Find the slope and the y-intercept of each straight line.

37. $x + 4y = 12$

38. $-2x + 3y + 9 = 0$

39. $4x - 2y + 14 = 0$

40. $3x - 6y = 0$

41. $y = 6$

42. $x = -4$

Graph each equation.

43. $y = 3x - 2$

44. $y = -2x + 5$

45. $5x - 2y + 4 = 0$

46. $4x + 3y + 6 = 0$

47. $x = 7$

48. $x = -2$

49. $y = -3$

50. $y = 2$

51. $6x + 8y = 24$

52. $3x - 5y = 30$

53. $x - 3y = -12$

54. $x + 6y = 8$

55. A metal rod is 43.0 cm long at temperature $-15.0°C$ and 43.2 cm long at $55.0°C$. These data can be listed in (x, y) form as $(-15.0, 43.0)$ and $(55.0, 43.2)$. Find the slope (as a simplified fraction) of the straight line passing through these two points.

1.4 PARALLEL AND PERPENDICULAR LINES

PARALLEL LINES

Two lines are parallel if either one of the following conditions holds:

1. They are both perpendicular to the x-axis [see Fig. 1.29(a)].

2. They both have the same slope [see Fig. 1.29(b)]. That is, if the equations of the lines are

$$L_1: \quad y = m_1x + b_1 \quad \text{and} \quad L_2: \quad y = m_2x + b_2$$

then

$$m_1 = m_2$$

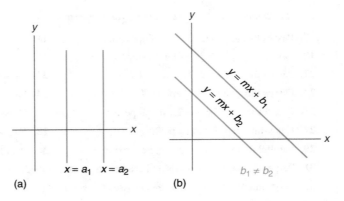

Figure 1.29

PERPENDICULAR LINES

Two lines are perpendicular if either one of the following conditions holds:

1. One line is vertical with equation $x = a$ and the other is horizontal with equation $y = b$.

2. Neither is vertical and the slope of one line is the negative reciprocal of the other. That is, if the equations of the lines are

$$L_1: \quad y = m_1 x + b_1 \quad \text{and} \quad L_2: \quad y = m_2 x + b_2$$

then

$$m_1 = -\frac{1}{m_2}$$

To show this second relationship, consider the triangle in Fig. 1.30, where L_1 is perpendicular to L_2. Let

$(c, 0)$ represent the point P

$(d, 0)$ represent the point R

(e, f) represent the point Q

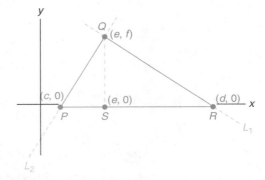

Figure 1.30

Draw QS perpendicular to the x-axis. Then S must be represented by $(e, 0)$.

Triangles PSQ and QSR in Fig. 1.30 are similar. (Note $\angle PQS = \angle QRS$.) From geometry we know that

$$\frac{PS}{QS} = \frac{QS}{SR} \tag{1}$$

In this case,

$$PS = e - c \qquad \text{(the distance from } c \text{ to } e \text{ on the } x\text{-axis)}$$
$$QS = f \qquad \text{(the distance from } 0 \text{ to } f \text{ on the } y\text{-axis)}$$
$$SR = d - e \qquad \text{(the distance from } e \text{ to } d \text{ on the } x\text{-axis)}$$

Substituting these values in Equation (1), we have

$$\frac{e - c}{f} = \frac{f}{d - e}$$

Multiplying each side of the equation by $(d - e)f$ gives

$$f^2 = (d - e)(e - c) \qquad\qquad (2)$$

Compute slopes m_1 and m_2 as follows:

$$m_1 = \frac{f - 0}{e - d} = \frac{f}{e - d}$$

$$m_2 = \frac{f - 0}{e - c} = \frac{f}{e - c}$$

$$(m_1)(m_2) = \frac{f}{e - d} \cdot \frac{f}{e - c} = \frac{f^2}{(e - d)(e - c)}$$

Substituting from Equation (2), we have

$$(m_1)(m_2) = \frac{(d - e)(e - c)}{(e - d)(e - c)} = \frac{d - e}{e - d} = -\left(\frac{e - d}{e - d}\right) = -1$$

or

$$(m_1)(m_2) = -1$$

Dividing each side of this equation by m_2, we have

$$m_1 = \frac{-1}{m_2}$$

EXAMPLE 1

Determine whether the lines given by the equations $3y + 6x - 5 = 0$ and $2y - x + 7 = 0$ are perpendicular.

Change each equation into slope-intercept form; that is, solve for y.

$$y = -2x + \frac{5}{3} \qquad \text{(Slope is } -2.)$$

and

$$y = \frac{1}{2}x - \frac{7}{2} \qquad \left(\text{Slope is } \frac{1}{2}.\right)$$

Since

$$-2 = \frac{-1}{\frac{1}{2}} \qquad \left(-2 \text{ is the negative reciprocal of } \frac{1}{2}.\right)$$

the lines are perpendicular.

EXAMPLE 2

Find the equation of the line through $(-3, 2)$ and perpendicular to $2y - 3x + 5 = 0$.

We can find the slope of the desired line by finding the negative reciprocal of the slope of the given line. First, find the slope of the line $2y - 3x + 5 = 0$. Writing this equation in slope-intercept form, we have

$$y = \frac{3}{2}x - \frac{5}{2}$$

The slope of this line is $m = \frac{3}{2}$. The slope of the line perpendicular to this line is then $-\frac{2}{3}$, the negative reciprocal of $\frac{3}{2}$. Now, using the point-slope form, we have

$$y - y_1 = m(x - x_1)$$

$$y - 2 = -\frac{2}{3}[x - (-3)]$$

$$y - 2 = -\frac{2}{3}(x + 3)$$

or

$$2x + 3y = 0$$

EXAMPLE 3

Find the equation of the line through $(2, -5)$ and parallel to $3x + y = 7$.

First, find the slope of the given line by solving its equation for y.

$$y = -3x + 7$$

Its slope is -3. The slope of any line parallel to this line has the same slope. Now, write the equation of the line with slope -3 passing through $(2, -5)$.

$$y - y_1 = m(x - x_1)$$
$$y - (-5) = -3(x - 2)$$
$$y + 5 = -3x + 6$$
$$y = -3x + 1 \quad \text{or} \quad 3x + y = 1$$

EXAMPLE 4

Judging the slopes of lines using a graphing calculator can be misleading unless a "square" viewing window is chosen. In particular, perpendicular lines don't look like they are intersecting at a 90° angle unless incremental changes along the x- and y-axes have the same meaning. The **ZoomSqr** feature squares up the current viewing window by choosing the *smaller* unit and using it on both axes (the effect is to zoom *out* to square the viewing window). As the sixth frame shows, **ZoomDec** is a square viewing window to begin with (each pixel on the x- and y-axes represents 0.1 units).

Graph $y = 3x - 4$ and $y = -\frac{1}{3}x - 2$.

green diamond Y=   **F2   6   (ZoomStandard)**   (not a square viewing window)

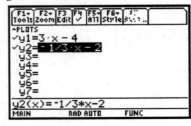   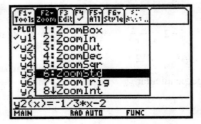   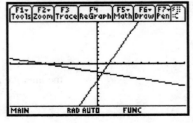

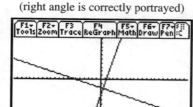

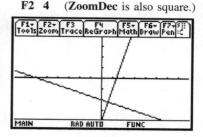

Exercises 1.4

Determine whether each given pair of equations represents lines that are parallel, perpendicular, or neither.

1. $x + 3y - 7 = 0; -3x + y + 2 = 0$ **2.** $x + 2y - 11 = 0; x + 2y + 4 = 0$

3. $-x + 4y + 7 = 0; x + 4y - 5 = 0$ **4.** $2x + 7y + 4 = 0; 7x - 2y - 5 = 0$

5. $y - 5x + 13 = 0; y - 5x + 9 = 0$ **6.** $-3x + 9y + 22 = 0; x + 3y - 17 = 0$

Find the equation of the line that satisfies each set of conditions.

7. Passes through $(-1, 5)$ and is parallel to $-2x + y + 13 = 0$.

8. Passes through $(2, -2)$ and is perpendicular to $3x - 2y - 14 = 0$.

9. Passes through $(-7, 4)$ and is perpendicular to $5y = x$.

10. Passes through $(2, -10)$ and is parallel to $2x + 3y - 7 = 0$.

11. Passes through the origin and is parallel to $3x - 4y = 12$.

12. Passes through the origin and is perpendicular to $4x + 5y = 17$.

13. Has x-intercept 6 and is perpendicular to $4x + 6y = 9$.

14. Has y-intercept -2 and is parallel to $6x - 4y = 11$.

15. Has y-intercept 8 and is parallel to $y = 2$.

16. Has x-intercept -4 and is perpendicular to $y = 6$.

17. Has x-intercept 7 and is parallel to $x = -4$.

18. Has y-intercept -9 and is perpendicular to $x = 5$.

19. The vertices of a quadrilateral are $A(-2, 3)$, $B(2, 2)$, $C(9, 6)$, and $D(5, 7)$.
 (a) Is the quadrilateral a parallelogram? Why or why not?
 (b) Is the quadrilateral a rectangle? Why or why not?

20. The vertices of a quadrilateral are $A(-4, 1)$, $B(0, -2)$, $C(6, 6)$, and $D(2, 9)$.
 (a) Is the quadrilateral a parallelogram? Why or why not?
 (b) Is the quadrilateral a rectangle? Why or why not?

1.5   THE DISTANCE AND MIDPOINT FORMULAS

We now wish to find the distance between two points on a straight line. Suppose P has the coordinates (x_1, y_1) and Q has the coordinates (x_2, y_2). Then a triangle similar to that in Fig. 1.31 can be constructed. Note that R must have the coordinates (x_2, y_1). (Point R has the same x-coordinate as Q and the same y-coordinate as P.)

Using the Pythagorean theorem, we have

$$PQ^2 = PR^2 + QR^2 \tag{3}$$

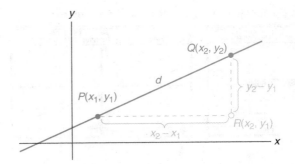

Figure 1.31 *d* is the distance between points *P* and *Q*.

Observe that

$$PR = x_2 - x_1 \qquad \text{(the horizontal distance between } x_1 \text{ and } x_2 \text{ on the } x\text{-axis)}$$
$$QR = y_2 - y_1 \qquad \text{(the vertical distance between } y_1 \text{ and } y_2 \text{ on the } y\text{-axis)}$$

Substituting these values for *PR* and *QR* in Equation (3) gives

$$PQ^2 = (x_2 - x_1)^2 + (y_2 - y_1)^2$$

DISTANCE FORMULA

The distance between two points $P(x_1, y_1)$ and $Q(x_2, y_2)$ is given by the formula

$$d = PQ = \sqrt{(x_2 - x_1)^2 + (y_2 - y_1)^2}$$

EXAMPLE 1

Find the distance, *d*, between $(3, 4)$ and $(-2, 7)$.

$$d = \sqrt{(x_2 - x_1)^2 + (y_2 - y_1)^2}$$
$$d = \sqrt{(-2 - 3)^2 + (7 - 4)^2}$$
$$= \sqrt{(-5)^2 + (3)^2} = \sqrt{25 + 9} = \sqrt{34}$$

Note that we can reverse the order of $(3, 4)$ and $(-2, 7)$ in the formula for computing *d* without affecting the result.

$$d = \sqrt{[3 - (-2)]^2 + (4 - 7)^2}$$
$$= \sqrt{(5)^2 + (-3)^2} = \sqrt{25 + 9} = \sqrt{34}$$

MIDPOINT FORMULA

The coordinates of a point $Q(x_m, y_m)$ which is midway between two points $P(x_1, y_1)$ and $R(x_2, y_2)$ are given by

$$x_m = \frac{x_1 + x_2}{2} \qquad y_m = \frac{y_1 + y_2}{2}$$

Figure 1.32 illustrates the midpoint formula. First look at points *P*, *Q*, and *R*. Triangles *PSQ* and *QTR* are congruent. This means that

$$PS = QT$$

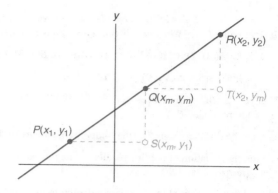

Figure 1.32 Point Q is the midpoint between points P and R.

Since

$$PS = x_m - x_1 \quad \text{and} \quad QT = x_2 - x_m$$

then

$$x_m - x_1 = x_2 - x_m$$
$$2x_m - x_1 = x_2$$
$$2x_m = x_1 + x_2$$
$$x_m = \frac{x_1 + x_2}{2}$$

The formula for y_m is found in the same manner.

EXAMPLE 2

Find the point midway between $(2, -3)$ and $(-4, 6)$.

$$x_m = \frac{x_1 + x_2}{2} = \frac{2 + (-4)}{2} = \frac{-2}{2} = -1$$
$$y_m = \frac{y_1 + y_2}{2} = \frac{-3 + 6}{2} = \frac{3}{2}$$

The midpoint is $(-1, \frac{3}{2})$.

Exercises 1.5

Find the distance between each pair of points.

1. $(4, -7); (-5, 5)$ **2.** $(4, 3); (-2, -1)$ **3.** $(3, -2); (10, -2)$

4. $(6, -2); (6, 4)$ **5.** $(5, -2); (1, 2)$ **6.** $(2, -3); (-1, 1)$

7. $(3, -5); (3, 2)$ **8.** $(2, -4); (6, -4)$

Find the coordinates of the point midway between each pair of points.

9. $(2, 3); (5, 7)$ **10.** $(0, 5); (2, -4)$ **11.** $(3, -2); (0, 0)$

12. $(2, -3); (4, -3)$ **13.** $(11, 4); (-11, -9)$ **14.** $(4, 10); (-6, -8)$

The vertices of each △ABC are given below. For each triangle, find (a) the perimeter, (b) whether it is a right triangle, (c) whether it is isosceles, and (d) its area if it is a right triangle.

15. $A(2, 8)$; $B(10, 2)$; $C(10, 8)$ **16.** $A(0, 0)$; $B(3, 3)$; $C(3, -3)$

17. $A(-3, 6)$; $B(5, 0)$; $C(4, 9)$ **18.** $A(-6, 3)$; $B(-3, 7)$; $C(1, 4)$

19. Given △ABC with vertices $A(7, -1)$, $B(9, 1)$, and $C(-3, 5)$, find the distance from A to the midpoint of side BC.

20. Find the distance from B to the midpoint of side AC in Exercise 19.

21. Find the equation of the line parallel to the line $3x - 6y = 10$ and through the midpoint of AB, where $A(4, 2)$ and $B(8, -6)$.

22. Find the equation of the line perpendicular to the line $2x + 5y = 12$ and through the midpoint of AB, where $A(-3, -4)$ and $B(7, -8)$.

23. Find the equation of the line perpendicular to the line $4x + 8y = 16$ and through the midpoint of AB, where $A(-8, 12)$ and $B(6, 10)$.

24. Find the equation of the line parallel to the line $5x - 6y = 30$ and through the midpoint of AB, where $A(3, 11)$ and $B(7, -5)$.

In Exercises 25 through 28, start with a graph and then use the distance formula and the slopes to confirm the given geometric figure.

25. Show that the figure ABCD with vertices $A(-2, 2)$, $B(1, 3)$, $C(2, 0)$, and $D(-1, -1)$ is a rectangle.

26. Show that the figure ABCD with vertices $A(2, 6)$, $B(7, 2)$, $C(8, 5)$, and $D(3, 9)$ is a parallelogram.

27. Show that the figure ABCD with vertices $A(-12, 8)$, $B(3, 2)$, $C(5, 7)$, and $D(-5, 11)$ is a trapezoid with one right angle.

28. Show that if the coordinates of the vertices of a triangle are (a, b), $(a + c, b)$, and $(a + c, b + c)$, the triangle is a right triangle.

1.6 THE CIRCLE

Equations in two variables of second degree in the form

$$Ax^2 + Bxy + Cy^2 + Dx + Ey + F = 0$$

are called **conics.** We begin a systematic study of conics with the circle.

The **circle** consists of the set of points located the same distance from a given point, called the **center.** The distance at which all points are located from the center is called the **radius.** A circle may thus be graphed in the plane given its center and radius.

EXAMPLE 1

Graph the circle with center at $(1, -2)$ and radius $r = 3$.

Plot all points in the plane located 3 units away from the point $(1, -2)$ as in Fig. 1.33. (You may wish to use a compass.)

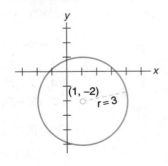

Figure 1.33

From the definition of a circle we can determine its equation. Let (h, k) be the coordinates of the center and let r represent the radius. If any point (x, y) is located on the circle, it must be a distance r from the center (h, k) as in Fig. 1.34.

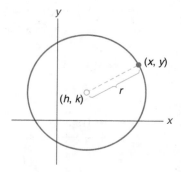

Figure 1.34 The set of points (x, y) located at the same distance r from the given point (h, k).

Using the distance formula, we have

$$\sqrt{(x_2 - x_1)^2 + (y_2 - y_1)^2} = d$$
$$\sqrt{(x - h)^2 + (y - k)^2} = r$$

Squaring each side, we have the following result:

STANDARD FORM OF A CIRCLE

$$(x - h)^2 + (y - k)^2 = r^2$$

where r is the radius and (h, k) is the center.

Any point (x, y) satisfying this equation lies on the circle.

EXAMPLE 2

Find the equation of the circle with radius 3 and center $(1, -2)$ (see Example 1).
Using the standard form of the equation of a circle, we have

$$(x - h)^2 + (y - k)^2 = r^2$$
$$(x - 1)^2 + [y - (-2)]^2 = (3)^2$$
$$(x - 1)^2 + (y + 2)^2 = 9$$

EXAMPLE 3

Find the equation of the circle with center at $(3, -2)$ and passing through $(-1, 1)$.
To write the equation, we need to know the radius r of the circle. Although r has not been stated, we do know that every point on the circle is a distance r from the center, $(3, -2)$. In

particular, the point $(-1, 1)$ is a distance r from $(3, -2)$ (see Fig. 1.35). Using the distance formula, we obtain

$$d = \sqrt{(x_2 - x_1)^2 + (y_2 - y_1)^2}$$
$$d = r = \sqrt{(x - h)^2 + (y - k)^2}$$
$$r = \sqrt{(-1 - 3)^2 + [1 - (-2)]^2}$$
$$= \sqrt{(-4)^2 + 3^2} = \sqrt{16 + 9} = \sqrt{25} = 5$$

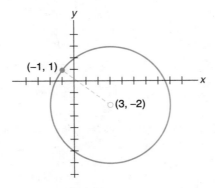

Figure 1.35

Now write the equation of the circle.

$$(x - h)^2 + (y - k)^2 = r^2$$
$$(x - 3)^2 + [y - (-2)]^2 = 5^2$$
$$(x - 3)^2 + (y + 2)^2 = 25$$

If we remove parentheses in the equation

$$(x - h)^2 + (y - k)^2 = r^2$$

we have

$$x^2 - 2xh + h^2 + y^2 - 2yk + k^2 = r^2$$

Rearranging terms, we have

$$x^2 + y^2 - 2hx - 2ky + h^2 + k^2 - r^2 = 0$$

If we let $D = -2h$, $E = -2k$, and $F = h^2 + k^2 - r^2$, we obtain the following equation:

GENERAL FORM OF A CIRCLE
$$x^2 + y^2 + Dx + Ey + F = 0$$

Any equation in this form represents a circle.

EXAMPLE 4

Write the equation $(x - 3)^2 + (y + 2)^2 = 25$ obtained in Example 3 in general form.

$$(x - 3)^2 + (y + 2)^2 = 25$$
$$x^2 - 6x + 9 + y^2 + 4y + 4 = 25$$
$$x^2 + y^2 - 6x + 4y - 12 = 0$$

EXAMPLE 5

Find the center and radius of the circle given by the equation

$$x^2 + y^2 - 4x + 2y - 11 = 0$$

Looking back at how we arrived at the general equation of a circle, we see that if we rearrange the terms of the equation as

$$(x^2 - 4x \quad) + (y^2 + 2y \quad) = 11$$

then $(x^2 - 4x \quad)$ represents the first two terms of

$$(x - h)^2 = x^2 - 2hx + h^2$$

and $(y^2 + 2y \quad)$ represents the first two terms of

$$(y - k)^2 = y^2 - 2ky + k^2$$

This means that

$$-4 = -2h \quad \text{and} \quad 2 = -2k$$
$$h = 2 \qquad\qquad k = -1$$

To complete the squares $(x - h)^2$ and $(y - k)^2$, we must add $h^2 = 2^2 = 4$ and $k^2 = (-1)^2 = 1$ to each side of the equation.

$$(x^2 - 4x \quad) + (y^2 + 2y \quad) = 11$$
$$(x^2 - 4x + 4) + (y^2 + 2y + 1) = 11 + 4 + 1$$
$$(x - 2)^2 + (y + 1)^2 = 16$$
$$(x - 2)^2 + [y - (-1)]^2 = 16 = 4^2$$

From this we see that we have the standard form of the equation of a circle with radius 4 and center at the point $(2, -1)$.

This process is called **completing the square** of the x- and y-terms. In general, if the coefficients of x^2 and y^2 are both equal to 1, then these values can be found as follows: Add h^2 and k^2 to each side of the equation, where

$$h^2 = (\tfrac{1}{2} \text{ the coefficient of } x)^2 = (\tfrac{1}{2}D)^2$$
$$k^2 = (\tfrac{1}{2} \text{ the coefficient of } y)^2 = (\tfrac{1}{2}E)^2$$

EXAMPLE 6

Find the center and radius of the circle given by the equation

$$x^2 + y^2 + 6x - 4y - 12 = 0$$

Sketch the graph of the circle. Write

$$h^2 = [(\tfrac{1}{2})(6)]^2 = 3^2 = 9$$
$$k^2 = [\tfrac{1}{2}(-4)]^2 = (-2)^2 = 4$$

Rewrite the equation and add 9 and 4 to each side.

$$(x^2 + 6x \quad) + (y^2 - 4y \quad) = 12$$
$$(x^2 + 6x + 9) + (y^2 - 4y + 4) = 12 + 9 + 4$$
$$(x + 3)^2 + (y - 2)^2 = 25 = 5^2$$

The center is at $(-3, 2)$ and the radius is 5. Plot all points that are at a distance of 5 from the point $(-3, 2)$ as in Fig. 1.36.

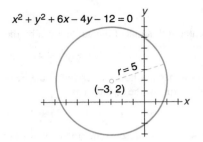

$x^2 + y^2 + 6x - 4y - 12 = 0$

$r = 5$

$(-3, 2)$

Figure 1.36

If the center of a circle is at the origin, then $h = 0$ and $k = 0$, and its standard equation becomes

$$x^2 + y^2 = r^2$$

where r is the radius and the center is at the origin.

EXAMPLE 7

Find the equation of the circle with radius 3 and center at the origin. Also, graph the circle.

$x^2 + y^2 = r^2$
$x^2 + y^2 = (3)^2$
$x^2 + y^2 = 9$ (See Fig. 1.37.)

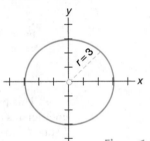

$r = 3$

Figure 1.37

Exercises 1.6

Graph the circle with the given center and radius.

1. Center at $(2, -1)$, $r = 3$.

2. Center at $(3, 3)$, $r = 2$.

3. Center at $(0, 2)$, $r = 4$.

4. Center at $(-4, -5)$, $r = 3$.

Find the equation of the circle (in standard form) with the given properties.

5. Center at $(1, -1)$, radius 4.

6. Center at $(-2, 3)$, radius $\sqrt{5}$.

7. Center at $(-2, -4)$, passing through $(1, -9)$.

8. Center at $(5, 2)$, passing through $(-2, -6)$.

9. Center at $(0, 0)$, radius 6.

10. Center at $(0, 0)$, passing through $(3, -4)$.

Find the center and radius of the given circle.

11. $x^2 + y^2 = 16$

12. $x^2 + y^2 - 4x - 5 = 0$

13. $x^2 + y^2 + 6x - 8y - 39 = 0$

14. $x^2 + y^2 - 6x + 14y + 42 = 0$

15. $x^2 + y^2 - 8x + 12y - 8 = 0$

16. $x^2 + y^2 + 10x + 2y - 14 = 0$

17. $x^2 + y^2 - 12x - 2y - 12 = 0$

18. $x^2 + y^2 + 4x - 9y + 4 = 0$

19. $x^2 + y^2 + 7x + 3y - 9 = 0$

20. $x^2 + y^2 - 5x - 8y = 0$

21. Find the equation of the circle or circles whose center is on the *y*-axis and that contain the points $(1, 4)$ and $(-3, 2)$. Give the center and radius.

22. Find the equation of the circle with center in the first quadrant on the line $y = 2x$, tangent to the *x*-axis, and radius 6. Give its center.

23. Find the equation of the circle containing the points $(3, 1)$, $(0, 0)$, and $(8, 4)$. Give its center and radius.

24. Find the equation of the circle containing the points $(1, -4)$, $(-3, 4)$, and $(4, 5)$. Give its center and radius.

1.7   THE PARABOLA

While the parabola may not be as familiar a geometric curve as the circle, examples of the parabola are found in many technical applications. A **parabola** consists of all points that are the same distance from a given fixed point and a given fixed line. The fixed point is called the **focus.** The fixed line is called the **directrix.** This relationship is shown in Fig. 1.38 for the points *P*, *Q*, and *V*, which lie on a parabola with focus *F* and directrix *D*.

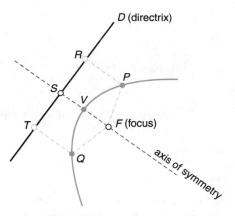

Figure 1.38   A parabola is a set of points that are the same distance from a given fixed point (focus) and a given fixed line (directrix).

Note:

$$RP = PF$$
$$SV = VF$$
$$TQ = QF$$

The point *V* midway between the directrix and the focus is called the **vertex.** The vertex and the focus lie on a line perpendicular to the directrix, which is called the **axis of symmetry.**

There are two standard forms for the equation of a parabola. The form depends on the position of the parabola in the plane. We first discuss the parabola with focus on the x-axis at $(p, 0)$ and directrix the line $x = -p$ as in Fig. 1.39. Let $P(x, y)$ represent any point on this parabola. Vertex V is then at the origin, and the axis of symmetry is the x-axis.

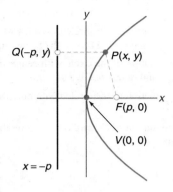

Figure 1.39

By the way we have described the parabola, the distance between P and F must equal the distance between P and Q. Using the distance formula, we have

$$PF = PQ$$
$$\sqrt{(x - p)^2 + (y - 0)^2} = \sqrt{[x - (-p)]^2 + (y - y)^2}$$
$$(x - p)^2 + y^2 = (x + p)^2 \quad \text{(Square each side.)}$$
$$x^2 - 2xp + p^2 + y^2 = x^2 + 2xp + p^2$$
$$y^2 = 4px$$

STANDARD FORM OF A PARABOLA

$$y^2 = 4px$$

with focus at $(p, 0)$ and with the line $x = -p$ as the directrix.

Note that in Fig. 1.39, $p > 0$.

EXAMPLE 1

Find the equation of the parabola with focus at $(3, 0)$ and directrix $x = -3$.
  In this case $p = 3$, so we have

$$y^2 = 4(3)x$$
$$y^2 = 12x$$

EXAMPLE 2

Find the focus and equation of the directrix of the parabola $y^2 = 24x$.

$$y^2 = 24x$$
$$y^2 = 4(6)x$$
$$y^2 = 4px$$

Since p must be 6, the focus is $(6, 0)$ and the directrix is the line $x = -6$.

EXAMPLE 3

Find the equation of the parabola with focus at $(-2, 0)$ and with directrix $x = 2$. Sketch the graph.

Here $p = -2$. The equation becomes

$$y^2 = 4(-2)x$$
$$y^2 = -8x \qquad \text{(See Fig. 1.40.)}$$

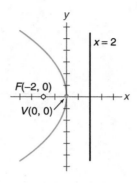

Figure 1.40

Observe the following:

1. If $p > 0$, the coefficient of x in the equation $y^2 = 4px$ is *positive* and the parabola opens to the *right* (see Fig. 1.41a).

2. If $p < 0$, the coefficient of x in the equation $y^2 = 4px$ is *negative* and the parabola opens to the *left* (see Fig. 1.41b).

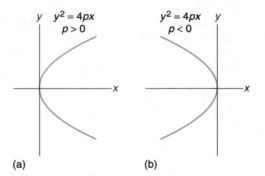

Figure 1.41   Standard form of the parabola $y^2 = 4px$.

We obtain the other standard form of the parabola when the focus lies on the y-axis and the directrix is parallel to the x-axis. Let $(0, p)$ be the focus F and $y = -p$ be the directrix. The vertex is still at the origin, but the axis of symmetry is now the y-axis (see Fig. 1.42).

$$x^2 = 4py$$

with focus at $(0, p)$ and with the line $y = -p$ as the directrix. (See Fig. 1.42.)

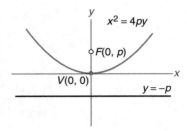

Figure 1.42

EXAMPLE 4

Find the equation of the parabola with focus at $(0, 3)$ and with directrix $y = -3$. Sketch the graph.

Since the focus lies on the y-axis and the directrix is parallel to the x-axis, we use the equation $x^2 = 4py$ with $p = 3$ (see Fig. 1.43).

$$x^2 = 4(3)y$$
$$x^2 = 12y$$

EXAMPLE 5

Find the equation of the parabola with focus at $(0, -1)$ and with directrix $y = 1$. Sketch the graph.

Again the focus lies on the y-axis with directrix parallel to the x-axis, so we use the equation $x^2 = 4py$ with $p = -1$ (see Fig. 1.44).

$$x^2 = 4(-1)y$$
$$x^2 = -4y$$

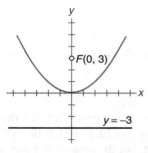

Figure 1.43

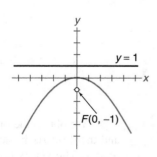

Figure 1.44

Observe the following:

1. If $p > 0$, the coefficient of y in the equation $x^2 = 4py$ is *positive* and the parabola opens *upward* (see Fig. 1.45a).

2. If $p < 0$, the coefficient of y in the equation $x^2 = 4py$ is *negative* and the parabola opens *downward* (see Fig. 1.45b).

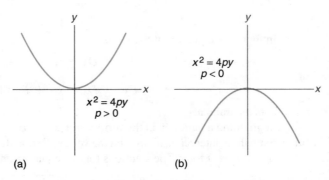

(a)   (b)

Figure 1.45   Standard form of the parabola $x^2 = 4py$.

We are now able to describe the graph of a parabola by inspection of its equation in standard form. We can also find the focus and directrix.

EXAMPLE 6

Describe the graph of the equation $y^2 = 20x$.

    This is an equation of a parabola in the form $y^2 = 4px$. Since $p = 5$, this parabola has its focus at $(5, 0)$ and its directrix is the line $x = -5$. The parabola opens to the right (since $p > 0$).

EXAMPLE 7

Describe the graph of the equation $x^2 = -2y$.

    This is an equation of a parabola in the form $x^2 = 4py$, where $p = -\frac{1}{2}$ [as $4(-\frac{1}{2}) = -2$]. The focus is at $(0, -\frac{1}{2})$ and the directrix is the line $y = \frac{1}{2}$. The parabola opens downward (since $p < 0$).

Of course, not all parabolas are given in standard position.

EXAMPLE 8

Find the equation of the parabola with focus at $(1, 3)$ and with the line $y = -1$ as directrix. We must use the definition of the parabola (see Fig. 1.46).

$$PF = PQ$$
$$\sqrt{(x - 1)^2 + (y - 3)^2} = \sqrt{(x - x)^2 + [y - (-1)]^2}$$
$$x^2 - 2x + 1 + y^2 - 6y + 9 = y^2 + 2y + 1 \qquad \text{(Square each side and}$$
$$x^2 - 2x - 8y + 9 = 0 \qquad\qquad\qquad \text{remove parentheses.)}$$

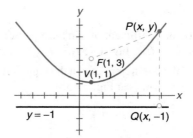

Figure 1.46

In fact, any equation of the form

$$Ax^2 + Dx + Ey + F = 0$$

or

$$Cy^2 + Dx + Ey + F = 0$$

represents a parabola.

In graphing a parabola in the form $y = f(x) = ax^2 + bx + c, a \neq 0$, it is most help-ful to graph the x-intercepts, if any, and the vertex. To find the x-intercepts, let $y = 0$ and solve $ax^2 + bx + c = 0$ for x. The solutions for this equation are given by the quadratic formula:

$$x = \frac{-b \pm \sqrt{b^2 - 4ac}}{2a}$$

Recall that the solutions are real numbers only if the *discriminant*, $b^2 - 4ac$, is nonnega-tive and that the solutions are imaginary if $b^2 - 4ac < 0$. Thus, the graph of the parabola $y = f(x) = ax^2 + bx + c, a \neq 0$, has

1. two different x-intercepts if $b^2 - 4ac > 0$,
2. only one x-intercept if $b^2 - 4ac = 0$ (the graph is tangent to the x-axis),
3. no x-intercepts if $b^2 - 4ac < 0$.

The **axis of symmetry** of the parabola in the form $y = f(x) = ax^2 + bx + c$ is a vertical line halfway between the x-intercepts. The equation of the axis is the vertical line passing through the midpoint of the line segment joining the two x-intercepts (see Fig. 1.47). This midpoint is

$$\frac{x_1 + x_2}{2} = \frac{\dfrac{-b - \sqrt{b^2 - 4ac}}{2a} + \dfrac{-b + \sqrt{b^2 - 4ac}}{2a}}{2} = \frac{\dfrac{-2b}{2a}}{2} = -\frac{b}{2a}$$

Thus, the equation of the axis is $x = -\dfrac{b}{2a}$.

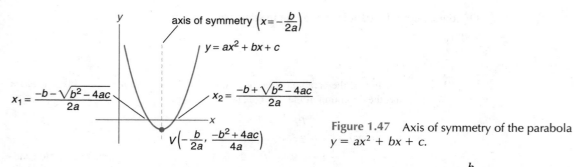

Figure 1.47 Axis of symmetry of the parabola $y = ax^2 + bx + c$.

Since the parabola contains the vertex, its x-coordinate is $-\dfrac{b}{2a}$. Its y-coordinate is then $f\left(-\dfrac{b}{2a}\right)$. To find the y-coordinate, evaluate

$$f(x) = ax^2 + bx + c$$

$$f\left(-\frac{b}{2a}\right) = a\left(-\frac{b}{2a}\right)^2 + b\left(-\frac{b}{2a}\right) + c$$

$$= \frac{b^2}{4a} - \frac{b^2}{2a} + c$$

$$= \frac{b^2}{4a} - \frac{2b^2}{4a} + \frac{4ac}{4a}$$

$$= \frac{-b^2 + 4ac}{4a}$$

AXIS AND VERTEX OF A PARABOLA

Given the parabola $y = f(x) = ax^2 + bx + c$, its axis is the vertical line $x = -\dfrac{b}{2a}$ and its vertex is the point

$$\left(-\frac{b}{2a}, f\left(-\frac{b}{2a}\right)\right) = \left(-\frac{b}{2a}, \frac{-b^2 + 4ac}{4a}\right)$$

The vertex is a maximum point if $a < 0$ and a minimum point if $a > 0$.

EXAMPLE 9

Graph $y = f(x) = 2x^2 - 8x + 11$. Find its vertex and the equation of the axis.
     First, note that $b^2 - 4ac = (-8)^2 - 4(2)(11) = -24 < 0$, which means that the graph has no x-intercepts. The equation of the axis is

$$x = -\frac{b}{2a} = -\frac{-8}{2(2)} = 2$$

The vertex is the point $(2, f(2))$ or $(2, 2 \cdot 2^2 - 8 \cdot 2 + 11) = (2, 3)$.

This y-coordinate may also be found using the formula

$$\frac{-b^2 + 4ac}{4a} = \frac{-(-8)^2 + 4 \cdot 2 \cdot 11}{4 \cdot 2} = \frac{24}{8} = 3$$

Since $a > 0$, the vertex $(2, 3)$ is a minimum point and the graph opens upward. You may also find some additional ordered pairs to graph this equation depending on whether you need only a rough sketch or a fairly accurate graph. The graph is shown in Fig. 1.48.

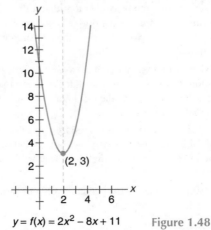

$y = f(x) = 2x^2 - 8x + 11$

Figure 1.48

Since the vertex of a parabola in the form $y = f(x) = ax^2 + bx + c$ is the highest point or the lowest point on the graph, we can use this fact to find a maximum or a minimum value of a quadratic function.

EXAMPLE 10

An object is thrown upward with an initial velocity of 48 ft/s. Its height after t seconds is given by $h = f(t) = 48t - 16t^2$. Find its maximum height and the time it takes the object to hit the ground.

First, find the vertex.

$$x = -\frac{b}{2a} = -\frac{48}{2(-16)} = \frac{3}{2}$$

Then the vertex is

$$\left(\frac{3}{2}, f\left(\frac{3}{2}\right)\right) = \left(\frac{3}{2}, 48\left(\frac{3}{2}\right) - 16\left(\frac{3}{2}\right)^2\right) = \left(\frac{3}{2}, 36\right)$$

Since $a = -16 < 0$, the vertex is a maximum point, and the maximum height is 36 ft.

The first coordinate of the vertex gives the amount of time it takes for the object to reach its maximum height. The time it takes for such a projectile to reach its maximum height is the same as the time it takes to drop back to the ground. Thus, the object hits the ground $2 \cdot \frac{3}{2}$ or 3 s after it is thrown.

Exercises 1.7

Find the focus and the directrix of each parabola. Sketch each graph.

1. $x^2 = 4y$ **2.** $x^2 = -8y$ **3.** $y^2 = -16x$ **4.** $x^2 = -6y$

5. $y^2 = x$ **6.** $y^2 = -4x$ **7.** $x^2 = 16y$ **8.** $y^2 = -12x$

9. $y^2 = 8x$ **10.** $x^2 = -y$

Find the equation of the parabola with given focus and directrix.

11. $(2, 0)$, $x = -2$ **12.** $(0, -3)$, $y = 3$ **13.** $(-8, 0)$, $x = 8$

14. $(5, 0)$, $x = -5$ **15.** $(0, 6)$, $y = -6$ **16.** $(0, -1)$, $y = 1$

17. Find the equation of the parabola with focus at $(-4, 0)$ and vertex at $(0, 0)$.

18. Find the equation of the parabola with vertex at $(0, 0)$ and directrix $y = -2$.

19. Find the equation of the parabola with focus $(-1, 3)$ and directrix $x = 3$.

20. Find the equation of the parabola with focus $(2, -5)$ and directrix $y = -1$.

21. The surface of a roadway over a bridge follows a parabolic curve with vertex at the middle of the bridge. The span of the bridge is 400 m. The roadway is 16 m higher in the middle than at the end supports. How far above the end supports is a point 50 m from the middle? 150 m from the middle?

22. The shape of a wire hanging between two poles closely approximates a parabola. Find the equation of a wire that is suspended between two poles 40 m apart and whose lowest point is 10 m below the level of the insulators. (Choose the lowest point as the origin of your coordinate system.)

23. A suspension bridge is supported by two cables that hang between two supports. The curve of these cables is approximately parabolic. Find the equation of this curve if the focus lies 8 m above the lowest point of the cable. (Set up the xy-coordinate system so that the vertex is at the origin.)

24. A culvert is shaped like a parabola, 120 cm across the top and 80 cm deep. How wide is the culvert 50 cm from the top?

Graph each parabola. Find its vertex and the equation of the axis.

25. $y = 2x^2 + 7x - 15$ **26.** $y = -x^2 - 6x - 8$

27. $f(x) = -2x^2 + 4x + 16$ **28.** $f(x) = 3x^2 + 6x + 10$

29. Starting at $(0, 0)$, a projectile travels along the path $y = f(x) = -\frac{1}{256}x^2 + 4x$, where x is in metres. Find **(a)** the maximum height and **(b)** the range of the projectile.

30. The height of a bullet fired vertically upward is given by $h = f(t) = 1200t - 16t^2$ (initial velocity is 1200 ft/s). Find **(a)** its maximum height and **(b)** the time it takes to hit the ground.

31. Enclose a rectangular area with 240 m of fencing. Find the largest possible area that can be enclosed.

32. A 36-in.-wide sheet of metal is bent into a rectangular trough with a cross section as shown in Fig. 1.49. What dimensions will maximize the flow of water? That is, what dimensions will maximize the cross-sectional area?

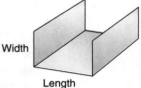

Figure 1.49

1.8 THE ELLIPSE

An **ellipse** consists of the set of points in a plane, the *sum* of whose distances from two fixed points is a positive constant. These two fixed points are called **foci**. As in Fig. 1.50, let the foci lie on the x-axis at $(-c, 0)$ and $(c, 0)$. Then any point $P(x, y)$ lies on the ellipse if its distance d_1 from P to the point $(-c, 0)$ plus its distance d_2 from P to the point $(c, 0)$ is equal to a given constant k. Let the constant be written as $k = 2a$; then

$$d_1 + d_2 = 2a$$

Again using the formula for computing the distance between two points, we have

$$\sqrt{[x - (-c)]^2 + (y - 0)^2} + \sqrt{(x - c)^2 + (y - 0)^2} = 2a$$

Rewrite the previous equation as follows:

$$\sqrt{(x + c)^2 + y^2} = 2a - \sqrt{(x - c)^2 + y^2}$$

$$(x + c)^2 + y^2 = 4a^2 - 4a\sqrt{(x - c)^2 + y^2} + (x - c)^2 + y^2 \quad \text{(Square each side.)}$$

$$x^2 + 2cx + c^2 + y^2 = 4a^2 - 4a\sqrt{(x - c)^2 + y^2} + x^2 - 2cx + c^2 + y^2$$

$$4cx - 4a^2 = -4a\sqrt{(x - c)^2 + y^2}$$

$$a^2 - cx = a\sqrt{(x - c)^2 + y^2} \quad \text{(Divide each side by } -4.)$$

$$(a^2 - cx)^2 = a^2[(x - c)^2 + y^2] \quad \text{(Square each side.)}$$

$$a^4 - 2a^2cx + c^2x^2 = a^2[x^2 - 2cx + c^2 + y^2]$$

$$a^4 - 2a^2cx + c^2x^2 = a^2x^2 - 2a^2cx + a^2c^2 + a^2y^2$$

$$a^4 - a^2c^2 = a^2x^2 - c^2x^2 + a^2y^2$$

$$a^2(a^2 - c^2) = (a^2 - c^2)x^2 + a^2y^2 \quad \text{(Factor.)}$$

$$1 = \frac{x^2}{a^2} + \frac{y^2}{a^2 - c^2} \quad \text{[Divide each side by } a^2(a^2 - c^2).]$$

If we now let $y = 0$ in this equation, we find that $x^2 = a^2$. The points $(-a, 0)$ and $(a, 0)$, which lie on the graph, are called **vertices** of the ellipse. Observe that $a > c$.

If we let $b^2 = a^2 - c^2$, the preceding equation becomes

$$\frac{x^2}{a^2} + \frac{y^2}{b^2} = 1$$

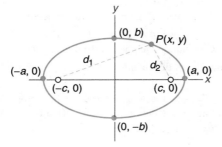

Figure 1.50   An ellipse is a set of points in a plane, the sum of whose distances from two fixed points (called foci) is a positive constant.

The line segment connecting the vertices $(a, 0)$ and $(-a, 0)$ is called the **major axis.** The point midway between the vertices is called the **center** of the ellipse. In this case the major axis lies on the x-axis and the center is at the origin. If we let $x = 0$ in the above equation, we find $y^2 = b^2$. The line connecting $(0, b)$ and $(0, -b)$ is perpendicular to the major axis and passes through the center (see Fig. 1.50). This line is called the **minor axis** of the ellipse. In this case the minor axis lies on the y-axis. Note that $2a$ is the length of the major axis and $2b$ is the length of the minor axis.

STANDARD FORM OF AN ELLIPSE

$$\frac{x^2}{a^2} + \frac{y^2}{b^2} = 1$$

with center at the origin and with the major axis lying on the x-axis.
Note: $a > b$.

One easy way to approximate the curve of an ellipse is to fix a string at two points (foci) on a piece of paper as in Fig. 1.51(a). Then, using a pencil to keep the string taut, trace out the curve as illustrated. Note that $d_1 + d_2$ is always constant—namely, the length of the string. Detach the string and compare the length of the string with the length of the major axis; note that the lengths are the same, $2a$.

The relationship $b^2 = a^2 - c^2$ or $a^2 = b^2 + c^2$ can also be seen from this string demonstration, as in Fig. 1.51(b). Put a pencil inside the taut string and on an end of the minor axis; this bisects the length of string and sets up a right triangle with a as its hypotenuse and b and c as the legs.

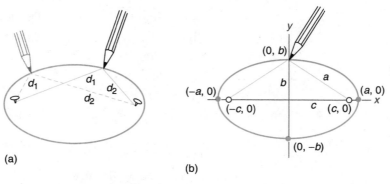

(a)

(b)

Figure 1.51   Drawing an ellipse with the use of a string.

EXAMPLE 1

Find the vertices, the foci, and the lengths of the major and minor axes of the ellipse

$$\frac{x^2}{25} + \frac{y^2}{9} = 1$$

Sketch the graph.

Since $a^2 = 25$, the vertices are at $(5, 0)$ and $(-5, 0)$. The length of the major axis is $2a = 2(5) = 10$. Since $b^2 = 9$, then $b = 3$, and the length of the minor axis is $2b = 2(3) = 6$. We need the value of c to determine the foci. Since $b^2 = a^2 - c^2$, we can write

$$c^2 = a^2 - b^2 = 25 - 9 = 16$$
$$c = 4$$

The foci are thus $(4, 0)$ and $(-4, 0)$. The graph of the ellipse is shown in Fig. 1.52.

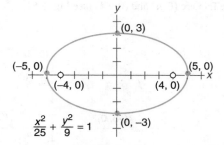

Figure 1.52

You will want to remember the equation relating a, b, and c for the ellipse:

$$c^2 = a^2 - b^2$$

When the major axis lies on the y-axis with center at the origin as in Fig. 1.53, the **standard form** of the equation of the ellipse becomes as follows:

STANDARD FORM OF AN ELLIPSE

$$\frac{y^2}{a^2} + \frac{x^2}{b^2} = 1$$

with center at the origin and with the major axis lying on the y-axis.
   Note: $a > b$

This result may be shown similarly as the derivation of the first standard form. Notice that the larger denominator now lies below y^2 instead of below x^2 as in the first case. The vertices are now $(0, a)$ and $(0, -a)$.

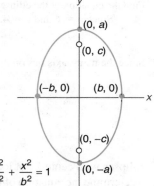

Figure 1.53 $\dfrac{y^2}{a^2} + \dfrac{x^2}{b^2} = 1$

EXAMPLE 2

Given the ellipse $25x^2 + 9y^2 = 225$, find the foci, vertices, and lengths of the major and minor axes. Sketch the graph.

First divide each side of the equation by 225 to put the equation in standard form.

$$\frac{x^2}{9} + \frac{y^2}{25} = 1$$

Since the larger denominator belongs to the y^2 term, this ellipse has its major axis on the y-axis and a^2 must then be 25. So $a = 5$ and $b = 3$. The vertices are $(0, 5)$ and $(0, -5)$. The length of the major axis is $2a = 10$ and the length of the minor axis is $2b = 6$.

$$c^2 = a^2 - b^2 = 25 - 9 = 16$$
$$c = 4$$

Thus the foci are $(0, 4)$ and $(0, -4)$ (see Fig. 1.54).

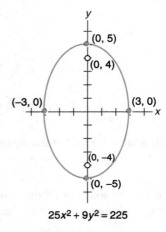

$$25x^2 + 9y^2 = 225$$

Figure 1.54

In general, a is always greater than b for an ellipse. The following are also true:

1. If the larger denominator belongs to the x^2-term, then its denominator is a^2, the major axis lies on the x-axis, and the vertices are $(a, 0)$ and $(-a, 0)$.

2. If the larger denominator belongs to the y^2-term, then its denominator is a^2, the major axis lies on the y-axis, and the vertices are $(0, a)$ and $(0, -a)$.

EXAMPLE 3

Find the equation of the ellipse with vertices at $(6, 0)$ and $(-6, 0)$ and foci at $(4, 0)$ and $(-4, 0)$.

Since $a = 6$ and $c = 4$, we have $a^2 = 36$ and $c^2 = 16$. Thus

$$b^2 = a^2 - c^2 = 36 - 16 = 20$$

Since the major axis lies on the x-axis, the equation in standard form is

$$\frac{x^2}{a^2} + \frac{y^2}{b^2} = 1$$
$$\frac{x^2}{36} + \frac{y^2}{20} = 1$$

Ellipses with centers not located at the origin will be presented in Section 1.10. If we were to determine the equation of the ellipse where the sum of the distances of all points from the foci $(-2, 3)$ and $(6, 3)$ is always 10, we would have

$$9x^2 + 25y^2 - 36x - 150y + 36 = 0$$

In general, an equation of the form

$$Ax^2 + Cy^2 + Dx + Ey + F = 0$$

represents an ellipse with axes parallel to the coordinate axes, where A and C are both positive (or both negative) and, unlike a circle, $A \neq C$.

Exercises 1.8

Find the vertices, foci, and lengths of the major and minor axes of each ellipse. Sketch each graph.

1. $\dfrac{x^2}{25} + \dfrac{y^2}{16} = 1$
2. $\dfrac{x^2}{36} + \dfrac{y^2}{64} = 1$
3. $9x^2 + 16y^2 = 144$

4. $25x^2 + 16y^2 = 400$
5. $36x^2 + y^2 = 36$
6. $4x^2 + 3y^2 = 12$

7. $16x^2 + 9y^2 = 144$
8. $x^2 + 4y^2 = 16$

Find the equation of each ellipse satisfying the given conditions.

9. Vertices at $(4, 0)$ and $(-4, 0)$; foci at $(2, 0)$ and $(-2, 0)$.

10. Vertices at $(0, 7)$ and $(0, -7)$; foci at $(0, 5)$ and $(0, -5)$.

11. Vertices at $(0, 9)$ and $(0, -9)$; foci at $(0, 6)$ and $(0, -6)$.

12. Vertices at $(12, 0)$ and $(-12, 0)$; foci at $(10, 0)$ and $(-10, 0)$.

13. Vertices at $(6, 0)$ and $(-6, 0)$; length of minor axis is 10.

14. Vertices at $(0, 10)$ and $(0, -10)$; length of minor axis is 18.

15. Foci at $(0, 5)$ and $(0, -5)$; length of major axis is 16.

16. Foci at $(3, 0)$ and $(-3, 0)$; length of major axis is 8.

17. A weather satellite with an orbit about the earth reaches a minimum altitude of 1000 mi and a maximum altitude of 1600 mi. The path of its orbit is approximately an ellipse with the center of the earth at one focus. Find the equation of this curve. Assume the radius of the earth is 4000 mi and the x-axis is the major axis.

18. An arch is in the shape of the upper half of an ellipse with a horizontal major axis supporting a foot bridge 40 m long over a stream in a park. The center of the arch is 8 m above the bridge supports. Find an equation of the ellipse. (Choose the point midway between the bridge supports as the origin.)

1.9   THE HYPERBOLA

A **hyperbola** consists of the set of points in a plane, the *difference* of whose distances from two fixed points is a positive constant. The two fixed points are called the **foci.**

Assume now as in Fig. 1.55 that the foci lie on the x-axis at $(-c, 0)$ and $(c, 0)$. Then a point $P(x, y)$ lies on the hyperbola if the difference between its distances to the foci is

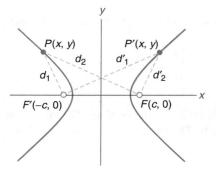

Figure 1.55 A hyperbola is the set of points in a plane, the difference of whose distances from two fixed points (called foci) is a positive constant.

equal to a given constant k. That is, $d_1 - d_2 = k$ or $d_2 - d_1 = k$. Again, this constant k equals $2a$; that is,

$$d_2 - d_1 = 2a$$

To obtain the equation of the hyperbola, use the distance formula.

$$d_2 - d_1 = 2a$$

$$\sqrt{(x - c)^2 + (y - 0)^2} - \sqrt{[x - (-c)]^2 + (y - 0)^2} = 2a$$

Rewrite the equation above as follows:

$$\sqrt{(x - c)^2 + y^2} = 2a + \sqrt{(x + c)^2 + y^2}$$

$$(x - c)^2 + y^2 = 4a^2 + 4a\sqrt{(x + c)^2 + y^2} + (x + c)^2 + y^2 \quad \text{(Square each side.)}$$

$$x^2 - 2cx + c^2 + y^2 = 4a^2 + 4a\sqrt{(x + c)^2 + y^2} + x^2 + 2cx + c^2 + y^2$$

$$-4a^2 - 4cx = 4a\sqrt{(x + c)^2 + y^2}$$

$$-a^2 - cx = a\sqrt{(x + c)^2 + y^2} \quad \text{(Divide each side by 4.)}$$

$$a^4 + 2a^2cx + c^2x^2 = a^2[(x + c)^2 + y^2] \quad \text{(Square each side.)}$$

$$a^4 + 2a^2cx + c^2x^2 = a^2[x^2 + 2cx + c^2 + y^2]$$

$$a^4 + 2a^2cx + c^2x^2 = a^2x^2 + 2a^2cx + a^2c^2 + a^2y^2$$

$$a^4 - a^2c^2 = a^2x^2 - c^2x^2 + a^2y^2$$

$$a^2(a^2 - c^2) = (a^2 - c^2)x^2 + a^2y^2 \quad \text{(Factor.)}$$

$$1 = \frac{x^2}{a^2} + \frac{y^2}{a^2 - c^2} \quad \text{[Divide each side by } a^2(a^2 - c^2).]$$

$$1 = \frac{x^2}{a^2} - \frac{y^2}{c^2 - a^2}$$

In triangle $F'PF$

$$PF' < PF + FF' \quad \text{(The sum of any two sides of a triangle is greater than the third side.)}$$

$$PF' - PF < FF'$$

$$2a < 2c \quad (PF' - PF = 2a \text{ by the definition of a hyperbola and } FF' = 2c.)$$

$$a < c$$

$$a^2 < c^2 \quad \text{(Since } a > 0 \text{ and } c > 0.)$$

$$0 < c^2 - a^2$$

Since $c^2 - a^2$ is positive, we may replace it by the positive number, b^2, as follows:

$$1 = \frac{x^2}{a^2} - \frac{y^2}{b^2}$$

where $b^2 = c^2 - a^2$.

The equation of the hyperbola with foci on the x-axis at $(c, 0)$ and $(-c, 0)$ is

$$\boxed{\frac{x^2}{a^2} - \frac{y^2}{b^2} = 1}$$

The points $(a, 0)$ and $(-a, 0)$ are called the **vertices.** The line segment connecting the vertices is called the **transverse axis.** The vertices and transverse axis in this case lie on the

x-axis. The length of the transverse axis is $2a$. The line segment connecting the points $(0, b)$ and $(0, -b)$ is called the **conjugate axis** and in this case lies on the y-axis. The length of the conjugate axis is $2b$. The **center** lies at the intersection of the conjugate and transverse axes.

STANDARD FORM OF A HYPERBOLA

$$\frac{x^2}{a^2} - \frac{y^2}{b^2} = 1$$

with center at the origin and with the transverse axis lying on the x-axis.

If we draw the central rectangle as in Fig. 1.56 and draw lines passing through opposite vertices of the rectangle, we obtain lines called the **asymptotes** of the hyperbola. In this case the equations of these lines are

$$y = \frac{b}{a}x$$

$$y = -\frac{b}{a}x$$

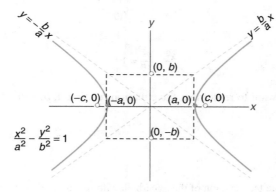

Figure 1.56

Asymptotes serve as guidelines to the branches of the hyperbola. That is, as the distance from the center of the hyperbola increases, the points on the branches get closer and closer to the asymptotes but never cross or touch them.

To sketch the graph of a hyperbola:

1. Locate the vertices $(a, 0)$ and $(-a, 0)$.
2. Locate the points $(0, b)$ and $(0, -b)$.
3. Sketch the central rectangle as in Fig. 1.56. [The coordinates of the vertices are (a, b), $(a, -b)$, $(-a, b)$, and $(-a, -b)$.]
4. Sketch the two asymptotes (the lines passing through the pairs of opposite vertices of the rectangle).
5. Sketch the branches of the hyperbola.

EXAMPLE 1

Find the vertices, foci, and lengths of the transverse and conjugate axes of the hyperbola

$$\frac{x^2}{9} - \frac{y^2}{16} = 1$$

Sketch the graph. Find the equations of the asymptotes.

Since 9 is the denominator of the x^2-term, $a^2 = 9$ and $a = 3$. The vertices are therefore $(3, 0)$ and $(-3, 0)$, and the length of the transverse axis is $2a = 2(3) = 6$. Since 16 is the denominator of the y^2-term, $b^2 = 16$ and $b = 4$. So the length of the conjugate axis is $2b = 2(4) = 8$.

To find the foci we need to know c^2. Since $b^2 = c^2 - a^2$, we have

$$c^2 = a^2 + b^2 = (3)^2 + (4)^2 = 25$$
$$c = 5$$

The foci are $(5, 0)$ and $(-5, 0)$. The asymptotes are $y = \frac{4}{3}x$ and $y = -\frac{4}{3}x$ (see Fig. 1.57).

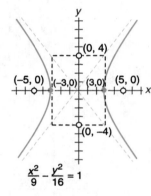

Figure 1.57

You will want to remember the equation relating a, b, and c for the hyperbola.

$$c^2 = a^2 + b^2$$

EXAMPLE 2

Write the equation of the hyperbola with foci at $(5, 0)$ and $(-5, 0)$ and whose transverse axis is 8 units in length.

Here we have $c = 5$. Since $2a = 8$, $a = 4$,

$$c^2 = a^2 + b^2$$
$$25 = 16 + b^2$$
$$b^2 = 9$$

The equation is then

$$\frac{x^2}{16} - \frac{y^2}{9} = 1$$

STANDARD FORM OF A HYPERBOLA

$$\frac{y^2}{a^2} - \frac{x^2}{b^2} = 1$$

with center at the origin and with the transverse axis lying on the y-axis.

We obtain a graph as shown in Fig. 1.58.

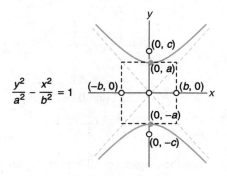

$$\frac{y^2}{a^2} - \frac{x^2}{b^2} = 1$$

Figure 1.58

Note that the difference between this equation and the first equation is that a^2 is now the denominator of the y^2-term, which is the positive term. This means that the vertices (and transverse axis) now lie on the y-axis.

The equations of the asymptotes are

$$y = \frac{a}{b}x$$

$$y = -\frac{a}{b}x$$

In general, the positive term indicates on which axis the vertices, foci, and transverse axis lie.

1. If the x^2 term is positive, then the denominator of x^2 is a^2 and the denominator of y^2 is b^2. The transverse axis lies along the x-axis and the vertices are $(a, 0)$ and $(-a, 0)$.
2. If the y^2 term is positive, then the denominator of y^2 is a^2 and the denominator of x^2 is b^2. The transverse axis lies along the y-axis and the vertices are $(0, a)$ and $(0, -a)$.

EXAMPLE 3

Sketch the graph of the hyperbola

$$\frac{y^2}{36} - \frac{x^2}{49} = 1$$

Since the y^2-term is positive, the vertices lie on the y-axis and $a^2 = 36$. Then $b^2 = 49$, $a = 6$, and $b = 7$. The graph is sketched in Fig. 1.59.

EXAMPLE 4

Write the equation of the hyperbola with foci at $(0, 8)$ and $(0, -8)$ and vertices at $(0, 6)$ and $(0, -6)$.

In this case $a = 6$ and $c = 8$, so $b^2 = c^2 - a^2 = 64 - 36 = 28$. Since the vertices and foci lie on the y-axis, the y^2-term is positive with denominator a^2. The equation is

$$\frac{y^2}{36} - \frac{x^2}{28} = 1$$

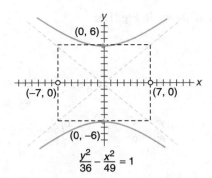

$$\frac{y^2}{36} - \frac{x^2}{49} = 1$$

Figure 1.59

As with the ellipse, not all hyperbolas are located with their centers at the origin. We have seen the standard forms of the equation of the hyperbola with center at the origin and whose transverse and conjugate axes lie on the *x*-axis and *y*-axis. In general, however, the equation of a hyperbola is of the form

$$Ax^2 + Bxy + Cy^2 + Dx + Ey + F = 0$$

where either (1) $B = 0$ and A and C differ in sign or (2) $A = 0$, $C = 0$, and $B \neq 0$.

A simple example of this last case is the equation $xy = k$. The foci and vertices lie on the line $y = x$ if $k > 0$ or on the line $y = -x$ if $k < 0$.

EXAMPLE 5

Sketch the graph of the hyperbola $xy = -6$.

Since there are no easy clues for sketching this equation (unlike hyperbolas in standard position), set up a table of values for x and y. Then plot the corresponding points in the plane as in Fig. 1.60.

x	y
6	−1
3	−2
2	−3
1	−6
−1	6
−2	3
−3	2
−6	1

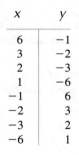

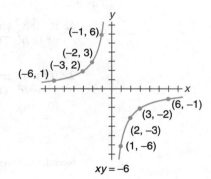

Figure 1.60

Exercises 1.9

Find the vertices, foci, and lengths of the transverse and conjugate axes of each hyperbola. Find the equations of the asymptotes and sketch each graph.

1. $\dfrac{x^2}{25} - \dfrac{y^2}{144} = 1$ **2.** $\dfrac{x^2}{144} - \dfrac{y^2}{25} = 1$ **3.** $\dfrac{y^2}{9} - \dfrac{x^2}{16} = 1$

4. $\dfrac{y^2}{16} - \dfrac{x^2}{9} = 1$ **5.** $5x^2 - 2y^2 = 10$ **6.** $3y^2 - 2x^2 = 6$

7. $4y^2 - x^2 = 4$ **8.** $4x^2 - y^2 = 4$

Find the equation of the hyperbola satisfying each of the given conditions.

9. Vertices at $(4, 0)$ and $(-4, 0)$; foci at $(6, 0)$ and $(-6, 0)$.

10. Vertices at $(0, 5)$ and $(0, -5)$; foci at $(0, 7)$ and $(0, -7)$.

11. Vertices at $(0, 6)$ and $(0, -6)$; foci at $(0, 8)$ and $(0, -8)$.

12. Vertices at $(2, 0)$ and $(-2, 0)$; foci at $(5, 0)$ and $(-5, 0)$.

13. Vertices at $(3, 0)$ and $(-3, 0)$; length of conjugate axis is 10.

14. Vertices at $(0, 6)$ and $(0, -6)$; length of conjugate axis is 8.

15. Foci at $(6, 0)$ and $(-6, 0)$; length of transverse axis is 10.

16. Foci at $(0, 8)$ and $(0, -8)$; length of transverse axis is 12.

17. Sketch the graph of the hyperbola given by $xy = 8$.

18. Sketch the graph of the hyperbola given by $xy = -4$.

1.10 TRANSLATION OF AXES

We have seen the difficulty in determining the equations of the parabola, ellipse, and hyperbola when these are not in standard position in the plane. It is still possible to find the equation of these curves fairly easily if the axes of these curves lie on lines parallel to the coordinate axes. This is accomplished by the translation of axes. We shall demonstrate this method with four examples.

EXAMPLE 1

Find the equation of the ellipse with foci at $(-2, 3)$ and $(6, 3)$ and vertices at $(-3, 3)$ and $(7, 3)$.

  The center of the ellipse is at $(2, 3)$, which is midway between the foci or the vertices. The distance between the foci $(-2, 3)$ and $(6, 3)$ is 8. So $c = 4$. The distance between $(-3, 3)$ and $(7, 3)$ is 10. So $a = 5$.

$$c^2 = a^2 - b^2$$
$$16 = 25 - b^2$$
$$b^2 = 9$$
$$b = 3$$

Sketch the graph as in Fig. 1.61(a). Next, plot the same ellipse in another coordinate system with center at the origin as in Fig. 1.61(b). Label the coordinate axes of this new system x' and y'. We know that in this $x'y'$-coordinate system, the equation for this ellipse is

$$\frac{(x')^2}{a^2} + \frac{(y')^2}{b^2} = 1$$

Since $a = 5$ and $b = 3$, we have

$$\frac{(x')^2}{25} + \frac{(y')^2}{9} = 1$$

Each point on the ellipse can now be seen as having coordinates (x, y) in the xy-plane and coordinates (x', y') in the $x'y'$-plane. If we compare coordinates in the two coordinate systems, we see, for example, that the right-hand vertex has coordinates $(7, 3)$ in the xy-plane, but the same point has coordinates $(5, 0)$ in the $x'y'$-plane. Likewise, the point at the upper end of the minor axis has coordinates $(2, 6)$ in the xy-plane, but the same point has coordinates $(0, 3)$ in the $x'y'$-plane.

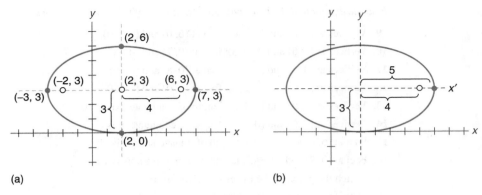

(a) (b)

Figure 1.61

In general, the x- and x'-coordinates are related as follows:

$$x = x' + 2$$

That is, the original x-coordinates are 2 larger than the new x'-coordinates. Note that this is the distance that the new origin was moved along the x-axis: the x-coordinate of the center of the ellipse. (See Fig. 1.61b.)

Similarly, the y- and y'-coordinates are related as follows:

$$y = y' + 3$$

Note that 3 is the distance that the new origin was moved along the y-axis: the y-coordinate of the center of the ellipse. (See Fig. 1.61b.) We now rearrange terms and have

$$x' = x - 2$$
$$y' = y - 3$$

Now replace x' by $x - 2$ and y' by $y - 3$ in the equation

$$\frac{(x')^2}{25} + \frac{(y')^2}{9} = 1$$

$$\frac{(x - 2)^2}{25} + \frac{(y - 3)^2}{9} = 1$$

This is the equation of the ellipse with center at $(2, 3)$ in the xy-plane.

To write an equation for a parabola, ellipse, or hyperbola whose axes are parallel to the x-axis and y-axis:

1. For a parabola, identify (h, k) as the vertex; for an ellipse or hyperbola identify (h, k) as the center.

2. Translate xy-coordinates to a new $x'y'$-coordinate system by using the translation equations

$$x' = x - h$$
$$y' = y - k$$

where (h, k) has been identified as in Step 1.

3. Write the equation of the conic, which is now in standard position in the $x'y'$-coordinate system.

4. Translate the equation derived in Step 3 back into the original coordinate system by making the following substitutions for x and y into the derived equation:

$$x' = x - h$$
$$y' = y - k$$

The resulting equation is an equation for the conic in the xy-coordinate system.

EXAMPLE 2

Find the equation of the parabola with focus $(-1, 2)$ and directrix $x = -7$.

Step 1:   The vertex of this parabola is halfway along the line $y = 2$ between the focus $(-1, 2)$ and the directrix $x = -7$ (see Fig. 1.62). Thus the vertex has coordinates $(-4, 2)$. This becomes the origin of the new coordinate system, so $h = -4$ and $k = 2$.

Step 2:

$$x' = x - h = x - (-4) = x + 4$$
$$y' = y - k = y - 2$$

The new $x'y'$-coordinates of the focus become

$$x' = x - h = -1 - (-4) = 3$$
$$y' = y - k = 2 - 2 = 0$$

and the equation of the directrix $x = -7$ becomes

$$x' = x - h = -7 - (-4)$$
$$x' = -3$$

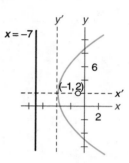

Figure 1.62

Step 3:   Since the parabola is now in standard position in the new coordinate system with focus $(3, 0)$, we have $p = 3$. The equation in this system becomes

$$(y')^2 = 4px'$$
$$(y')^2 = 4(3)x'$$
$$(y')^2 = 12x'$$

Step 4:   Replace x' with $x + 4$ and y' with $y - 2$.

$$(y')^2 = 12x'$$
$$(y - 2)^2 = 12(x + 4)$$
$$y^2 - 4y - 12x - 44 = 0$$

We sometimes know the equation of a curve and need to identify the curve and sketch its graph, as in the following example.

EXAMPLE 3

Describe and sketch the graph of the equation

$$\frac{(y - 4)^2}{9} - \frac{(x + 2)^2}{16} = 1$$

If we let

$$x' = x - h = x + 2 = x - (-2)$$
$$y' = y - k = y - 4$$

we have

$$\frac{(y')^2}{9} - \frac{(x')^2}{16} = 1$$

This is the equation of a hyperbola with center at $(-2, 4)$. Since $a^2 = 9$ and $b^2 = 16$, we have

$$c^2 = a^2 + b^2 = 9 + 16 = 25$$

so

$$a = 3 \qquad b = 4 \qquad \text{and} \qquad c = 5$$

In terms of the $x'y'$-coordinates, the foci are at $(0, 5)$ and $(0, -5)$, the vertices are at $(0, 3)$ and $(0, -3)$, the length of the transverse axis is 6, and the length of the conjugate axis is 8.

To translate the $x'y'$-coordinates to xy-coordinates, we use the equations

$$x = x' + h \qquad y = y' + k$$

In this case

$$x = x' + (-2) \qquad y = y' + 4$$

So, in the xy-plane the foci are at $(-2, 9)$ and $(-2, -1)$, the vertices are at $(-2, 7)$ and $(-2, 1)$, the length of the transverse axis is 6, and the length of the conjugate axis is 8 (see Fig. 1.63).

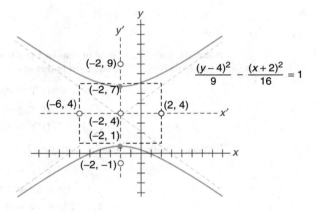

Figure 1.63

EXAMPLE 4

Name the equation $16x^2 + 9y^2 + 64x + 54y + 1 = 0$. Locate the vertex if it is a parabola or the center if it is an ellipse or a hyperbola.

First complete the square for x and y. (See Section 1.6.)

$$(16x^2 + 64x \quad) + (9y^2 + 54y \quad) = -1$$
$$16(x^2 + 4x \quad) + 9(y^2 + 6y \quad) = -1 \qquad \text{(Factor out the coefficients of } x^2 \text{ and } y^2 \text{ before completing the square. The coefficients of } x^2 \text{ and } y^2 \text{ must be one.)}$$

$$16(x^2 + 4x + 4) + 9(y^2 + 6y + 9) = -1 + 16(4) + 9(9)$$
$$16(x + 2)^2 + 9(y + 3)^2 = 144$$
$$\frac{(x + 2)^2}{9} + \frac{(y + 3)^2}{16} = 1 \qquad \text{(Divide each side by 144.)}$$

This is an equation of an ellipse. Noting that

$$x' = x - h = x + 2 = x - (-2)$$
$$y' = y - k = y + 3 = y - (-3)$$

we see that the center is at $(-2, -3)$.

GENERAL FORMS OF CONICS WITH AXES PARALLEL TO THE COORDINATE AXES

1. $(y - k)^2 = 4p(x - h)$
   is a parabola with vertex at (h, k) and axis parallel to the x-axis.

2. $(x - h)^2 = 4p(y - k)$
   is a parabola with vertex at (h, k) and axis parallel to the y-axis.

3. $\dfrac{(x - h)^2}{a^2} + \dfrac{(y - k)^2}{b^2} = 1 \qquad (a > b)$
   is an ellipse with center at (h, k) and major axis parallel to the x-axis.

4. $\dfrac{(y - k)^2}{a^2} + \dfrac{(x - h)^2}{b^2} = 1 \qquad (a > b)$
   is an ellipse with center at (h, k) and major axis parallel to the y-axis.

5. $\dfrac{(x - h)^2}{a^2} - \dfrac{(y - k)^2}{b^2} = 1$
   is a hyperbola with center at (h, k) and transverse axis parallel to the x-axis.

6. $\dfrac{(y - k)^2}{a^2} - \dfrac{(x - h)^2}{b^2} = 1$
   is a hyperbola with center at (h, k) and transverse axis parallel to the y-axis.

Exercises 1.10

Find the equation of each curve from the given information.

1. Ellipse with center at $(1, -1)$, vertices at $(5, -1)$ and $(-3, -1)$, and foci at $(3, -1)$ and $(-1, -1)$.

2. Parabola with vertex at $(-1, 3)$, focus at $(-1, 4)$, and directrix $y = 2$.

3. Hyperbola with center at $(1, 1)$, vertices at $(1, 7)$ and $(1, -5)$, and foci at $(1, 9)$ and $(1, -7)$.

4. Ellipse with center at $(-2, -3)$, vertices at $(4, -3)$ and $(-8, -3)$, and minor axis length 10.

5. Parabola with vertex at $(3, -1)$, focus at $(5, -1)$, and directrix $x = 1$.

6. Hyperbola with center at $(-2, -2)$, vertices at $(1, -2)$ and $(-5, -2)$, and conjugate axis length 10.

Name and graph each equation.

7. $(x - 2)^2 = 4(y + 3)$

8. $\dfrac{(x + 1)^2}{36} + \dfrac{(y - 2)^2}{64} = 1$

9. $\dfrac{y^2}{9} - \dfrac{(x + 2)^2}{16} = 1$

10. $y^2 = 8(x + 1)$

11. $9(x - 2)^2 + 16y^2 = 144$

12. $\dfrac{(x + 1)^2}{9} - \dfrac{(y + 3)^2}{16} = 1$

13. $\dfrac{(x - 3)^2}{36} + \dfrac{(y - 1)^2}{16} = 1$

14. $\dfrac{(x - 3)^2}{36} - \dfrac{(y - 1)^2}{16} = 1$

15. $(y + 3)^2 = 8(x - 1)$

16. $(x - 5)^2 = 12(y + 2)$

17. $\dfrac{(y + 1)^2}{9} - \dfrac{(x + 1)^2}{9} = 1$

18. $\dfrac{(y + 4)^2}{4} + \dfrac{(x - 2)^2}{9} = 1$

Name and sketch the graph of each equation. Locate the vertex if it is a parabola or the center if it is an ellipse or a hyperbola.

19. $x^2 - 4x + 2y + 6 = 0$

20. $9x^2 + 4y^2 - 18x + 24y + 9 = 0$

21. $x^2 + 4y^2 + 4x - 8y - 8 = 0$

22. $-2x^2 + 3y^2 + 8x - 14 = 0$

23. $4x^2 - y^2 - 8x + 2y + 3 = 0$

24. $y^2 + 6y - x + 12 = 0$

25. $25y^2 - 4x^2 - 24x - 150y + 89 = 0$

26. $25x^2 + 9y^2 - 100x - 54y - 44 = 0$

27. $x^2 + 16x - 12y + 40 = 0$

28. $9x^2 - 4y^2 + 54x + 40y - 55 = 0$

29. $4x^2 + y^2 + 48x + 4y + 84 = 0$

30. $y^2 - 10x - 6y + 39 = 0$

1.11 THE GENERAL SECOND-DEGREE EQUATION

The circle, parabola, ellipse, and hyperbola are all special cases of the second-degree equation

$$Ax^2 + Bxy + Cy^2 + Dx + Ey + F = 0$$

When $B = 0$ and at least one of the coefficients A or C is not zero, the following summarizes the conditions for each curve.

1. If $A = C$, we have a *circle*.
In special cases, the graph of the equation may be a point or there may be no graph. (The equation may have only one or no solution.)

2. If $A = 0$ and $C \neq 0$, or $C = 0$ and $A \neq 0$, then we have a *parabola*.

3. If $A \neq C$, and A and C are either both positive or both negative, then we have an *ellipse*.
In special cases, the graph of the equation may be a point or there may be no graph. (The equation may have only one or no solution.)

4. If A is positive and C is negative, or A is negative and C is positive, then we have a *hyperbola*.
In some special cases the graph may be a pair of intersecting lines.

If $D \neq 0$ or $E \neq 0$ or both are not equal to zero, the curve does not have its center (or vertex in the case of the parabola) at the origin (see Section 1.10). If $B \neq 0$, then the axis of the curve does not lie along the x-axis or y-axis. The hyperbola $xy = k$ is the only such example we have studied (see Section 1.9).

EXAMPLE

Identify the curve

$$x^2 + 3y^2 - 2x + 4y - 7 = 0$$

Since $A \neq C$, A and C are both positive, and $B = 0$, the curve is an ellipse. (The center is not the origin since $D \neq 0$ and $E \neq 0$.)

The curves represented by the second-degree equation

$$Ax^2 + Bxy + Cy^2 + Dx + Ey + F = 0$$

are called **conic sections** because they can be obtained by cutting the cones with a plane, as in Fig. 1.64.

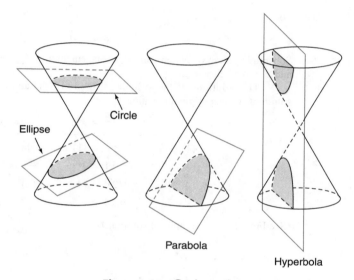

Figure 1.64 Conic sections.

Exercises 1.11

Determine whether each equation represents a circle, a parabola, an ellipse, or a hyperbola.

1. $x^2 + 3y^2 + 4x - 5y - 40 = 0$ **2.** $x^2 + y^2 + 4x - 6y - 12 = 0$

3. $4y^2 - 8y + 3x - 2 = 0$ **4.** $9x^2 + 4y^2 + 36x - 8y + 4 = 0$

5. $4x^2 - 5y^2 - 16x + 10y + 20 = 0$ **6.** $x^2 + y^2 + 3x - 2y - 14 = 0$

7. $3x^2 + 3y^2 + x - y - 6 = 0$ **8.** $x^2 + 4x - 3y - 52 = 0$

9. $x^2 + y^2 + 2x - 3y - 21 = 0$ **10.** $x^2 - y^2 - 6x + 3y - 100 = 0$

11. $9x^2 + 4y^2 - 18x + 8y + 4 = 0$ **12.** $3x^2 - 2y^2 + 6x - 8y - 17 = 0$

13. $3x^2 - 3y^2 - 2x - 4y - 13 = 0$ **14.** $4x^2 + 4y^2 - 16x - 4y - 5 = 0$

15. $x^2 - 6x - 6y + 3 = 0$ **16.** $4x^2 - 4x - 4y - 5 = 0$

1.12   SYSTEMS OF QUADRATIC EQUATIONS

To solve systems of equations involving conics algebraically, try to eliminate a variable.

Substitution Method

EXAMPLE 1

Solve the system of equations using the substitution method.

$$y^2 = x$$
$$y = x - 2$$

Since $y^2 = x$, we can substitute y^2 for x in the second equation.

$$y = x - 2$$
$$y = (y^2) - 2$$
$$y^2 - y - 2 = 0$$
$$(y - 2)(y + 1) = 0$$

So

$$y = 2 \quad \text{or} \quad y = -1$$

Substituting these values for y in the second equation, $y = x - 2$, we have $x = 1$ when $y = -1$ and $x = 4$ when $y = 2$.

The solutions of the system are then $(1, -1)$ and $(4, 2)$. Check by substituting the solutions in each original equation.

	$y^2 = x$	$y = x - 2$
$(1, -1)$	$(-1)^2 = (1)$	$(-1) = (1) - 2$
	$1 = 1$	$-1 = -1$
$(4, 2)$	$(2)^2 = (4)$	$(2) = (4) - 2$
	$4 = 4$	$2 = 2$

(See Fig. 1.65 for a graphical solution.)

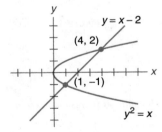

Figure 1.65

EXAMPLE 2

Solve the system of equations using the substitution method.

$$4x^2 - 3y^2 = 4$$
$$x^2 - 4x + y^2 = 0$$

If we solve the second equation for y^2, we have $y^2 = 4x - x^2$. We can now substitute $4x - x^2$ for y^2 in the first equation.

$$4x^2 - 3(4x - x^2) = 4$$
$$4x^2 - 12x + 3x^2 = 4$$
$$7x^2 - 12x - 4 = 0$$
$$(x - 2)(7x + 2) = 0$$
$$x = 2 \quad \text{or} \quad x = -\frac{2}{7}$$

To find y we substitute each of these values for x in one of the original equations. We use the second equation.

For $x = 2$:

$$(2)^2 - 4(2) + y^2 = 0$$
$$4 - 8 + y^2 = 0$$
$$y^2 = 4$$

Thus $y = 2$ or -2 when $x = 2$.

For $x = -\frac{2}{7}$:

$$\left(-\frac{2}{7}\right)^2 - 4\left(-\frac{2}{7}\right) + y^2 = 0$$

$$\frac{4}{49} + \frac{8}{7} + y^2 = 0$$

$$y^2 = -\frac{60}{49}$$

Since y^2 can never be negative, we conclude that there are no real solutions when $x = -\frac{2}{7}$. (This is what we call an *extraneous root*.) The solutions of the system are $(2, 2)$ and $(2, -2)$. The solutions should be checked in each original equation (see Fig. 1.66 for a graphical solution).

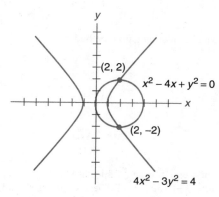

Figure 1.66

Addition-Subtraction Method

EXAMPLE 3

Solve the system of equations using the addition-subtraction method.

$$3x^2 + y^2 = 14$$
$$x^2 - y^2 = 2$$

By adding the two equations we can eliminate the y^2-term.

$$3x^2 + y^2 = 14$$
$$\underline{x^2 - y^2 = 2}$$
$$4x^2 = 16$$

Solving for x,

$$x^2 = 4$$
$$x = 2 \quad \text{or} \quad x = -2$$

Using the second equation, $x^2 - y^2 = 2$, we find the corresponding values for y. For $x = 2$:

$$(2)^2 - y^2 = 2$$
$$4 - y^2 = 2$$
$$y^2 = 2$$
$$y = \sqrt{2} \quad \text{or} \quad y = -\sqrt{2}$$

For $x = -2$:

$$(-2)^2 - y^2 = 2$$
$$4 - y^2 = 2$$
$$y^2 = 2$$
$$y = \sqrt{2} \quad \text{or} \quad y = -\sqrt{2}$$

The solutions are $(2, \sqrt{2})$, $(2, -\sqrt{2})$, $(-2, \sqrt{2})$, and $(-2, -\sqrt{2})$. These should be checked in each original equation.

When solving a system of two equations where one represents a conic and the other a line, the substitution method is usually preferred. Example 4 shows how the addition-subtraction method may be helpful in some cases.

EXAMPLE 4

Solve the system of equations.

$$y + 6x = 2$$
$$y^2 = 6x$$

We use the addition-subtraction method.

$$y + 6x = 2$$
$$\underline{y^2 - 6x = 0}$$
$$y^2 + y = 2 \qquad \text{(Add.)}$$
$$y^2 + y - 2 = 0$$
$$(y + 2)(y - 1) = 0$$
$$y = -2 \quad \text{or} \quad y = 1$$

Using the first equation, we find that when $y = -2$, $x = \frac{2}{3}$, and when $y = 1$, $x = \frac{1}{6}$, so the solutions are $\left(\frac{2}{3}, -2\right)$ and $\left(\frac{1}{6}, 1\right)$. These solutions should be checked in each original equation. Using a calculator, we obtain

2nd CUSTOM F3 4 *twelve* left arrows y+6x=2 *five* right arrows y^2=6x **ENTER** up arrow **2nd** right arrow

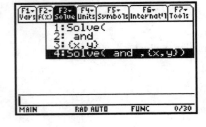 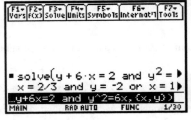 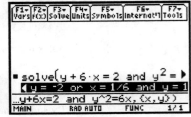

Exercises 1.12

Solve each system of equations.

1. $x^2 = 3y$
$y = 2x - 3$

2. $x^2 - 2y^2 = 1$
$3x^2 + 2y^2 = 3$

3. $x^2 + 4x + y^2 - 8 = 0$
$x^2 + y^2 = 4$

4. $x^2 + 2y^2 = 12$
$y = -x$

5. $y^2 - x^2 = 12$
$x^2 = 4y$

6. $x^2 + y^2 = 9$
$y = 4$

7. $x^2 + y^2 = 4$
$x^2 - y^2 = 4$

8. $x^2 + y^2 - 6y = 0$
$y = x$

9. $x^2 = 6y$
$y = 6$

10. $\dfrac{y^2}{16} + \dfrac{x^2}{9} = 1$
$4x + 3y = 12$

11. $y^2 = 4x + 12$
$y^2 = -4x - 4$

12. $x^2 - y^2 = 2$
$y^2 = x$

13. $x^2 + y^2 = 36$
$y = x^2$

14. $y = x^2 - 3x - 10$
$2x + y + 4 = 0$

15. $x^2 - y^2 = 9$
$x^2 + 9y^2 = 169$

16. $x^2 + 4y^2 = 36$
$x^2 + y^2 = 16$

17. $x^2 + y^2 = 17$
$xy = 4$

18. $3x^2 + 4y^2 = 48$
$xy = 6$

1.13 POLAR COORDINATES

Each point in the number plane has been associated with an ordered pair of real numbers (x, y), which are called rectangular or Cartesian coordinates. Point $P(x, y)$ is shown in Fig. 1.67. Point P can also be located by specifying an angle θ from the positive x-axis and a directed distance r from the origin, and described by the ordered pair (r, θ) called *polar coordinates*. The polar coordinate system has a fixed point in the number plane called the *pole* or *origin*. From the pole draw a horizontal ray directed to the right, which is called the *polar axis* (see Fig. 1.68).

Angle θ is a directed angle: $\theta > 0$ is measured counterclockwise; $\theta < 0$ is measured clockwise. Angle θ is commonly expressed in either degrees or radians. Distance r is a directed distance: $r > 0$ is measured in the direction of the ray (terminal side of θ); $r < 0$ is measured in the direction opposite the direction of the ray.

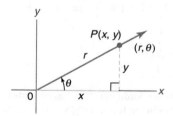

Figure 1.67   Polar coordinates.

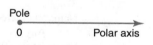

Figure 1.68   Polar axis.

EXAMPLE 1

Graph each point whose polar coordinates are given: (a) $(2, 120°)$, (b) $(4, 4\pi/3)$, (c) $(4, -2\pi/3)$, (d) $(-5, 135°)$, (e) $(-2, -60°)$, (f) $(-3, 570°)$ (see Fig. 1.69).

From the results of Example 1, you can see that there is a major difference between the rectangular coordinate system and the polar coordinate system. In the rectangular system there is a one-to-one correspondence between points in the plane and ordered pairs

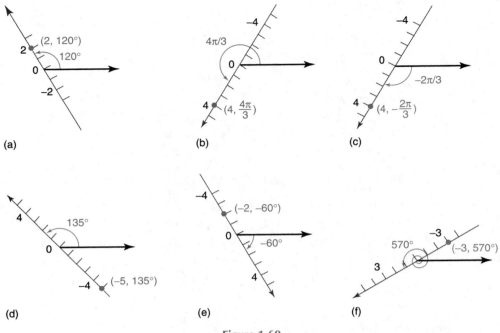

(a) (b) (c)

(d) (e) (f)

Figure 1.69

of real numbers. That is, each point is named by exactly one ordered pair, and each ordered pair corresponds to exactly one point. This one-to-one correspondence is not a property of the polar coordinate system. In Example 1, the point described by parts (a) and (e) is the same, and the point described by parts (b) and (c) is the same. In fact, each point may be named by infinitely many polar coordinates. In general, the point $P(r, \theta)$ may be represented by

$$(r, \theta + k \cdot 360°) \quad \text{or} \quad (r, \theta + k \cdot 2\pi)$$

where k is any integer. $P(r, \theta)$ may also be represented by

$$(-r, \theta + k \cdot 180°) \quad \text{or} \quad (-r, \theta + k\pi)$$

where k is any odd integer.

EXAMPLE 2

Name an ordered pair of polar coordinates that corresponds to the pole or origin.

Any set of coordinates in the form $(0, \theta)$, where θ is any angle, corresponds to the pole. For example, $(0, 64°)$, $(0, 2\pi/3)$, and $(0, -\pi/6)$ name the pole.

Polar graph paper is available for working with polar coordinates. Figure 1.70 shows graph paper in both degrees and radians.

EXAMPLE 3

Plot each point whose polar coordinates are given. Use polar graph paper in degrees (see Fig. 1.71).

$A(6, 60°), \quad B(4, 270°), \quad C(3, -210°), \quad D(-6, 45°), \quad E(-2, -150°), \quad F(8, 480°)$

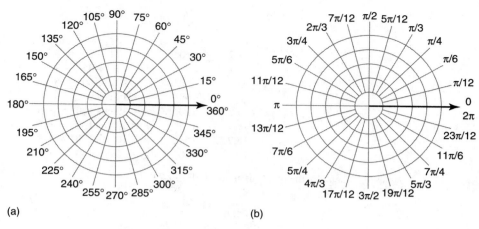

(a)

(b)

Figure 1.70 Polar graph paper.

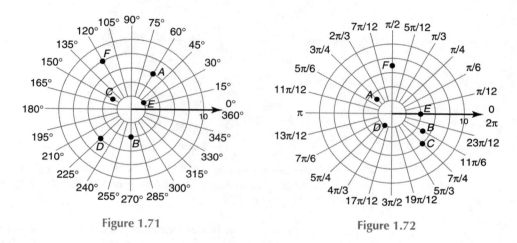

Figure 1.71

Figure 1.72

EXAMPLE 4

Plot each point whose polar coordinates are given. Use polar graph paper in radians (see Fig. 1.72).

$$A\left(3, \frac{3\pi}{4}\right), \quad B\left(5, \frac{11\pi}{6}\right), \quad C\left(6, -\frac{\pi}{4}\right), \quad D\left(-2, \frac{\pi}{3}\right), \quad E(-4, -\pi), \quad F\left(7, \frac{13\pi}{2}\right)$$

EXAMPLE 5

Given the point $P(4, 150°)$, name three other sets of polar coordinates for P such that $-360° \leq \theta \leq 360°$.

For $r > 0$ and $\theta < 0$: $(4, -210°)$

For $r < 0$ and $\theta > 0$: $(-4, 330°)$

For $r < 0$ and $\theta < 0$: $(-4, -30°)$

EXAMPLE 6

Graph $r = 10 \cos \theta$ by plotting points. Assign θ values of $0°$, $30°$, $45°$, $60°$, and so on until you have a smooth curve.

Make a table for the ordered pairs as follows. *Note:* Although r and θ are given in the same order as the ordered pair (r, θ), θ is actually the independent variable.

r	θ	$r = 10 \cos \theta$
10	0°	$r = 10 \cos 0° = 10$
8.7	30°	$r = 10 \cos 30° = 8.7$
7.1	45°	$r = 10 \cos 45° = 7.1$
5	60°	$r = 10 \cos 60° = 5$
0	90°	$r = 10 \cos 90° = 0$
-5	120°	$r = 10 \cos 120° = -5$
-7.1	135°	$r = 10 \cos 135° = -7.1$
-8.7	150°	$r = 10 \cos 150° = -8.7$
-10	180°	$r = 10 \cos 180° = -10$

Then plot the points as shown in Fig. 1.73.

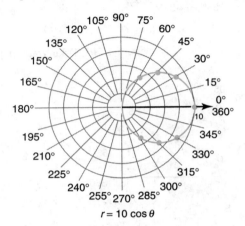

$r = 10 \cos \theta$

Figure 1.73

Note: You should plot values of θ from 0° to 360°, since the period of the cosine function is 360°. In this case choosing values of θ between 180° and 360° will give ordered pairs that duplicate those in Fig. 1.73.

Let point $P(x, y)$ be any point in the rectangular plane. Let the polar plane coincide with the rectangular plane so that $P(x, y)$ and $P(r, \theta)$ represent the same point, as shown in Fig. 1.74. Note the following relationships:

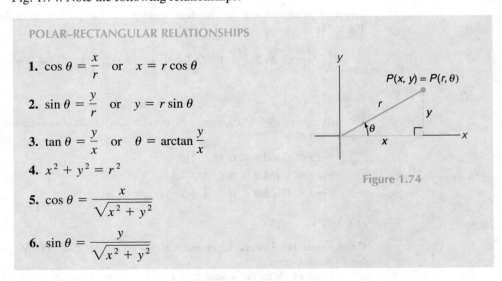

POLAR–RECTANGULAR RELATIONSHIPS

1. $\cos \theta = \dfrac{x}{r}$ or $x = r \cos \theta$

2. $\sin \theta = \dfrac{y}{r}$ or $y = r \sin \theta$

3. $\tan \theta = \dfrac{y}{x}$ or $\theta = \arctan \dfrac{y}{x}$

4. $x^2 + y^2 = r^2$

5. $\cos \theta = \dfrac{x}{\sqrt{x^2 + y^2}}$

6. $\sin \theta = \dfrac{y}{\sqrt{x^2 + y^2}}$

$P(x, y) = P(r, \theta)$

Figure 1.74

Suppose that we wish to change coordinates from one system to the other.

EXAMPLE 7

Change $A(4, 60°)$ and $B(8, 7\pi/6)$ to rectangular coordinates.
For point $A(4, 60°)$:

$$x = r \cos \theta \qquad y = r \sin \theta$$
$$x = 4 \cos 60° \qquad y = 4 \sin 60°$$
$$= 4\left(\frac{1}{2}\right) \qquad = 4\left(\frac{\sqrt{3}}{2}\right)$$
$$= 2 \qquad = 2\sqrt{3}$$

Thus $A(4, 60°) = (2, 2\sqrt{3})$.
For point $B(8, 7\pi/6)$:

$$x = r \cos \theta \qquad y = r \sin \theta$$
$$x = 8 \cos \frac{7\pi}{6} \qquad y = 8 \sin \frac{7\pi}{6}$$
$$= 8\left(-\frac{\sqrt{3}}{2}\right) \qquad = 8\left(-\frac{1}{2}\right)$$
$$= -4\sqrt{3} \qquad = -4$$

Thus $B(8, 7\pi/6) = (-4\sqrt{3}, -4)$.

EXAMPLE 8

Find polar coordinates for each point: $C(2\sqrt{3}, 2)$ in degrees, $0° \le \theta < 360°$, and $D(6, -6)$ in radians, $0 \le \theta < 2\pi$.

Note: The signs of x and y determine the quadrant for θ. That is, the signs of x and y determine in which quadrant the point lies and hence the quadrant in which θ must lie.
For point $C(2\sqrt{3}, 2)$:

$$r^2 = x^2 + y^2 \qquad\qquad \theta = \arctan \frac{y}{x}$$
$$r^2 = (2\sqrt{3})^2 + 2^2 = 16 \qquad \theta = \arctan \frac{2}{2\sqrt{3}}$$
$$r = 4 \qquad\qquad \theta = 30°$$

Thus $C(2\sqrt{3}, 2) = (4, 30°)$.
For point $D(6, -6)$:

$$r^2 = x^2 + y^2 \qquad\qquad \theta = \arctan \frac{y}{x}$$
$$r^2 = 6^2 + (-6)^2 = 72 \qquad \theta = \arctan \left(\frac{-6}{6}\right) = \arctan(-1)$$
$$r = 6\sqrt{2} \qquad\qquad \theta = \frac{7\pi}{4} \qquad \left(\text{\textit{Note:} the reference angle } \alpha = \frac{\pi}{4}.\right)$$

Thus $D(6, -6) = (6\sqrt{2}, 7\pi/4)$.

Some curves are most simply expressed and easiest to work with in rectangular coordinates; others are most simply expressed and easiest to work with in polar coordinates. As a result, you must be able to change a polar equation to a rectangular equation and to change a rectangular equation to a polar equation.

SECTION 1.13   Polar Coordinates   **67**

EXAMPLE 9

Change $x^2 + y^2 - 4x = 0$ to polar form.

Substituting $x^2 + y^2 = r^2$ and $x = r \cos \theta$, we have

$$r^2 - 4r \cos \theta = 0$$

$$r(r - 4 \cos \theta) = 0 \qquad \text{(Factor.)}$$

So

$$r = 0 \quad \text{or} \quad r - 4 \cos \theta = 0$$

But $r = 0$ (the pole) is a point that is included in the graph of the equation $r - 4 \cos \theta = 0$. Note that $(0, \pi/2)$ is an ordered pair that satisfies the second equation and names the pole. Thus the simplest polar equation is

$$r = 4 \cos \theta$$

EXAMPLE 10

Change $r = 4 \sin \theta$ to rectangular form.

Multiply both sides of the equation by r:

$$r^2 = 4r \sin \theta$$

Substituting $r^2 = x^2 + y^2$ and $r \sin \theta = y$, we have

$$x^2 + y^2 = 4y$$

Note that by multiplying both sides of the given equation by r, we added the root $r = 0$. But the point represented by that root is already included in the original equation. So no new points are added to those represented by the original equation.

EXAMPLE 11

Change $r \cos^2 \theta = 6 \sin \theta$ to rectangular form.

First multiply both sides by r:

$$r^2 \cos^2 \theta = 6r \sin \theta$$

$$(r \cos \theta)^2 = 6r \sin \theta$$

Substituting $r \cos \theta = x$ and $r \sin \theta = y$, we have

$$x^2 = 6y$$

EXAMPLE 12

Change $r = \dfrac{2}{1 - \cos \theta}$ to rectangular form.

$$r = \frac{2}{1 - \cos \theta} \qquad \qquad \text{(1)}$$

First multiply both sides by $1 - \cos \theta$:

$$r(1 - \cos \theta) = 2$$

$$r - r \cos \theta = 2$$

$$r = 2 + r \cos \theta \qquad \qquad \text{(2)}$$

Substituting $r = \pm\sqrt{x^2 + y^2}$ and $r \cos \theta = x$, we have

$$\pm\sqrt{x^2 + y^2} = 2 + x$$

Squaring both sides, we have

$$x^2 + y^2 = 4 + 4x + x^2$$
$$y^2 = 4x + 4$$

Note that squaring both sides was a risky operation because we introduced the possible extraneous solutions

$$r = -(2 + r \cos \theta) \qquad \text{(3)}$$

However, in this case both Equations (2) and (3) have the same graph. To show this, solve Equation (3) for r:

$$r = \frac{-2}{1 + \cos \theta} \qquad \text{(4)}$$

Recall that the ordered pairs (r, θ) and $(-r, \theta + \pi)$ represent the same point. Let us replace (r, θ) by $(-r, \theta + \pi)$ in Equation (4):

$$-r = \frac{-2}{1 + \cos (\theta + \pi)}$$

$$r = \frac{2}{1 - \cos \theta} \qquad [\text{Recall } \cos (\theta + \pi) = -\cos \theta.]$$

Equations (2) and (3) and thus Equations (1) and (4) have the same graph, and no extraneous solutions were introduced when we squared both sides. So our result $y^2 = 4x + 4$ is correct.

Exercises 1.13

Plot each point whose polar coordinates are given.

1. $A(3, 150°)$, $B(7, -45°)$, $C(2, -120°)$, $D(-4, 225°)$

2. $A(5, -90°)$, $B(2, -210°)$, $C(6, -270°)$, $D(-5, 30°)$

3. $A\left(4, \frac{\pi}{3}\right)$, $B\left(5, -\frac{\pi}{4}\right)$, $C\left(3, -\frac{7\pi}{6}\right)$, $D\left(-6, \frac{11\pi}{6}\right)$

4. $A\left(4, \frac{5\pi}{3}\right)$, $B\left(5, -\frac{3\pi}{2}\right)$, $C\left(3, -\frac{19\pi}{12}\right)$, $D\left(-6, -\frac{2\pi}{3}\right)$

For each point, name three other sets of polar coordinates such that $-360° \leq \theta \leq 360°$.

5. $(3, 60°)$ **6.** $(2, 240°)$ **7.** $(-5, 315°)$

8. $(-6, 90°)$ **9.** $(4, -135°)$ **10.** $(-1, -180°)$

For each point, name three other sets of polar coordinates such that $-2\pi \leq \theta \leq 2\pi$.

11. $\left(3, \frac{\pi}{6}\right)$ **12.** $\left(-7, \frac{\pi}{2}\right)$ **13.** $\left(-9, \frac{2\pi}{3}\right)$

14. $\left(-2, -\frac{5\pi}{6}\right)$ **15.** $\left(-4, -\frac{7\pi}{4}\right)$ **16.** $\left(5, -\frac{5\pi}{3}\right)$

Graph each equation by plotting points. Assign θ values of $0°, 30°, 45°, 60°$, and so on, until you have a smooth curve.

17. $r = 10 \sin \theta$ **18.** $r = -10 \sin \theta$ **19.** $r = 4 + 4 \cos \theta$

20. $r = 4 + 4 \sin \theta$ **21.** $r \cos \theta = 4$ **22.** $r \sin \theta = -4$

Graph each equation by plotting points. Assign θ values of 0, $\pi/6$, $\pi/4$, $\pi/3$, and so on, until you have a smooth curve.

23. $r = -10 \cos \theta$ **24.** $r = 6 \sin \theta$ **25.** $r = 4 - 4 \sin \theta$

26. $r = 4 - 4 \cos \theta$ **27.** $r = \theta, 0 \le \theta \le 4\pi$ **28.** $r = 2\theta, 0 \le \theta \le 2\pi$

Change each set of polar coordinates to rectangular coordinates.

29. $(3, 30°)$ **30.** $(2, 180°)$ **31.** $\left(2, \dfrac{\pi}{3}\right)$

32. $\left(7, \dfrac{5\pi}{6}\right)$ **33.** $(-4, 150°)$ **34.** $(1, 420°)$

35. $\left(-6, \dfrac{3\pi}{2}\right)$ **36.** $(3, -\pi)$ **37.** $(-5, -240°)$

38. $(2, -120°)$ **39.** $\left(2, -\dfrac{7\pi}{4}\right)$ **40.** $\left(-1, -\dfrac{5\pi}{3}\right)$

Change each set of rectangular coordinates to polar coordinates in degrees, $0° \le \theta \le 360°$.

41. $(5, 5)$ **42.** $(-\sqrt{3}, 1)$ **43.** $(0, 4)$

44. $(-3, 0)$ **45.** $(-2, -2\sqrt{3})$ **46.** $(-1, 1)$

Change each set of rectangular coordinates to polar coordinates in radians, $0 \le \theta < 2\pi$.

47. $(-4, 4)$ **48.** $(-1, -\sqrt{3})$ **49.** $(-\sqrt{6}, \sqrt{2})$

50. $(5\sqrt{2}, -5\sqrt{2})$ **51.** $(0, -4)$ **52.** $(0, 0)$

Change each equation to polar form.

53. $x = 3$ **54.** $y = 5$ **55.** $x^2 + y^2 = 36$

56. $y^2 = 5x$ **57.** $x^2 + y^2 + 2x + 5y = 0$ **58.** $2x + 3y = 6$

59. $4x - 3y = 12$ **60.** $ax + by = c$ **61.** $9x^2 + 4y^2 = 36$

62. $4x^2 - 9y^2 = 36$ **63.** $x^3 = 4y^2$ **64.** $x^4 - 2x^2y^2 + y^4 = 0$

Change each equation to rectangular form.

65. $r \sin \theta = -3$ **66.** $r \cos \theta = 7$ **67.** $r = 5$

68. $r = 3 \sec \theta$ **69.** $\theta = \dfrac{\pi}{4}$ **70.** $\theta = -\dfrac{2\pi}{3}$

71. $r = 5 \cos \theta$ **72.** $r = 6 \sin \theta$ **73.** $r = 6 \cos\left(\theta + \dfrac{\pi}{3}\right)$

74. $r = 4 \sin\left(\theta - \dfrac{\pi}{4}\right)$ **75.** $r \sin^2 \theta = 3 \cos \theta$ **76.** $r^2 = \tan^2 \theta$

77. $r^2 \sin 2\theta = 2$ **78.** $r^2 \cos 2\theta = 6$ **79.** $r^2 = \sin 2\theta$

80. $r^2 = \cos 2\theta$ **81.** $r = \tan \theta$ **82.** $r = 4 \tan \theta \sec \theta$

83. $r = \dfrac{3}{1 + \sin \theta}$ **84.** $r = \dfrac{-4}{1 + \cos \theta}$ **85.** $r = 4 \sin 3\theta$

86. $r = 4 \cos 2\theta$ **87.** $r = 2 + 4 \sin \theta$ **88.** $r = 1 - \cos \theta$

89. Find the distance between the points whose polar coordinates are $(3, 60°)$ and $(2, 330°)$.

90. Find the distance between the points whose polar coordinates are $(5, \pi/2)$ and $(1, 7\pi/6)$.

91. Find a formula for the distance between two points whose polar coordinates are $P_1(r_1, \theta_1)$ and $P_2(r_2, \theta_2)$.

As you undoubtedly know, a graph of any equation may be made by finding and plotting "enough" ordered pairs that satisfy the equation and connecting them with a curve. As you also undoubtedly know, this is often tedious and time-consuming at best. We need a method for sketching the graph of a polar equation that minimizes the number of ordered pairs that must be found and plotted. One such method involves symmetry. We shall present tests for three kinds of symmetry:

SYMMETRY WITH RESPECT TO THE

1. *Horizontal axis:* Replace θ by $-\theta$ in the original equation. If the resulting equation is equivalent to the original equation, then the graph of the original equation is symmetric with respect to the *horizontal* axis.

2. *Vertical axis:* Replace θ by $\pi - \theta$ in the original equation. If the resulting equation is equivalent to the original equation, then the graph of the original equation is symmetric with respect to the *vertical* axis.

3. *Pole:*
   (a) Replace r by $-r$ in the original equation. If the resulting equation is equivalent to the original equation, then the graph of the original equation is symmetric with respect to the *pole*.
   (b) Replace θ by $\pi + \theta$ in the original equation. If the resulting equation is equivalent to the original equation, then the graph of the original equation is symmetric with respect to the *pole*.

You should note that these tests for symmetry are sufficient conditions for symmetry; that is, they are sufficient to assure symmetry. You should also note that these are not necessary conditions for symmetry; that is, symmetry may exist even though the test fails.

If either Test 3(a) or 3(b) is satisfied, then the graph is symmetric with respect to the pole. It is also true that if any two of the three kinds of symmetry hold, then the remaining third symmetry automatically holds. Can you explain why?

To help you quickly test for symmetry, the following identities are listed for your convenience.

POLAR COORDINATE IDENTITIES FOR TESTING SYMMETRY

$$\sin(-\theta) = -\sin\theta$$
$$\cos(-\theta) = \cos\theta$$
$$\tan(-\theta) = -\tan\theta$$
$$\sin(\pi - \theta) = \sin\theta$$
$$\cos(\pi - \theta) = -\cos\theta$$
$$\tan(\pi - \theta) = -\tan\theta$$
$$\sin(\pi + \theta) = -\sin\theta$$
$$\cos(\pi + \theta) = -\cos\theta$$
$$\tan(\pi + \theta) = \tan\theta$$

EXAMPLE 1

Graph $r = 4 + 2 \cos \theta$.

Replacing θ by $-\theta$, we see that the graph is symmetric with respect to the horizontal axis. The other tests fail. Thus we need to make a table as follows (note that because of symmetry with respect to the horizontal axis, we need only generate ordered pairs for $0° \leq \theta \leq 180°$):

r	θ	$r = 4 + 2 \cos \theta$
6	0°	$r = 4 + 2 \cos 0° = 6$
5.7	30°	$r = 4 + 2 \cos 30° = 5.7$
5	60°	$r = 4 + 2 \cos 60° = 5$
4	90°	$r = 4 + 2 \cos 90° = 4$
3	120°	$r = 4 + 2 \cos 120° = 3$
2.3	150°	$r = 4 + 2 \cos 150° = 2.3$
2	180°	$r = 4 + 2 \cos 180° = 2$

Plot the points as shown in Fig. 1.75(a). Because of the symmetry with respect to the horizontal axis, plot the corresponding mirror-image points below the horizontal axis (see Fig. 1.75b).

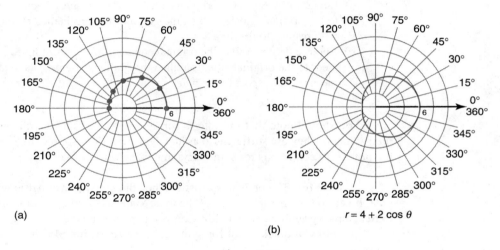

(a)

(b)

$r = 4 + 2 \cos \theta$

Figure 1.75

EXAMPLE 2

Graph $r = 4 + 4 \sin \theta$.

Replacing θ by $\pi - \theta$, we see that the graph is symmetric with respect to the vertical axis. The other tests fail. Thus, make a table as follows (note that because of symmetry with respect to the vertical axis, we need only generate ordered pairs for $-\pi/2 \leq \theta \leq \pi/2$):

r	θ	$r = 4 + 4 \sin \theta$
4	0	$r = 4 + 4 \sin 0 = 4$
6	$\pi/6$	$r = 4 + 4 \sin \pi/6 = 6$
7.5	$\pi/3$	$r = 4 + 4 \sin \pi/3 = 7.5$
8	$\pi/2$	$r = 4 + 4 \sin \pi/2 = 8$
2	$-\pi/6$	$r = 4 + 4 \sin (-\pi/6) = 2$
0.54	$-\pi/3$	$r = 4 + 4 \sin (-\pi/3) = 0.54$
0	$-\pi/2$	$r = 4 + 4 \sin (-\pi/2) = 0$

Plot the points as shown in Fig. 1.76(a). Because of the symmetry with respect to the vertical axis, plot the corresponding mirror-image points to the left of the vertical axis (see Fig. 1.76(b)).

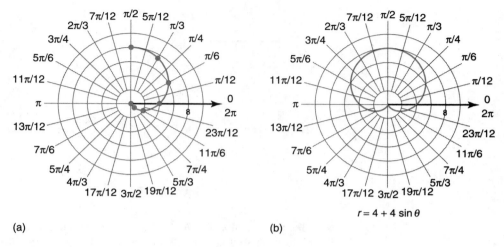

$r = 4 + 4 \sin \theta$

(a)   (b)

Figure 1.76

EXAMPLE 3

Graph $r^2 = 16 \sin \theta$.

Replacing r by $-r$, we see that the graph is symmetric with respect to the pole. Replacing θ by $\pi - \theta$, we see that the graph is also symmetric with respect to the vertical axis. Since two of the three kinds of symmetry hold, the graph is also symmetric with respect to the horizontal axis. (*Note:* Replacing θ by $-\theta$ gives the resulting equation $r^2 = -16 \sin \theta$, which is different from the original equation. However, its solutions when graphed give the same curve.)

r	θ	$r^2 = 16 \sin \theta$
0	0°	$r^2 = 16 \sin 0° = 0; r = 0$
2.8	30°	$r^2 = 16 \sin 30° = 8; r = 2.8$
3.7	60°	$r^2 = 16 \sin 60° = 13.9; r = 3.7$
4	90°	$r^2 = 16 \sin 90° = 16; r = 4$

Plot the points as shown in Fig. 1.77(a). Because of the symmetry with respect to the horizontal and vertical axes, plot the corresponding mirror-image points below the horizontal axis. Then plot the mirror image points of all resulting points to the left of the vertical axis (see Fig. 1.77(b)).

EXAMPLE 4

Graph $r^2 = 25 \cos 2\theta$.

By replacing θ by $-\theta$ and r by $-r$, we have symmetry with respect to the horizontal axis and the pole, respectively. Thus we also have symmetry with respect to the vertical axis. Working in the first quadrant, we have

r	θ	$r^2 = 25 \cos 2\theta$
5	0	$r^2 = 25 \cos 2(0) = 25; r = 5$
4.7	$\pi/12$	$r^2 = 25 \cos 2(\pi/12) = 21.7; r = 4.7$
3.5	$\pi/6$	$r^2 = 25 \cos 2(\pi/6) = 12.5; r = 3.5$
0	$\pi/4$	$r^2 = 25 \cos 2(\pi/4) = 0; r = 0$

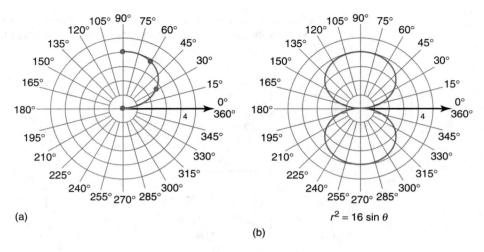

(a)

(b)

$r^2 = 16 \sin \theta$

Figure 1.77

Note: For the interval $\pi/4 < \theta \le \pi/2$, $r^2 < 0$ and r is undefined.

Plot the points as shown in Fig. 1.78(a). Because of the symmetry with respect to the horizontal and vertical axes, plot the corresponding mirror-image points below the horizontal axis and to the left of the vertical axis (see Fig. 1.78b).

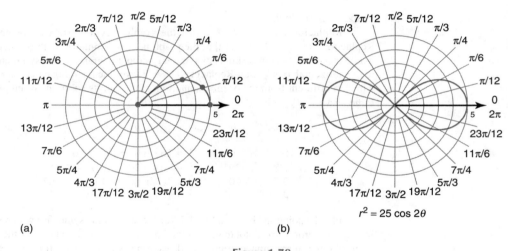

(a)

(b)

$r^2 = 25 \cos 2\theta$

Figure 1.78

There are various general polar equations whose graphs may be classified as shown in Fig. 1.79. What are the graphs of the various forms of $r = a + b \sin \theta$ like?

Equations in the form

$$r = a \sin n\theta \quad \text{or} \quad r = a \cos n\theta$$

where n is a positive integer, are called *petal* or *rose curves*. The number of petals is equal to n if n is an *odd* integer, and is equal to $2n$ if n is an *even* integer. This is because the graph "retraces" itself as θ goes from $0°$ to $360°$ when n is odd, so there are only half as many distinct petals. (For $n = 1$ there is one circular petal. See Example 6, Section 1.13). The value of a corresponds to the length of each petal.

Limaçons ($r = a + b \cos \theta$)

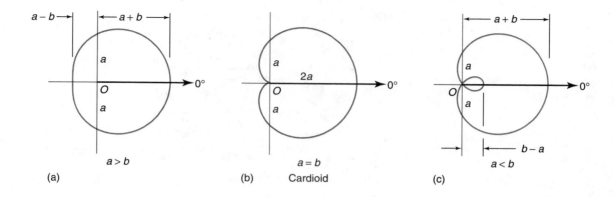

(a) $a > b$

(b) $a = b$ — Cardioid

(c) $a < b$

Lemniscates

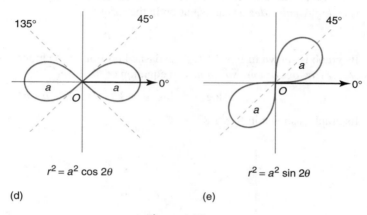

(d) $r^2 = a^2 \cos 2\theta$

(e) $r^2 = a^2 \sin 2\theta$

Figure 1.79

The tests for symmetry may be used to graph petal curves. However, we shall illustrate a method that is somewhat different, as well as easier and quicker, for graphing petal curves.

EXAMPLE 5

Graph $r = 6 \cos 2\theta$.

First, note that $n = 2$, which is even. Therefore, we have four petals. The petals are always uniform; each petal occupies $360°/4$, or $90°$, of the polar coordinate system. Next, find the tip of a petal; this occurs when r is maximum or when

$$\cos 2\theta = 1$$
$$2\theta = 0°$$
$$\theta = 0°$$

That is, $r = 6$ when $\theta = 0°$.

Finally, sketch four petals, each having a maximum length of six and occupying $90°$ (see Fig. 1.80). For more accuracy, you may graph the ordered pairs corresponding to a "half petal" ($0° \leq \theta \leq 45°$ in this case).

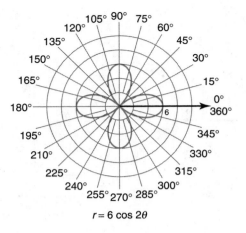

$r = 6 \cos 2\theta$

Figure 1.80

Polar coordinates are especially useful for the study and graphing of *spirals*. The *spiral of Archimedes* has an equation in the form

$$r = a\theta$$

Its graph is shown in Fig. 1.81. (The dashed portion of the graph corresponds to $\theta < 0$.)
The *logarithmic spiral* has an equation of the form

$$\log_b r = \log_b a + k\theta \quad \text{or} \quad r = a \cdot b^{k\theta}$$

Its graph is shown in Fig. 1.82.

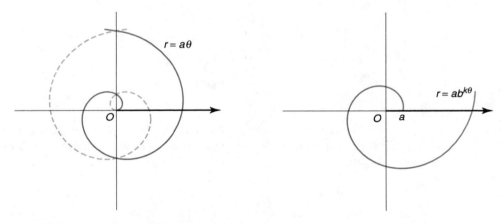

Figure 1.81   Spiral of Archimedes.   Figure 1.82   Logarithmic spiral.

For graphing calculator examples in polar coordinates, see Appendix C, Section C.5 (TI-83 Plus), or Appendix D, Section D.7 (TI-89).

Exercises 1.14

Graph each equation.

1. $r = 6$ **2.** $r = 3$ **3.** $r = -2$

4. $r = -4$ **5.** $\theta = 30°$ **6.** $\theta = -120°$

7. $\theta = -\dfrac{\pi}{3}$ **8.** $\theta = \dfrac{7\pi}{6}$ **9.** $r = 5 \sin \theta$

10. $r = 8 \cos \theta$ **11.** $r = 6 \cos\left(\theta + \dfrac{\pi}{3}\right)$ **12.** $r = 4 \sin\left(\theta - \dfrac{\pi}{4}\right)$

13. $r = 4 + 2 \sin \theta$ **14.** $r = 8 + 2 \cos \theta$ **15.** $r = 4 - 2 \cos \theta$

16. $r = 4 - 2 \sin \theta$ **17.** $r = 3 + 3 \cos \theta$ **18.** $r = 5 + 5 \sin \theta$

19. $r = 2 + 4 \sin \theta$ **20.** $r = 2 + 8 \cos \theta$ **21.** $r = 2 - 4 \cos \theta$

22. $r = 2 - 4 \sin \theta$ **23.** $r = 3 - 3 \cos \theta$ **24.** $r = 5 - 5 \sin \theta$

25. $r \cos \theta = 6$ **26.** $r \sin \theta = -4$ **27.** $r^2 = 25 \cos \theta$

28. $r^2 = -9 \sin \theta$ **29.** $r^2 = 9 \sin 2\theta$ **30.** $r^2 = 16 \cos 2\theta$

31. $r^2 = -36 \cos 2\theta$ **32.** $r = -36 \sin 2\theta$ **33.** $r = 5 \sin 3\theta$

34. $r = 4 \cos 5\theta$ **35.** $r = 3 \cos 2\theta$ **36.** $r = 6 \sin 4\theta$

37. $r = 9 \sin^2 \theta$ **38.** $r = 16 \cos^2 \theta$ **39.** $r = 4 \cos \dfrac{\theta}{2}$

40. $r = 5 \sin^2 \dfrac{\theta}{2}$ **41.** $r = \tan \theta$ **42.** $r = 2 \csc \theta$

43. $r = 3\theta, \theta > 0$ **44.** $r = \dfrac{3}{\theta}, \theta > 0$ **45.** $r = 2^{3\theta}$

46. $r = 2 \cdot 3^{2\theta}$ **47.** $r = \dfrac{4}{\sin \theta + \cos \theta}$ **48.** $r = \dfrac{-2}{\sin \theta + \cos \theta}$

49. $r(1 + \cos \theta) = 4$ **50.** $r(1 + 2 \sin \theta) = -4$

CHAPTER 1 SUMMARY

1. *Basic terms:*
   (a) *Analytic geometry:* Study of relationships between algebra and geometry.
   (b) *Relation:* Set of ordered pairs, usually in the form (x, y).
   (c) *Independent variable:* First element of an ordered pair, usually x.
   (d) *Dependent variable:* Second element of an ordered pair, usually y.
   (e) *Domain:* Set of all first elements in a relation or set of all x's.
   (f) *Range:* Set of all second elements in a relation or set of all y's.
   (g) *Function:* A set of ordered pairs in which no two distinct ordered pairs have the same first element.
   (h) *Functional notation:* To write an equation in variables x and y in functional notation, solve for y, and replace y with $f(x)$.
   (i) *Linear equation with two unknowns:* An equation of degree one in the form $ax + by = c$ where a and b are not both 0.
   (j) *Positive integers:* $1, 2, 3, \ldots$.
   (k) *Negative integers:* $-1, -2, -3, \ldots$.
   (l) *Integers:* $\ldots, -3, -2, -1, 0, 1, 2, 3, \ldots$.
   (m) *Rational numbers:* Numbers that can be represented as the ratio of two integers $a/b, b \neq 0$.
   (n) *Irrational numbers:* Numbers that cannot be represented as the ratio of two integers.
   (o) *Real numbers:* Set of numbers consisting of the rational numbers and the irrational numbers.
   (p) *Inequalities:* Statements involving less than or greater than, which may be used to describe various intervals on the number line as follows:

Type of interval	Symbols	Meaning	Number line graph
Open	$x > a$	x is greater than a	
	$x < b$	x is less than b	
	$a < x < b$	x is between a and b	
Half-open	$x \geq a$	x is greater than or equal to a	
	$x \leq b$	x is less than or equal to b	
	$a < x \leq b$	x is between a and b, including b but excluding a	
	$a \leq x < b$	x is between a and b, including a but excluding b	
Closed	$a \leq x \leq b$	x is between a and b, including both a and b	

2. *Slope of a line:* If $P_1(x_1, y_1)$ and $P_2(x_2, y_2)$ represent any two points on a line, then the slope m of the line is

$$m = \frac{y_2 - y_1}{x_2 - x_1}$$

(a) If a line has positive slope, the line slopes upward from left to right.
(b) If a line has negative slope, the line slopes downward from left to right.
(c) If a line has zero slope, the line is horizontal.
(d) If a line has undefined slope, the line is vertical.

3. *Point-slope form of a line:* If m is the slope and $P_1(x_1, y_1)$ is any point on a nonvertical line, its equation is

$$y - y_1 = m(x - x_1)$$

4. *Slope-intercept form of a line:* If m is the slope and $(0, b)$ is the y-intercept of a non-vertical line, its equation is

$$y = mx + b$$

5. *Equation of a horizontal line:* If a horizontal line passes through the point (a, b), its equation is

$$y = b$$

6. *Equation of a vertical line:* If a vertical line passes through the point (a, b), its equation is

$$x = a$$

7. *General form of the equation of a straight line:*

$$Ax + By + C = 0 \qquad \text{where } A \text{ and } B \text{ are not both } 0$$

8. *Parallel lines:* Two lines are parallel if either one of the following conditions holds:
   (a) They are both perpendicular to the x-axis.
   (b) They both have the same slope. That is, if the equations of the lines are

$$L_1: \quad y = m_1 x + b_1 \quad \text{and} \quad L_2: \quad y = m_2 x + b_2$$

then

$$m_1 = m_2$$

9. *Perpendicular lines:* Two lines are perpendicular if either one of the following conditions holds:
   (a) One line is vertical with equation $x = a$ and the other is horizontal with equation $y = b$.
   (b) Neither is vertical and the slope of one line is the negative reciprocal of the other. That is, if the equations of the lines are

$$L_1: \quad y = m_1 x + b_1 \quad \text{and} \quad L_2: \quad y = m_2 x + b_2$$

then

$$m_1 = -\frac{1}{m_2}$$

10. *Distance formula:* The distance between two points $P(x_1, y_1)$ and $Q(x_2, y_2)$ is given by the formula

$$d = PQ = \sqrt{(x_2 - x_1)^2 + (y_2 - y_1)^2}$$

11. *Midpoint formula:* The coordinates of the point $Q(x_m, y_m)$ that is midway between two points $P(x_1, y_1)$ and $R(x_2, y_2)$ are given by

$$x_m = \frac{x_1 + x_2}{2} \quad \text{and} \quad y_m = \frac{y_1 + y_2}{2}$$

12. *Conics:* Equations in the form $Ax^2 + Bxy + Cy^2 + Dx + Ey + F = 0$ are called conics.

13. *Circle:*
    (a) *Standard form:* $(x - h)^2 + (y - k)^2 = r^2$, where r is the radius and (h, k) is the center.
    (b) *General form:* $x^2 + y^2 + Dx + Ey + F = 0$.
    (c) *Center at the origin:* $x^2 + y^2 = r^2$, where r is the radius.

14. *Parabola with vertex at the origin:*
    (a) $y^2 = 4px$ with focus at $(p, 0)$ and $x = -p$ as the directrix.
       (i) When $p > 0$, the parabola opens to the right.
       (ii) When $p < 0$, the parabola opens to the left.
    (b) $x^2 = 4py$ with focus at $(0, p)$ and $y = -p$ as the directrix.
       (i) When $p > 0$, the parabola opens upward.
       (ii) When $p < 0$, the parabola opens downward.

15. *Ellipse with center at the origin:*
    (a) $\dfrac{x^2}{a^2} + \dfrac{y^2}{b^2} = 1$ with the major axis on the x-axis and $a > b$.
    (b) $\dfrac{y^2}{a^2} + \dfrac{x^2}{b^2} = 1$ with the major axis on the y-axis and $a > b$.

16. *Hyperbola with center at the origin:*
    (a) $\dfrac{x^2}{a^2} - \dfrac{y^2}{b^2} = 1$ with the transverse axis on the x-axis.
    (b) $\dfrac{y^2}{a^2} - \dfrac{x^2}{b^2} = 1$ with the transverse axis on the y-axis.

17. *Translation equations:* $x' = x - h$ and $y' = y - k$.

18. *General forms of conics with axes parallel to the coordinate axes:*
    (a) $(y - k)^2 = 4p(x - h)$
       is a parabola with vertex at (h, k) and axis parallel to the x-axis.
    (b) $(x - h)^2 = 4p(y - k)$
       is a parabola with vertex at (h, k) and axis parallel to the y-axis.
    (c) $\dfrac{(x - h)^2}{a^2} + \dfrac{(y - k)^2}{b^2} = 1,$ $(a > b)$
       is an ellipse with center at (h, k) and major axis parallel to the x-axis.
    (d) $\dfrac{(y - k)^2}{a^2} + \dfrac{(x - h)^2}{b^2} = 1,$ $(a > b)$
       is an ellipse with center at (h, k) and major axis parallel to the y-axis.
    (e) $\dfrac{(x - h)^2}{a^2} - \dfrac{(y - k)^2}{b^2} = 1$
       is a hyperbola with center at (h, k) and transverse axis parallel to the x-axis.
    (f) $\dfrac{(y - k)^2}{a^2} - \dfrac{(x - h)^2}{b^2} = 1$
       is a hyperbola with center at (h, k) and transverse axis parallel to the y-axis.

19. *The general second-degree equation:* The circle, parabola, ellipse, and hyperbola are all special cases of the second-degree equation

$$Ax^2 + Bxy + Cy^2 + Dx + Ey + F = 0$$

When $B = 0$ and at least one of the coefficients A or C is not zero, the following summarizes the conditions for each curve:
    (a) If $A = C$, we have a *circle*.
       In special cases, the graph of the equation may be a point or there may be no graph. (The equation may have only one or no solution.)
    (b) If $A = 0$ and $C \neq 0$ or $C = 0$ and $A \neq 0$, then we have a *parabola*.
    (c) If $A \neq C$, and A and C are either both positive or both negative, then we have an *ellipse*.
       In special cases, the graph of the equation may be a point or there may be no graph. (The equation may have only one or no solution.)
    (d) If A and C differ in sign, then we have a *hyperbola*. In some special cases the graph may be a pair of intersecting lines.
       If $D \neq 0$ or $E \neq 0$ or both are not equal to zero, the curve does not have its center (or vertex in the case of the parabola) at the origin. If $B \neq 0$, then the axis of the curve does not lie along the x-axis or the y-axis.

20. Each point $P(x, y)$ in the rectangular coordinate system may be described by an ordered pair $P(r, \theta)$ in the polar coordinate system.

21. In the rectangular coordinate system, there is a one-to-one correspondence between points in the plane and ordered pairs of real numbers. This one-to-one correspondence is not a property of the polar coordinate system. In general the point $P(r, \theta)$ may be represented by

$$(r, \theta + k \cdot 360°) \quad \text{or} \quad (r, \theta + k \cdot 2\pi)$$

where k is any integer. $P(r, \theta)$ may also be represented by

$$(-r, \theta + k \cdot 180°) \quad \text{or} \quad (-r, \theta + k\pi)$$

where k is any odd integer.

22. *Relationships between the rectangular and polar coordinate systems* (see Fig. 1.83):

(a) $x = r \cos \theta$ (b) $y = r \sin \theta$

(c) $\tan \theta = \dfrac{y}{x}$ or $\theta = \arctan \dfrac{y}{x}$ (d) $x^2 + y^2 = r^2$

(e) $\cos \theta = \dfrac{x}{\sqrt{x^2 + y^2}}$ (f) $\sin \theta = \dfrac{y}{\sqrt{x^2 + y^2}}$

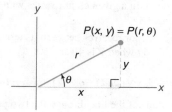

Figure 1.83

23. *Symmetry tests for graphing polar equations:*

(a) *Horizontal axis:* Replace θ by $-\theta$ in the original equation. If the resulting equation is equivalent to the original equation, then the graph of the original equation is symmetric with respect to the *horizontal* axis.

(b) *Vertical axis:* Replace θ by $\pi - \theta$ in the original equation. If the resulting equation is equivalent to the original equation, then the graph of the original equation is symmetric with respect to the *vertical* axis.

(c) *Pole*

    (i) Replace r by $-r$ in the original equation. If the resulting equation is equivalent to the original equation, then the graph of the original equation is symmetric with respect to the *pole.*

    (ii) Replace θ by $\pi + \theta$ in the original equation. If the resulting equation is equivalent to the original equation, then the graph of the original equation is symmetric with respect to the *pole.*

CHAPTER 1 REVIEW

Determine whether or not each relation is a function. Write its domain and its range.

1. $A = \{(2, 3), (3, 4), (4, 5), (5, 6)\}$ **2.** $B = \{(2, 6), (6, 4), (2, 1), (4, 3)\}$

3. $y = -4x + 3$ **4.** $y = x^2 - 5$

5. $x = y^2 + 4$ **6.** $y = \sqrt{4 - 8x}$

7. Given $f(x) = 5x + 14$, find

  (a) $f(2)$ (b) $f(0)$ (c) $f(-4)$

8. Given $g(t) = 3t^2 + 5t - 12$, find

  (a) $g(2)$ (b) $g(0)$ (c) $g(-5)$

9. Given $h(x) = \dfrac{4x^2 - 3x}{2\sqrt{x - 1}}$, find

  (a) $h(2)$ (b) $h(5)$ (c) $h(-15)$ (d) $h(1)$

10. Given $g(x) = x^2 - 6x + 4$, find

  (a) $g(a)$ (b) $g(2x)$ (c) $g(z - 2)$

Graph each equation.

11. $y = 4x + 5$ **12.** $y = x^2 + 4$ **13.** $y = x^2 + 2x - 8$

14. $y = 2x^2 + x - 6$

15. $y = -x^2 - x + 4$

16. $y = \sqrt{2x}$

17. $y = \sqrt{-2 - 4x}$

18. $y = x^3 - 6x$

Solve each graphically.

19. Exercise 12 for $y = 5, 7$, and 2.

20. Exercise 13 for $y = 0, -2$, and 3.

21. Exercise 15 for $y = 2, 0$, and -2.

22. Exercise 18 for $y = 0, 2$, and -3.

23. The current, i, in a given circuit varies with the time, t, according to $i = 2t^2$. Find t when $i = 2, 6$, and 8.

24. A given capacitor receives between its terminals a voltage, V, where $V = 4t^3 + t$ when t is in seconds. Find t when V is 40 and 60.

Use the points $(3, -4)$ and $(-6, -2)$ in Exercises 25 through 27.

25. Find the slope of the line through the two points.

26. Find the distance between the two points.

27. Find the coordinates of the point midway between the two points.

Find the equation of the line that satisfies each condition in Exercises 28 through 31.

28. Passes through $(4, 7)$ and $(6, -4)$.

29. Passes through $(-3, 1)$ with slope $\frac{2}{3}$.

30. Crosses the y-axis at -3 with slope $-\frac{1}{3}$.

31. Is parallel to and 3 units to the left of the y-axis.

32. Find the slope and the y-intercept of $3x - 2y - 6 = 0$.

33. Graph $3x - 4y = 12$.

Using the slope and the intercept of each line, determine whether each given pair of equations represents lines that are parallel, perpendicular, or neither.

34. $x - 2y + 3 = 0$; $8x + 4y - 9 = 0$

35. $2x - 3y + 4 = 0$; $-8x + 12y = 16$

36. $3x - 2y + 5 = 0$; $2x - 3y + 9 = 0$

37. $x = 2$; $y = -3$

38. $x = 4$; $y = 7$

39. Find the equation of the line parallel to the line $2x - y + 4 = 0$ that passes through the point $(5, 2)$.

40. Find the equation of the line perpendicular to the line $3x + 5y - 6 = 0$ that passes through the point $(-4, 0)$.

41. Write the equation of the circle with center at $(5, -7)$ and with radius 6.

42. Find the center and radius of the circle $x^2 + y^2 - 8x + 6y - 24 = 0$.

43. Find the focus and directrix of the parabola $x^2 = 6y$ and sketch its graph.

44. Write the equation of the parabola with focus at $(-4, 0)$ and directrix $x = 4$.

45. Write the equation of the parabola with focus at $(4, 3)$ and directrix $x = 0$.

46. Find the vertices and foci of the ellipse $4x^2 + 49y^2 = 196$ and sketch its graph.

47. Find the equation of the ellipse with vertices $(0, 4)$ and $(0, -4)$ and with foci at $(0, 2\sqrt{3})$ and $(0, -2\sqrt{3})$.

48. Find the vertices and foci of the hyperbola $4x^2 - 9y^2 = 144$ and sketch its graph.

49. Write the equation of the hyperbola with vertices at $(0, 5)$ and $(0, -5)$ and with foci at $(0, \sqrt{41})$ and $(0, -\sqrt{41})$.

50. Write the equation of the ellipse with center at $(3, -4)$, vertices at $(3, 1)$ and $(3, -9)$, and foci at $(3, 0)$ and $(3, -8)$.

51. Write the equation of the hyperbola with center at $(-7, 4)$ and vertices at $(2, 4)$ and $(-16, 4)$; the length of the conjugate axis is 6.

52. Name and sketch the graph of $16x^2 - 4y^2 - 64x - 24y + 12 = 0$.

Solve each system of equations.

53. $y^2 + 4y + x = 0$
$x = 2y$

54. $3x^2 - 4y^2 = 36$
$5x^2 - 8y^2 = 56$

Plot each point whose polar coordinates are given.

55. $A(6, 60°)$, $B(3, -210°)$, $C(-2, -270°)$, $D(-4, 750°)$

56. $A\left(5, \dfrac{\pi}{6}\right)$, $B\left(2, -\dfrac{5\pi}{4}\right)$, $C\left(-3, -\dfrac{\pi}{2}\right)$, $D\left(-5, \dfrac{19\pi}{2}\right)$

57. For point $A(5, 135°)$, name three other sets of polar coordinates for $-360° \leq \theta < 360°$.

58. For point $B(-2, 7\pi/6)$, name three other sets of polar coordinates for $-2\pi \leq \theta \leq 2\pi$.

59. Change each set of polar coordinates to rectangular coordinates.

   (a) $(3, 210°)$ (b) $(2, -120°)$ (c) $\left(-5, \dfrac{11\pi}{6}\right)$ (d) $\left(-6, -\dfrac{\pi}{2}\right)$

60. Change each set of rectangular coordinates to polar coordinates in degrees for $0° \leq \theta < 360°$.
   (a) $(-3, 3)$ (b) $(0, -6)$ (c) $(-1, \sqrt{3})$

61. Change each set of rectangular coordinates to polar coordinates in radians for $0 \leq \theta < 2\pi$.
   (a) $(-5, 0)$ (b) $(-6\sqrt{3}, 6)$ (c) $(1, -1)$

Change each equation to polar form.

62. $x^2 + y^2 = 49$ **63.** $y^2 = 9x$ **64.** $5x + 2y = 8$

65. $x^2 - 4y^2 = 12$ **66.** $y^3 = 6x^2$ **67.** $y(x^2 + y^2) = x^2$

Change each equation to rectangular form.

68. $r \cos \theta = 12$ **69.** $r = 9$ **70.** $\theta = \dfrac{2\pi}{3}$

71. $r = 8 \cos \theta$ **72.** $r \sin^2 \theta = 5 \cos \theta$ **73.** $r^2 \sin 2\theta = 8$

74. $r^2 = 4 \cos 2\theta$ **75.** $r = \csc \theta$ **76.** $r = 1 + \sin \theta$

77. $r = \dfrac{2}{1 - \sin \theta}$

Graph each equation.

78. $r = 7$ **79.** $\theta = -\dfrac{\pi}{4}$ **80.** $r = 5 \cos \theta$

81. $r = 6 + 3 \sin \theta$ **82.** $r = 6 - 3 \sin \theta$ **83.** $r = 4 + 4 \cos \theta$

84. $r = 3 - 6 \cos \theta$ **85.** $r \sin \theta = 5$ **86.** $r^2 = 36 \cos \theta$

87. $r = 6 \sin 5\theta$ **88.** $r^2 = 25 \sin 2\theta$ **89.** $r(1 - \sin \theta) = 6$

2
The Derivative

INTRODUCTION

Although algebra, trigonometry, and geometry are of fundamental importance to the mathematician and technician, a wide variety of technical problems cannot be solved using only these tools of mathematics. Many problems must be solved using the methods of the calculus. As early as the seventeenth century, scientists found the need for new techniques of mathematics to study the motion of projectiles, the motion of the moon and planets, and the motion of light. Scientists such as Isaac Newton began developing a new branch of mathematics to solve problems involving motion. This new branch of mathematics came to be known as the calculus. Today, the calculus remains a powerful development of mathematics. Even though the calculus began with the study of motion, it is useful in many varied technical areas today.

Objectives

- Find limits and instantaneous velocity.
- Find the slope and the equation of a tangent line to a curve at a point.
- Use the definition of derivative to find derivatives.
- Differentiate polynomials, products, and quotients of polynomials.
- Use the chain rule to find derivatives.
- Use implicit differentiation.

2.1 MOTION

Motion is usually defined as a continual change in position. Linear motion is motion along a straight line. In this section, we limit our discussion to linear motion. You are familiar with finding the average speed of an object in motion. For example, if you drive 150 mi in 3 hours (h), then by dividing 150 mi by 3 h, you find that you drove 50 mi/h on the average. This does not tell you how fast you were driving exactly 1 h and 32 minutes (min) after you began the trip. At that moment you may have been stopped at a traffic light or you may have been traveling 65 mi/h!

In attempting to solve this problem mathematically, we assume we can describe the distance traveled by an object as a function of time. That is, at each point in time t we can associate a number s representing the distance traveled by the object. For example, $s = 4t + 1$ is a function that describes the motion of an object as it moves along a straight line in terms of time, t. If t is measured in seconds (s) and s in metres (m), then after 2 s, the object is at $s = 4(2) + 1 = 9$ m along the line of motion. Three seconds later, $t = 2 + 3$, the object has moved to $s = 4(2 + 3) + 1 = 4(5) + 1 = 21$ m along the line of motion (see Fig. 2.1).

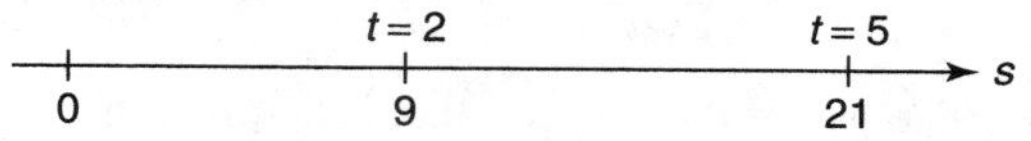

Figure 2.1 Distance traveled as a function of time.

The *average speed* $\bar{v}$ of an object in motion is the ratio of the distance traveled by the object to the time taken to travel that distance. In our previous example, the distance traveled by the object is 21 m − 9 m = 12 m. It traveled this distance in 3 s. The average speed over this time period is then

$$\bar{v} = \frac{12 \text{ m}}{3 \text{ s}} = 4 \text{ m/s}$$

The mathematical symbol Δ (the Greek letter delta) indicates a change between two values of a variable. In this section Δt (read "delta t") represents the change in time t and Δs (read "delta s") represents the change in distance s. (The letter s is commonly used to represent distance. The letter d is used to represent diameter.) Above, the time interval $\Delta t = 3$ s. This is the change in time needed for the object to go from 9 m to 21 m along the line of motion. The change in distance for this time interval $\Delta t = 3$ s is $\Delta s = 21$ m − 9 m = 12 m. Using this notation, we can write

$$\bar{v} = \frac{\Delta s}{\Delta t} = \frac{21 \text{ m} - 9 \text{ m}}{5 \text{ s} - 2 \text{ s}} = \frac{12 \text{ m}}{3 \text{ s}} = 4 \text{ m/s}$$

When both speed and direction are needed to describe motion, the term *velocity* is used. The **velocity** of an object is the time rate of change of its displacement, where displacement is the vector difference (net distance) between the initial and final positions of the object. Since both magnitude (speed) and direction are required to completely describe velocity, velocity is a vector quantity. The direction of velocity along a straight line is usually given as positive or negative.

Note: Since speed is the magnitude of velocity, it is common to use v for either speed or the magnitude of velocity. In addition, the terms *speed* and *velocity* are often used interchangeably because the direction of the motion is often understood. For example, velocity that results from motion in a straight line has the same direction as the direction of the motion, such as in a freely falling body.

Recall that a function is a set of ordered pairs, no two of which have the same first element. We find it helpful to use a special notation, called *functional notation,* to represent a functional relationship. For example, the function $y = x^2 + 3$ is written $f(x) = x^2 + 3$ using functional notation. The symbol $f(x)$, read "f of x," is used to represent the number y which corresponds to a number x under the given functional relationship. (See Section 1.1.) The following table gives $f(x)$ for various values of x:

x	$f(x) = x^2 + 3$
−3	$f(-3) = (-3)^2 + 3 = 12$
0	$f(0) = (0)^2 + 3 = 3$
1	$f(1) = (1)^2 + 3 = 4$
2	$f(2) = (2)^2 + 3 = 7$

x	$f(x) = x^2 + 3$
h	$f(h) = (h)^2 + 3 = h^2 + 3$
$3t$	$f(3t) = (3t)^2 + 3 = 9t^2 + 3$
$1 + \Delta x$	$f(1 + \Delta x) = (1 + \Delta x)^2 + 3 = 4 + 2\Delta x + (\Delta x)^2$

The use of the symbol $f(x)$ is helpful since we can use $f(x)$ to represent the number corresponding to x under the functional relationship without having to actually determine the number as done in the table above. For example, $f(3)$ represents the number corresponding to $x = 3$ under any given functional relationship. For this reason, $f(x)$ is often called the *value of the function at x*.

EXAMPLE 1

Find the value of the function $f(x) = x^3 - 2$ for (a) $x = -3$ and (b) $x = 2 + \Delta x$.

(a) $f(-3) = (-3)^3 - 2 = -27 - 2 = -29$

(b) $f(2 + \Delta x) = (2 + \Delta x)^3 - 2$
$$= 8 + 12(\Delta x) + 6(\Delta x)^2 + (\Delta x)^3 - 2$$
$$= 6 + 12(\Delta x) + 6(\Delta x)^2 + (\Delta x)^3$$

EXAMPLE 2

Evaluate the function $g(x) = \sqrt{2x + 3}$ at $x = 3$.
$$g(3) = \sqrt{2(3) + 3} = \sqrt{9} = 3$$

EXAMPLE 3

Evaluate the function $f(x) = x^2 + 3x - 5$ at $x = h + 2$.
$$f(h + 2) = (h + 2)^2 + 3(h + 2) - 5$$
$$= h^2 + 4h + 4 + 3h + 6 - 5$$
$$= h^2 + 7h + 5$$

On the previous pages we were considering an object that moved along a straight line according to the function $s = 4t + 1$. We can express this using functional notation: $s = f(t) = 4t + 1$.

Recall from this earlier discussion that Δs is the change in distance s and Δt is the change in time after $t = 2$ s. Then, using functional notation, the equation

$$\Delta s = f(2 + \Delta t) - f(2)$$

represents, as we saw earlier, the change in distance traveled for a given change in time Δt. When $\Delta t = 3$ s, we have

$$\Delta s = f(2 + \Delta t) - f(2)$$
$$= f(2 + 3) - f(2) \qquad (\Delta t = 3)$$
$$= f(5) - f(2)$$
$$= [4(5) + 1] - [4(2) + 1]$$
$$= 21 - 9$$
$$= 12 \text{ m}$$

So the average speed over this time period is

$$\bar{v} = \frac{\Delta s}{\Delta t} = \frac{f(2 + \Delta t) - f(2)}{\Delta t}$$

$$= \frac{12 \text{ m}}{3 \text{ s}} = 4 \text{ m/s}$$

as we determined earlier.

In general, the distance traveled by an object from time t to time $t + \Delta t$ is given in functional notation by

$$\Delta s = f(t + \Delta t) - f(t)$$

The average speed of this object over the time interval from t to $t + \Delta t$ is then given as follows:

> **AVERAGE SPEED**
>
> $$\bar{v} = \frac{\Delta s}{\Delta t} = \frac{f(t + \Delta t) - f(t)}{\Delta t}$$

EXAMPLE 4

Given that $s = f(t) = t^2 - 1$ describes the motion of an object moving along a straight line, where s is measured in feet (ft), (a) find Δs and $\bar{v}$, and (b) find the average velocity $\bar{v}$ over the time interval from 4 s to 7 s.

(a)
$$\Delta s = f(t + \Delta t) - f(t)$$
$$= [(t + \Delta t)^2 - 1] - (t^2 - 1)$$
$$= [t^2 + 2t(\Delta t) + (\Delta t)^2 - 1] - (t^2 - 1)$$
$$= 2t(\Delta t) + (\Delta t)^2$$

$$\bar{v} = \frac{\Delta s}{\Delta t} = \frac{2t(\Delta t) + (\Delta t)^2}{\Delta t}$$

$$= \frac{\Delta t(2t + \Delta t)}{\Delta t}$$

$$= 2t + \Delta t$$

(b)
$$\Delta t = 7 - 4 = 3 \text{ s}$$

From (a) we have

$$\bar{v} = 2t + \Delta t$$
$$= 2(4) + (3)$$
$$= 11 \text{ ft/s}$$

This same result can be obtained by calculating:

$$\bar{v} = \frac{f(4 + 3) - f(4)}{3} = \frac{\text{distance traveled}}{\text{time traveled}} = \frac{48 - 15}{3} = 11 \text{ ft/s}$$

From Example 4 we see that to calculate $\bar{v} = (\Delta s / \Delta t)$ we need to know the time t at which we begin measuring $\bar{v}$ as well as the change in time Δt. Note that both t and Δt can be negative. If $\Delta t = -1$, then $f(t + (-1))$ represents the position of the object 1 s before it reaches the position $f(t)$.

The use of functional notation, as well as the concept of function itself, will receive strong emphasis in the remaining material. The development of the calculus depends heavily on this concept.

To find instantaneous speeds, consider the motion of an object moving along a straight line described by $s = f(t) = 3t^2 + 1$ with s measured in feet. We will now find the "instantaneous" speed after exactly 2 s of travel.

The average speed over the time interval from 2 s to $(2 + \Delta t)$ s is given by

$$\bar{v} = \frac{\text{change in distance}}{\text{change in time}} = \frac{f(2 + \Delta t) - f(2)}{\Delta t}$$

$$= \frac{[3(2 + \Delta t)^2 + 1] - [3(2)^2 + 1]}{\Delta t}$$

$$= \frac{3[4 + 4(\Delta t) + (\Delta t)^2] + 1 - 13}{\Delta t}$$

$$= \frac{12(\Delta t) + 3(\Delta t)^2}{\Delta t}$$

$$= \frac{\Delta t[12 + 3(\Delta t)]}{\Delta t} = 12 + 3(\Delta t)$$

So, for example, with a change in time from $t = 2$ to $t = 6$, $\Delta t = 4$ s. The average speed is $12 + 3(4) = 24$ ft/s. We now tabulate $\bar{v}$ for different values of Δt:

Δt (s)	$\bar{v}$ (ft/s)
4	24
2	18
1	15
0.5	13.5
0.1	12.3
0.01	12.03
0.001	12.003
−0.001	11.997
−0.01	11.97
−0.1	11.7
−0.5	10.5
−2	6

From this table we can see that the closer Δt is to 0, the closer $\bar{v}$ is to 12 ft/s. As we consider the average speed over shorter and shorter time spans, we would expect that the average speed will better approximate the instantaneous speed of the object at 2 s. That is, $\bar{v} = 12.3$ ft/s after 0.1 s of travel (beyond the 2-s mark) is a better approximation than $\bar{v} = 24$ ft/s after 4 s of travel (beyond the 2-s mark). From this table, we see that the instantaneous speed at time $t = 2$ s appears to be 12 ft/s.

INSTANTANEOUS SPEED

To find the *instantaneous speed* of an object in motion at a given time t:

1. Find

$$\bar{v} = \frac{f(t + \Delta t) - f(t)}{\Delta t} = \frac{\Delta s}{\Delta t}$$

where $s = f(t)$ describes the motion of the object as a function of time.

2. Observe what number, if any, $\bar{v}$ approaches as values of Δt approach 0. If there is such a number, it is called the instantaneous speed v.

EXAMPLE 5

Find the instantaneous speed of an object moving according to $s = f(t) = 5t^2 - 4$ at $t = 3$ s.

Step 1: $\quad \bar{v} = \dfrac{f(3 + \Delta t) - f(3)}{\Delta t}$

$\qquad = \dfrac{[5(3 + \Delta t)^2 - 4] - [5(3)^2 - 4]}{\Delta t}$

$\qquad = \dfrac{45 + 30\Delta t + 5(\Delta t)^2 - 4 - 41}{\Delta t}$

$\qquad = \dfrac{30(\Delta t) + 5(\Delta t)^2}{\Delta t}$

$\qquad = \dfrac{\Delta t[30 + 5(\Delta t)]}{\Delta t}$

$\qquad = 30 + 5(\Delta t)$

Step 2: As Δt approaches (gets close to) 0, $\bar{v}$ approaches 30. We conclude that

$$v = 30 \text{ ft/s}$$

Note: It is tempting to simply substitute $\Delta t = 0$ in the formula for $\bar{v}$. This would be an attempt to compute an average velocity over a time interval of length 0 s. This gives us a zero time interval over which to average! We would be attempting to divide by zero, which is undefined.

$$\frac{f(3 + 0) - f(3)}{0} = \frac{0}{0}!!!$$

As in Example 5, we must find a way to simplify the expression for $\bar{v}$ so that Δt does not remain in the denominator. Only then can we begin to see what number $\bar{v}$ approaches as Δt approaches 0.

EXAMPLE 6

Find v at $t = 2$ when $s = f(t) = \dfrac{1}{t}$.

Step 1: $\quad \bar{v} = \dfrac{f(2 + \Delta t) - f(2)}{\Delta t}$

$\qquad = \dfrac{\dfrac{1}{2 + \Delta t} - \dfrac{1}{2}}{\Delta t}$

$\qquad = \dfrac{\dfrac{2 - (2 + \Delta t)}{2(2 + \Delta t)}}{\Delta t}$

$\qquad = \dfrac{-\Delta t}{2(2 + \Delta t)\Delta t}$

$\qquad = \dfrac{-1}{2(2 + \Delta t)}$

Step 2: As Δt approaches 0, $\bar{v}$ approaches $-\frac{1}{2(2)}$. So, $v = -\frac{1}{4}$.

Exercises 2.1

Evaluate each function at the given value.

1. $f(x) = 2x^2 + 7, x = 1$

2. $g(x) = x^3 - x + 3, x = -1$

3. $h(x) = 3x^3 - 2x + 4, x = -2$

4. $k(x) = 2x^3 + x - 5, x = 2$

5. $f(x) = \dfrac{x^2 - 3}{x + 5}, x = 2$

6. $g(x) = \dfrac{(x^3 - 2x + 3)\sqrt{x - 2}}{x - 4}, x = 3$

7. $f(z) = \sqrt{z^2 + 3}, z = -5$

8. $f(t) = \sqrt{t^2 - 1}, t = 4$

9. $f(x) = 3x - 2, x = h + 3$

10. $g(x) = x^2 + x - 3, x = w + 4$

11. $f(t) = 3t^2 + 2t - 5, t = 2 + \Delta t$

12. $f(t) = t^2 - 3t + 4, t = -3 + \Delta t$

*Find **(a)** Δs and **(b)** $\bar{v}$ for each function expressing distance s in terms of time t. (Express results in terms of t and Δt.)*

13. $s = 3t - 4$

14. $s = 2t + 2$

15. $s = 2t^2 + 5$

16. $s = 3t^2 - 7$

17. $s = t^2 - 2t + 8$

18. $s = 5t^2 + 3t - 9$

Find $\bar{v}$ for each function $s = f(t)$ at the values of t and Δt (s is measured in metres and t in seconds).

19. $s = 5t^2 + 6, t = 3, \Delta t = 4$

20. $s = 2t^2 - 5, t = 2, \Delta t = 3$

21. $s = 3t^2 - t + 4, t = 2, \Delta t = 2$

22. $s = 6t^2 + 2t - 7, t = 5, \Delta t = 1$

23. A charged particle moves from 0.2 m to 0.5 m from a fixed reference point in 0.5 μs. Find its average speed during that interval ($1 \mu s = 10^{-6}$ s).

24. An electron moved a distance of 0.2 m in 1 μs. Find its average speed in m/s during that interval.

25. The average current in a capacitor over a time interval Δt is given by $i_{av} = C(\Delta V / \Delta t)$ amperes (A), where C is the capacitance in farads (F) and V is the voltage across the capacitor in volts (V). Find the average current (in μA) in a 10-μF capacitor from 2 s to 5 s where the voltage is given by $V = t^2 + 3t + 160$.

26. Find the average current (in μA) in a 15-μF capacitor from 3 s to 7 s where the voltage is given by $V = 2t^2 - 4t + 200$ (see Exercise 25).

Find the instantaneous velocity v of an object moving along a straight line for each given expression for s (measured in metres) at the given value of t (measured in seconds).

27. $s = f(t) = 3t^2 - 6t + 1, t = 2$

28. $s = f(t) = -4t^2 + 8, t = 3$

29. $s = f(t) = 5t^2 - 7, t = 1$

30. $s = f(t) = 8t^2 + 3t - 11, t = 4$

31. $s = f(t) = \dfrac{1}{2t}, t = 3$

32. $s = f(t) = \dfrac{1}{t + 1}, t = 2$

33. $s = f(t) = \dfrac{1}{t - 2}, t = 4$

34. $s = f(t) = \dfrac{1}{3t}, t = 4$

35. A free-falling object (neglecting friction) falls from rest according to $s = 16t^2$ when time t is measured in seconds and distance s is measured in feet. Find the speed of an object after falling 2 s.

36. A circuit-breaker contact moves approximately $s = 200,000t^3$, where s is in centimetres (cm) and t is in seconds. Find the speed v of the contact when $t = 0.1$ s.

2.2 THE LIMIT

The process we developed in problems involving motion is very useful in other applications. The technique used is often called "the limit process." Given any function, we may find whether the functional values approach some number when the value of the variable approaches a specified number.

EXAMPLE 1

Let $f(x) = x^2 - 3x + 2$. What number, if any, does $f(x)$ approach as x approaches -1?

Since x^2 approaches $(-1)^2 = 1$ as x approaches -1 and $-3x$ approaches $(-3)(-1) = 3$ as x approaches -1, we conclude that $f(x) = x^2 - 3x + 2$ approaches $1 + 3 + 2 = 6$ as x approaches -1.

We use symbols to describe this limit process more compactly. The symbol " $\rightarrow$ " means "approaches," so x approaches -1 is written $x \rightarrow -1$.

LIMIT

If $f(x) \rightarrow L$ as $x \rightarrow a$, then L is called "the limit of the function as $x \rightarrow a$." This process is written as

$$\lim_{x \to a} f(x) = L$$

and read "the limit of f of x as x approaches a equals L."

The expression in Example 1 is written $\lim_{x \to -1} (x^2 - 3x + 2) = 6$.

Note in this case that the limit and the functional value are equal.

THEOREM

For any polynomial $f(x)$,

$$\lim_{x \to a} f(x) = f(a)$$

EXAMPLE 2

Given $f(x) = \dfrac{\tan x}{x}$, what number, if any, does $f(x)$ approach as x approaches 0?

Notice that $f(0)$ does not exist, but that does not mean that the limit does not exist, because finding a limit is not the same as finding the value of a function. That is, find $\lim_{x \to 0} \dfrac{\tan x}{x}$.

Let's use a calculator and make a table of values for x close to zero. (Be certain that your calculator is in the radian mode.)

x	$\dfrac{\tan x}{x}$	x	$\dfrac{\tan x}{x}$
0.5	1.092605	-0.5	1.092605
0.25	1.021368	-0.25	1.021368
0.15	1.007568	-0.15	1.007568
0.10	1.003347	-0.10	1.003347
0.05	1.000834	-0.05	1.000834
0.01	1.0000332	-0.01	1.0000332
0.001	1.0000005	-0.001	1.0000005

As you can see, as x gets closer and closer to 0, $\dfrac{\tan x}{x}$ approaches 1 (see Fig. 2.2). Thus

$$\lim_{x \to 0} \frac{\tan x}{x} = 1$$

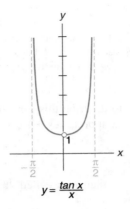

$$y = \frac{\tan x}{x}$$

Figure 2.2

Note: This example does not constitute a proof; it gives only an intuitive idea about limits.

This example leads to a fact that is of paramount importance in physics, namely that $\frac{\tan x}{x}$ approaches 1 if x approaches 0 and so $\tan x$ approaches x if x approaches 0.

EXAMPLE 3

Find $\lim\limits_{x \to 3} \left(\dfrac{x^2 - 9}{x - 3} \right)$

As $x \to 3$, the denominator approaches 0. We cannot divide by zero. However,

$$\frac{x^2 - 9}{x - 3} = \frac{(x + 3)(x - 3)}{x - 3} = x + 3 \qquad (x \neq 3)$$

In the limit process we are not concerned about what happens at $x = 3$, but only what happens as $x \to 3$ (Fig. 2.3). As $x \to 3$, $x + 3 \to 6$. So

$$\lim_{x \to 3} \left(\frac{x^2 - 9}{x - 3} \right) = \lim_{x \to 3} (x + 3) = 6$$

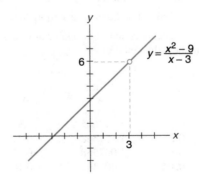

$$y = \frac{x^2 - 9}{x - 3}$$

Figure 2.3

Note that in Example 3 we can find the limit of $f(x) = \dfrac{x^2 - 9}{x - 3}$ as $x \to 3$ even though the function is not defined at $x = 3$. However, we will now see that limits do not always exist.

EXAMPLE 4

Find $\lim\limits_{x \to 0} \dfrac{|x|}{x}$.

Note that the function $\dfrac{|x|}{x} = 1$ for all $x > 0$, for example, $\dfrac{|0.002|}{0.002} = \dfrac{0.002}{0.002} = 1$. However, $\dfrac{|x|}{x} = -1$ for all $x < 0$, for example, $\dfrac{|-0.003|}{-0.003} = \dfrac{0.003}{-0.003} = -1$. Since the function is constantly -1 to the left of zero and 1 to the right of zero, we conclude that $\lim\limits_{x \to 0} \dfrac{|x|}{x}$ *does not exist* since there is no unique, specific value that $\dfrac{|x|}{x}$ gets close to as $x \to 0$.

Sometimes a function approaches a limiting number L as $x \to \infty$, that is, the function approaches L as x is allowed to get large without bound.

EXAMPLE 5

Find $\lim\limits_{x \to \infty} \dfrac{1}{x}$.

As the denominator $x \to \infty$, the fraction $\dfrac{1}{x}$ approaches 0. So

$$\lim_{x \to \infty} \frac{1}{x} = 0$$

Note in Fig. 2.4 that as x increases in value, the graph gets closer and closer to the x-axis. That is, y approaches 0. From the graph, also note that $\lim\limits_{x \to -\infty} \dfrac{1}{x} = 0$.

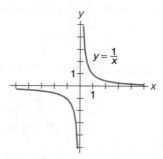

$y = \dfrac{1}{x}$

Figure 2.4

EXAMPLE 6

Find $\lim\limits_{x \to \infty} \dfrac{2x^2 + x}{7x^2 - 3}$.

As $x \to \infty$, both numerator and denominator approach ∞ separately. However, if we divide numerator and denominator by the highest power of x in the denominator, x^2, we have

$$\frac{2 + \dfrac{1}{x}}{7 - \dfrac{3}{x^2}}$$

We write

$$\lim_{x \to \infty} \frac{2x^2 + x}{7x^2 - 3} = \lim_{x \to \infty} \frac{2 + \dfrac{1}{x}}{7 - \dfrac{3}{x^2}} = \frac{2 + 0}{7 - 0} = \frac{2}{7}$$

Note: As $x \to \infty$, $\dfrac{1}{x} \to 0$ and $\dfrac{3}{x^2} \to 0$.

Using a calculator, we obtain

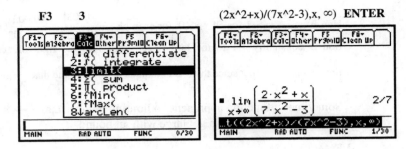

F3   3   (2x^2+x)/(7x^2-3),x, ∞) **ENTER**

Finding instantaneous velocity is an application of the limit process. As the time interval Δt decreases in the average velocity formula

$$\bar{v} = \frac{\Delta s}{\Delta t} = \frac{f(t + \Delta t) - f(t)}{\Delta t}$$

the average velocity approaches the instantaneous velocity v, the velocity at a given instant. That is,

$$v = \lim_{\Delta t \to 0} \frac{f(t + \Delta t) - f(t)}{\Delta t}$$

EXAMPLE 7

Find the instantaneous velocity v at $t = 3$ when $s = f(t) = t^2 - 7$.

$$v = \lim_{\Delta t \to 0} \frac{f(3 + \Delta t) - f(3)}{\Delta t}$$

$$= \lim_{\Delta t \to 0} \frac{[9 + 6(\Delta t) + (\Delta t)^2 - 7] - [9 - 7]}{\Delta t}$$

$$= \lim_{\Delta t \to 0} \frac{6(\Delta t) + (\Delta t)^2}{\Delta t}$$

$$= \lim_{\Delta t \to 0} \frac{\Delta t(6 + \Delta t)}{\Delta t}$$

$$= \lim_{\Delta t \to 0} (6 + \Delta t)$$

$$= 6$$

It can be shown that the limit process is described by the following formulas:

$$\lim_{x \to a} [f(x) \pm g(x)] = \lim_{x \to a} f(x) \pm \lim_{x \to a} g(x) \tag{1}$$

EXAMPLE 8

$$\lim_{x \to 3} (x^3 + x^2) = \lim_{x \to 3} x^3 + \lim_{x \to 3} x^2$$

$$36 = 27 + 9$$

$$\lim_{x \to a} [k \cdot f(x)] = k \cdot \lim_{x \to a} f(x), \qquad \text{where } k \text{ is a constant} \tag{2}$$

EXAMPLE 9

$$\lim_{x \to -2} 12x^2 = 12 \lim_{x \to -2} x^2$$

$$48 = 12(4)$$

$$\lim_{x \to a} k = k, \qquad \text{where } k \text{ is a constant} \tag{3}$$

EXAMPLE 10

$$\lim_{x \to 2} 8 = 8$$

Note: No matter what x approaches, $f(x) = 8$, so $f(x)$ not only approaches 8, but actually is 8.

$$\lim_{x \to a} [f(x) \cdot g(x)] = \lim_{x \to a} f(x) \cdot \lim_{x \to a} g(x) \tag{4}$$

EXAMPLE 11

$$\lim_{x \to 3} [x^2(x - 1)] = \lim_{x \to 3} x^2 \cdot \lim_{x \to 3} (x - 1)$$

$$18 = 9 \cdot 2$$

Using Formula (4), we can show that

$$\lim_{x \to a} x^n = a^n \qquad \text{(where } n \text{ is a positive integer)}$$

$$\lim_{x \to a} \frac{f(x)}{g(x)} = \frac{\lim_{x \to a} f(x)}{\lim_{x \to a} g(x)}, \qquad \text{where} \quad \lim_{x \to a} g(x) \neq 0 \tag{5}$$

Note: $\lim_{x \to a} f(x)$ and $\lim_{x \to a} g(x)$ must both exist in Formulas (1) through (5).

EXAMPLE 12

$$\lim_{x \to 1} \frac{x^2 - 4}{x + 2} = \frac{\lim_{x \to 1} (x^2 - 4)}{\lim_{x \to 1} (x + 2)}$$

$$-1 = \frac{-3}{3}$$

The idea of continuity is very closely related to the limit idea. A function is *continuous* if its graph is an unbroken curve. The function $f(x) = x^2$ is continuous, as you can see from its graph in Fig. 2.5.

The function

$$f(x) = \begin{cases} x & \text{if } x \geq 0 \\ 1 & \text{if } x < 0 \end{cases}$$

is not continuous because its graph in Fig. 2.6 is broken at $x = 0$.

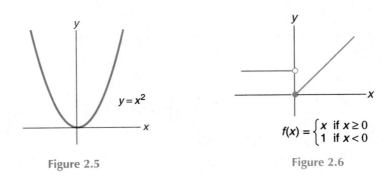

Figure 2.5

Figure 2.6

$$f(x) = \begin{cases} x & \text{if } x \geq 0 \\ 1 & \text{if } x < 0 \end{cases}$$

More formally, we have the following:

CONTINUITY

A function is continuous at $x = a$ if and only if

1. $f(a)$ is defined,
2. $\lim\limits_{x \to a} f(x)$ exists, and
3. $\lim\limits_{x \to a} f(x) = f(a)$.

Figure 2.7 shows the graphs of three functions that are not continuous at $x = a$.

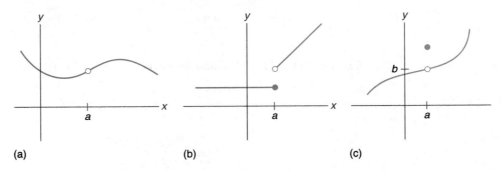

(a)   (b)   (c)

Figure 2.7   Functions not continuous at $x = a$.

Figure 2.7(a) is not continuous at $x = a$ because $f(a)$ is not defined.

Figure 2.7(b) is not continuous at $x = a$ because $\lim\limits_{x \to a} f(x)$ does not exist.

Figure 2.7(c) is not continuous at $x = a$ because $\lim\limits_{x \to a} f(x) = b \neq f(a)$.

If a function is continuous at all points in a given interval, it is continuous on that interval.

Exercises 2.2

Find each limit using a calculator. (For trigonometric functions, be certain that your calculator is in the radian mode.)

1. $\lim\limits_{x \to 2} \dfrac{x^2 - 4}{x - 2}$

2. $\lim\limits_{x \to -\frac{1}{2}} \dfrac{4x^2 - 1}{2x + 1}$

3. $\lim\limits_{x \to \infty} \dfrac{3x + 2}{x}$

4. $\lim\limits_{x \to \infty} \dfrac{3x^2 + 4x}{2x^2 - 1}$

5. $\lim\limits_{x \to 0} \dfrac{\sin x}{x}$

6. $\lim\limits_{x \to 0} \dfrac{\cos x - 1}{x}$

Find each limit without using a calculator.

7. $\lim\limits_{x \to 2} (x^2 - 5x)$

8. $\lim\limits_{x \to -1} (3x^2 + 7x + 1)$

9. $\lim\limits_{x \to -1} (2x^3 + 5x^2 - 2)$

10. $\lim\limits_{x \to 2} (x^3 - 3x^2 + x + 4)$

11. $\lim\limits_{x \to 1} \dfrac{x^2 - 1}{x - 1}$

12. $\lim\limits_{x \to -3} \dfrac{x^2 - 9}{x + 3}$

13. $\lim\limits_{x \to -3/2} \dfrac{4x^2 - 9}{2x + 3}$

14. $\lim\limits_{x \to 4/3} \dfrac{9x^2 - 16}{3x - 4}$

15. $\lim\limits_{x \to -1} \sqrt{2x + 3}$

16. $\lim\limits_{x \to 4} \sqrt{3x - 3}$

17. $\lim\limits_{x \to 6} \sqrt{4 - x}$

18. $\lim\limits_{x \to -1} \sqrt{2x + 1}$

19. $\lim\limits_{x \to \infty} \dfrac{1}{2x}$

20. $\lim\limits_{x \to \infty} \dfrac{1}{x^2}$

21. $\lim\limits_{x \to \infty} \dfrac{3x^2 - 5x + 2}{4x^2 + 8x - 11}$

22. $\lim\limits_{x \to \infty} \dfrac{7x^3 + 2x - 13}{4x^3 + x^2}$.

Find the instantaneous velocity v for each expression of s and value of t.

23. $s = f(t) = 4t^2 - 3t, t = 2$

24. $s = f(t) = 3t^2 - 5t + 2, t = 3$

25. $s = f(t) = t^2 + 3t - 10, t = 4$

26. $s = f(t) = 5t^2 - 7t + 8, t = 2$

Find each limit using Formulas (1) through (5).

27. $\lim\limits_{x \to 2} (x^2 + x)$

28. $\lim\limits_{x \to 3} (x^3 + x^2)$

29. $\lim\limits_{x \to 1} (4x^2 + 100x - 2)$

30. $\lim\limits_{x \to -1} (3x^2 + 5x - 8)$

31. $\lim\limits_{x \to 1} (x + 3)(x - 4)$

32. $\lim\limits_{x \to 4} (2x + 1)(x - 3)$

33. $\lim\limits_{x \to -2} (x^2 + 3x + 1)(x^4 - 2x^2 + 3)$

34. $\lim\limits_{x \to 2} (x^2 + 5x - 10)(x^3 + 6x^2 - x)$

35. $\lim\limits_{x \to 2} \dfrac{x^2 + 3x + 2}{x^2 + 1}$

36. $\lim\limits_{x \to 3} \dfrac{x^2 - 4x + 5}{x^2 + 2x}$

37. $\lim\limits_{x \to -7} \dfrac{x^2 - 49}{x + 7}$

38. $\lim\limits_{x \to 2} \dfrac{x^2 - 4}{x - 2}$

39. $\lim\limits_{x \to 5/2} \dfrac{4x^2 - 25}{2x - 5}$

40. $\lim\limits_{x \to -4/3} \dfrac{9x^2 - 16}{3x + 4}$

41. $\lim\limits_{x \to 3} \dfrac{(x^2 + 3x + 1)(x + 5)}{x - 2}$

42. $\lim\limits_{x \to -2} \dfrac{(x^2 + x - 5)(x - 3)}{x + 3}$

43. $\lim\limits_{h \to 0} \dfrac{(x + h)^2 - x^2}{h}$

44. $\lim\limits_{x \to a} \dfrac{x^3 - a^3}{x - a}$

45. $\lim\limits_{h \to 0} \dfrac{\dfrac{1}{x + h} - \dfrac{1}{x}}{h}$

46. $\lim\limits_{x \to a} \dfrac{\dfrac{1}{x^2} - \dfrac{1}{a^2}}{x - a}$

47. $\lim\limits_{x \to a} \dfrac{\sqrt{x} - \sqrt{a}}{x - a}$ (*Hint:* Rationalize the numerator.)

48. $\lim\limits_{h \to 0} \dfrac{\sqrt{x + h} - \sqrt{x}}{h}$

In Exercises 49 through 56, find $\lim\limits_{x \to a} f(x)$ if it exists.

49.
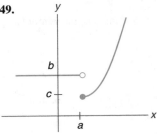

50.
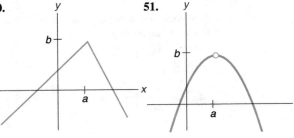

51.

52.
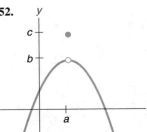

53.
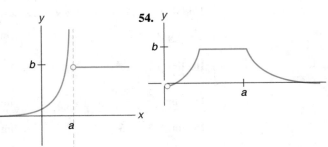

54.

55.
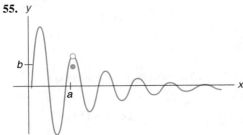

56.
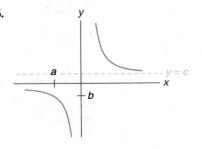

57–64. In Exercises 49 through 56, is the function continuous at $x = a$?

65. In Exercise 49, find $\lim\limits_{x \to +\infty} f(x)$ if it exists.

66. In Exercise 53, find $\lim\limits_{x \to +\infty} f(x)$ if it exists.

67. In Exercise 54, find $\lim\limits_{x \to +\infty} f(x)$ if it exists.

68. In Exercise 55, find $\lim\limits_{x \to +\infty} f(x)$ if it exists.

69. In Exercise 49, find $\lim\limits_{x \to -\infty} f(x)$ if it exists.

70. In Exercise 53, find $\lim\limits_{x \to -\infty} f(x)$ if it exists.

71. In Exercise 54, find $\lim\limits_{x \to -\infty} f(x)$ if it exists.

72. In Exercise 56, find $\lim\limits_{x \to +\infty} f(x)$ if it exists.

2.3   THE SLOPE OF A TANGENT LINE TO A CURVE

The limit process so far has been applied only to motion problems. We now look at its geometric application. We saw in Section 1.3 how to find the slope of a line. But how can we describe the slope of a tangent line to a nonlinear curve at a given point? As in Fig. 2.8, assume the curve is the graph of a given function $y = f(x)$. We wish to find the slope of the tangent line, m_{tan}, at the point P with coordinates $(x, f(x))$. We can determine the slope of a line passing through P and any other point Q on the curve (the secant line). Observe the slopes of these secant lines as we choose points Q closer and closer to the point P. As Q approaches P, the values of the slopes of these secant lines become closer and closer to the slope of the tangent line, m_{tan}. We can express this process in terms of the coordinates of P and Q as in Fig. 2.9. In this figure, $\Delta y = f(x + \Delta x) - f(x)$.

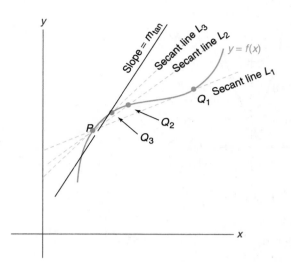

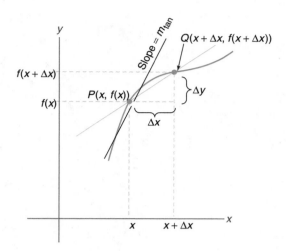

Figure 2.8 As Q approaches P, the slope of the secant line approaches the slope of the tangent line at point P.

Figure 2.9 As Δx approaches 0, Q approaches P and the slope of the secant line approaches the slope of the tangent line at P.

As we choose values of Δx closer to 0, point Q moves closer to P along the curve. Thus the slope of the secant line approaches m_{tan}, the slope of the tangent line. The slope of the secant line through P and Q is given by

$$\frac{f(x + \Delta x) - f(x)}{(x + \Delta x) - x} = \frac{f(x + \Delta x) - f(x)}{\Delta x} = \frac{\Delta y}{\Delta x}$$

so we have the following result:

SLOPE OF TANGENT LINE

$$m_{\text{tan}} = \lim_{\Delta x \to 0} \frac{\Delta y}{\Delta x} = \lim_{\Delta x \to 0} \frac{f(x + \Delta x) - f(x)}{\Delta x}$$

EXAMPLE 1

Find the slope of the tangent line to the curve $y = x^2 + 3$ at $(1, 4)$.

$$m_{\text{tan}} = \lim_{\Delta x \to 0} \frac{\Delta y}{\Delta x} = \lim_{\Delta x \to 0} \frac{f(x + \Delta x) - f(x)}{\Delta x}$$

$$= \lim_{\Delta x \to 0} \frac{[(1 + \Delta x)^2 + 3] - [(1)^2 + 3]}{\Delta x}$$

$$= \lim_{\Delta x \to 0} \frac{2(\Delta x) + (\Delta x)^2}{\Delta x}$$

$$= \lim_{\Delta x \to 0} \frac{\Delta x(2 + \Delta x)}{\Delta x}$$

$$= \lim_{\Delta x \to 0} (2 + \Delta x)$$

$$= 2$$

The curve and the tangent line appear in Fig. 2.10.

The process used to solve the geometric problem is the same as used for the motion problem. This process, the limit, is the foundation of the calculus.

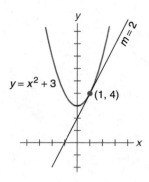

Figure 2.10

EXAMPLE 2

Find the equation of the tangent line to the curve $y = 2x^2 - 5$ at $(2, 3)$.

Step 1: Find m_{tan}:

$$m_{\text{tan}} = \lim_{\Delta x \to 0} \frac{\Delta y}{\Delta x} = \lim_{\Delta x \to 0} \frac{f(x + \Delta x) - f(x)}{\Delta x}$$

$$= \lim_{\Delta x \to 0} \frac{[2(2 + \Delta x)^2 - 5] - [2(2)^2 - 5]}{\Delta x}$$

$$= \lim_{\Delta x \to 0} \frac{\Delta x(8 + 2\Delta x)}{\Delta x}$$

$$= \lim_{\Delta x \to 0} (8 + 2\Delta x)$$

$$= 8$$

Step 2: Find the equation of the line:
Using the point-slope formula, we have

$$y - y_1 = m(x - x_1)$$
$$y - 3 = 8(x - 2)$$
$$y = 8x - 13$$

Exercises 2.3

Find the slope of the tangent line to each curve at the given point.

1. $y = x^2$; $(3, 9)$ **2.** $y = 3x^2$; $(1, 3)$

3. $y = 3x^2 - 4$; $(-1, -1)$ **4.** $y = 4x^2 + 3$; $(2, 19)$

5. $y = 2x^2 + x - 3$; $(2, 7)$ **6.** $y = 3x^2 + 8x - 10$; $(-2, -14)$

7. $y = -4x^2 + 3x - 2$; $(1, -3)$ **8.** $y = -5x^2 - 3x - 1$; $(2, -27)$

9. $y = x^3$; $(2, 8)$ **10.** $y = x^3 + 1$; $(-1, 0)$

Find the equation of the tangent line to each curve at the given point.

11. $y = x^2$; $(-2, 4)$ **12.** $y = -5x^2$; $(2, -20)$

13. $y = 2x^2 - 3$; $(-2, 5)$ **14.** $y = -4x^2 + 2$; $(-1, -2)$

15. $y = 5x^2 - 3x + 2$; $(-1, 10)$ **16.** $y = 4x^2 - 7x + 5$; $(3, 20)$

17. $y = -3x^2 + 5x + 2; x = 3$ **18.** $y = -2x^2 + 4x - 7; x = -2$

19. $y = x^3 + x - 1; x = 1$ **20.** $y = x^3 - 3x + 4; x = 2$

Find a point or points on the curve where the slope of the tangent line is the given value.

21. $y = x^2; m = -\frac{1}{3}$ **22.** $y = 3x^2 - 4; m = 6$

23. $y = x^3 + x; m = 4$ **24.** $y = x^3 - 3x^2 - 5x; m = 4$

2.4 THE DERIVATIVE

Instantaneous velocity and the slope of the tangent line to a curve are only two examples of the use of the concept of limit. A more general use of the limit is found in the derivative. When we developed instantaneous velocity and the slope of the tangent line, we applied the limit concept to related functions as follows:

$$v = \lim_{\Delta t \to 0} \frac{\Delta s}{\Delta t} = \lim_{\Delta t \to 0} \frac{f(t + \Delta t) - f(t)}{\Delta t}$$

and

$$m_{\text{tan}} = \lim_{\Delta x \to 0} \frac{\Delta y}{\Delta x} = \lim_{\Delta x \to 0} \frac{f(x + \Delta x) - f(x)}{\Delta x}$$

For any function $y = f(x)$,

$$\frac{\Delta y}{\Delta x} = \frac{f(x + \Delta x) - f(x)}{\Delta x}$$

is the *average rate of change* of the function f at x, and

> **DERIVATIVE**
>
> $$\lim_{\Delta x \to 0} \frac{\Delta y}{\Delta x} = \lim_{\Delta x \to 0} \frac{f(x + \Delta x) - f(x)}{\Delta x}$$

is the *derivative* of the function f at x. (The derivative could also be thought of as the instantaneous rate of change of f at x.) The process of finding this limit, the derivative, is called *differentiation*.

EXAMPLE 1

Find the derivative of $f(x) = x^2$ at $x = 3$.

$$\lim_{\Delta x \to 0} \frac{\Delta y}{\Delta x} = \lim_{\Delta x \to 0} \frac{f(x + \Delta x) - f(x)}{\Delta x}$$

$$= \lim_{\Delta x \to 0} \frac{(3 + \Delta x)^2 - (3)^2}{\Delta x}$$

$$= \lim_{\Delta x \to 0} \frac{9 + 6\Delta x + (\Delta x)^2 - 9}{\Delta x}$$

$$= \lim_{\Delta x \to 0} \frac{6\Delta x + (\Delta x)^2}{\Delta x}$$

$$= \lim_{\Delta x \to 0} \frac{\Delta x(6 + \Delta x)}{\Delta x}$$

$$= \lim_{\Delta x \to 0} (6 + \Delta x)$$

$$= 6$$

In Example 1 we found the derivative at $x = 3$. However, we can also find the derivative without specifying a value for x.

EXAMPLE 2

Find the derivative of $f(x) = x^2$.

$$\lim_{\Delta x \to 0} \frac{\Delta y}{\Delta x} = \lim_{\Delta x \to 0} \frac{f(x + \Delta x) - f(x)}{\Delta x}$$

$$= \lim_{\Delta x \to 0} \frac{(x + \Delta x)^2 - x^2}{\Delta x}$$

$$= \lim_{\Delta x \to 0} \frac{x^2 + 2x(\Delta x) + (\Delta x)^2 - x^2}{\Delta x}$$

$$= \lim_{\Delta x \to 0} \frac{\Delta x(2x + \Delta x)}{\Delta x}$$

$$= \lim_{\Delta x \to 0} (2x + \Delta x)$$

$$= 2x$$

Note that when finding the above limit, x is held constant. Only Δx is approaching 0. Note also that if we let $x = 3$ in Example 2, the derivative has the value $2x = 2(3) = 6$ as in Example 1.

The following notations for the derivative are often used in place of the symbol $\lim_{\Delta x \to 0} \frac{\Delta y}{\Delta x}$:

$$\frac{dy}{dx} \qquad y' \qquad \frac{d}{dx}[f(x)] \qquad f'(x) \qquad Dy$$

So, for Example 1 we can write

$$\frac{dy}{dx} = 6 \quad \text{at} \quad x = 3$$

$$y' = 6 \quad \text{at} \quad x = 3$$

$$\frac{d}{dx}[f(x)] = 6 \quad \text{at} \quad x = 3$$

$$f'(3) = 6$$

or

$$Dy = 6 \quad \text{at} \quad x = 3$$

For Example 2 we can write

$$\frac{dy}{dx} = 2x$$

$$y' = 2x$$

$$\frac{d}{dx}[f(x)] = 2x$$

$$f'(x) = 2x$$

or

$$Dy = 2x$$

Note that the expressions above for the derivative determined in Example 2 show that the derivative becomes a new function of x when the value for x is not specified. That is, $y' = 2x$ is a function that relates to each x the value $2x$.

EXAMPLE 3

Find the derivative of $y = x^3$.

$$\frac{dy}{dx} = \lim_{\Delta x \to 0} \frac{f(x + \Delta x) - f(x)}{\Delta x}$$

$$= \lim_{\Delta x \to 0} \frac{(x + \Delta x)^3 - x^3}{\Delta x}$$

$$= \lim_{\Delta x \to 0} \frac{x^3 + 3x^2(\Delta x) + 3x(\Delta x)^2 + (\Delta x)^3 - x^3}{\Delta x}$$

$$= \lim_{\Delta x \to 0} \frac{3x^2(\Delta x) + 3x(\Delta x)^2 + (\Delta x)^3}{\Delta x}$$

$$= \lim_{\Delta x \to 0} \frac{\Delta x[3x^2 + 3x(\Delta x) + (\Delta x)^2]}{\Delta x}$$

$$= \lim_{\Delta x \to 0} [3x^2 + 3x(\Delta x) + (\Delta x)^2]$$

$$= 3x^2$$

EXAMPLE 4

Find the derivative of $y = \dfrac{1}{x + 2}$.

$$\frac{dy}{dx} = \lim_{\Delta x \to 0} \frac{f(x + \Delta x) - f(x)}{\Delta x}$$

$$= \lim_{\Delta x \to 0} \frac{\dfrac{1}{x + \Delta x + 2} - \dfrac{1}{x + 2}}{\Delta x}$$

$$= \lim_{\Delta x \to 0} \frac{\dfrac{(x + 2) - (x + \Delta x + 2)}{(x + \Delta x + 2)(x + 2)}}{\Delta x}$$

$$= \lim_{\Delta x \to 0} \frac{\dfrac{-\Delta x}{(x + \Delta x + 2)(x + 2)}}{\Delta x}$$

$$= \lim_{\Delta x \to 0} \frac{-1}{(x + \Delta x + 2)(x + 2)}$$

$$= \frac{-1}{(x + 2)^2}$$

EXAMPLE 5

Find the derivative of $y = 3x^2 + 2x - 4$.

$$\frac{dy}{dx} = \lim_{\Delta x \to 0} \frac{f(x + \Delta x) - f(x)}{\Delta x}$$

$$= \lim_{\Delta x \to 0} \frac{[3(x + \Delta x)^2 + 2(x + \Delta x) - 4] - (3x^2 + 2x - 4)}{\Delta x}$$

$$= \lim_{\Delta x \to 0} \frac{3x^2 + 6x(\Delta x) + 3(\Delta x)^2 + 2x + 2(\Delta x) - 4 - 3x^2 - 2x + 4}{\Delta x}$$

$$= \lim_{\Delta x \to 0} \frac{6x(\Delta x) + 3(\Delta x)^2 + 2(\Delta x)}{\Delta x}$$

$$= \lim_{\Delta x \to 0} \frac{\Delta x[6x + 3(\Delta x) + 2]}{\Delta x}$$

$$= \lim_{\Delta x \to 0} [6x + 3(\Delta x) + 2]$$

$$= 6x + 2$$

EXAMPLE 6

Find the derivative of $f(x) = \sqrt{x}$.

$$\frac{dy}{dx} = \lim_{\Delta x \to 0} \frac{f(x + \Delta x) - f(x)}{\Delta x}$$

$$= \lim_{\Delta x \to 0} \frac{\sqrt{x + \Delta x} - \sqrt{x}}{\Delta x} \qquad \text{(\textit{Note:} To evaluate this limit, you must rationalize the numerator.)}$$

$$= \lim_{\Delta x \to 0} \frac{\sqrt{x + \Delta x} - \sqrt{x}}{\Delta x} \cdot \frac{\sqrt{x + \Delta x} + \sqrt{x}}{\sqrt{x + \Delta x} + \sqrt{x}}$$

$$= \lim_{\Delta x \to 0} \frac{x + \Delta x - x}{\Delta x(\sqrt{x + \Delta x} + \sqrt{x})}$$

$$= \lim_{\Delta x \to 0} \frac{\Delta x}{\Delta x(\sqrt{x + \Delta x} + \sqrt{x})}$$

$$= \lim_{\Delta x \to 0} \frac{1}{\sqrt{x + \Delta x} + \sqrt{x}}$$

$$= \frac{1}{\sqrt{x} + \sqrt{x}} = \frac{1}{2\sqrt{x}}$$

Using a calculator, we obtain

F3 3   **(2nd** $\sqrt{\ }$ **x+2nd CHAR 1 5** x)- **2nd** $\sqrt{\ }$ x)) / Δx,Δx,0) **ENTER**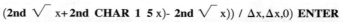

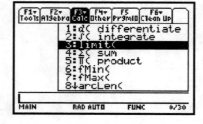    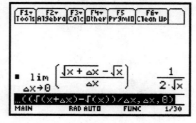

Note that the symbol Δ can be obtained on the TI-89 by using the keystrokes **2nd CHAR 1 5**.

Exercises 2.4

Find the derivative of each function.

1. $y = 3x + 4$ **2.** $y = 2 - 6x$ **3.** $y = 1 - 2x$ **4.** $y = 4x - 5$

5. $y = 3x^2$ **6.** $y = -4x^2$ **7.** $y = x^2 - 2x$ **8.** $y = x^2 + 1$

9. $y = 3x^2 - 4x + 1$ **10.** $y = 6x^2 - 8x + 2$ **11.** $y = 1 - 6x^2$ **12.** $y = 3 - 4x - 7x^2$

13. $y = x^3 + 4x$ **14.** $y = 1 - 2x^3$ **15.** $y = \dfrac{1}{x}$ **16.** $y = \dfrac{1}{x - 1}$

17. $y = \dfrac{2}{x - 3}$ **18.** $y = \dfrac{-1}{2x + 1}$ **19.** $y = \dfrac{1}{x^2}$ **20.** $y = \dfrac{1}{x^2 - 1}$

21. $y = \dfrac{1}{4 - x^2}$ **22.** $y = \dfrac{4}{x^2 + 1}$ **23.** $y = \sqrt{x + 1}$ **24.** $y = \sqrt{x - 2}$

25. $y = \sqrt{1 - 2x}$ **26.** $y = \sqrt{x^2 + 1}$ **27.** $y = \dfrac{1}{\sqrt{x - 1}}$ **28.** $y = \dfrac{1}{\sqrt{4 - x}}$

Find the slope of the tangent line to each curve at the given point.

29. $y = 3x^2 - 4;\ (1, -1)$ **30.** $y = \dfrac{1}{x - 4};\ \left(1, -\dfrac{1}{3}\right)$ **31.** $y = \dfrac{1}{1 - 3x^2};\ \left(1, -\dfrac{1}{2}\right)$

32. $y = \sqrt{x + 5};\ (4, 3)$

Find the equation of the tangent line to each curve at the given point.

33. $y = x^2 - 3x;\ (2, -2)$ **34.** $y = \dfrac{6}{x};\ (-2, -3)$ **35.** $y = \sqrt{x - 7};\ (11, 2)$

36. $y = \dfrac{2}{x^2 + 1};\ (-1, 1)$

Find a point or points on the curve where the slope of the tangent line is the given value.

37. $y = \dfrac{1}{x - 3};\ m = -1$ **38.** $y = \dfrac{1}{x^2};\ m = \dfrac{1}{4}$ **39.** $y = \sqrt{x + 4};\ m = \dfrac{1}{2}$

40. $y = \dfrac{2}{\sqrt{x}};\ m = -\dfrac{1}{8}$

2.5   DIFFERENTIATION OF POLYNOMIALS

Recall from algebra that a *polynomial* is defined as follows:

$$a_n x^n + a_{n-1} x^{n-1} + a_{n-2} x^{n-2} + \cdots + a_2 x^2 + a_1 x + a_0$$

where n is a positive integer and the coefficients $a_n, a_{n-1}, a_{n-2}, \ldots, a_2, a_1, a_0$ are real numbers. As we saw, the derivative definition in Section 2.4 can be used to find the derivative of a polynomial. However, the process is tedious. We now develop some formulas that will shorten the process of finding such a derivative.

First, let's find the derivative of a constant function.

EXAMPLE 1

Find $\dfrac{dy}{dx}$ when $y = C$, where C is a constant.

$$\frac{dy}{dx} = \lim_{\Delta x \to 0} \frac{f(x + \Delta x) - f(x)}{\Delta x}$$

$$= \lim_{\Delta x \to 0} \frac{C - C}{\Delta x}$$

$$= \lim_{\Delta x \to 0} \frac{0}{\Delta x}$$

$$= \lim_{\Delta x \to 0} 0$$

$$= 0$$

So, if $f(x)$ is a constant function, that is, $f(x) = C$ for all x, then $f'(x) = 0$ for all x.

EXAMPLE 2

Find the derivative of $f(x) = 10$.

Since this is a constant function, $f'(x) = 0$ for all x.

Suppose that $y = x^n$, where n is some positive integer. By using the binomial theorem (see Section 9.3), we have

$$(x + \Delta x)^n = x^n + nx^{n-1}(\Delta x) + \frac{n(n-1)}{2!}x^{n-2}(\Delta x)^2$$

$$+ \frac{n(n-1)(n-2)}{3!}x^{n-3}(\Delta x)^3 + \cdots$$

$$+ nx(\Delta x)^{n-1} + (\Delta x)^n$$

where the right-hand side consists of $(n + 1)$ terms, each of which has a factor of Δx except for the first term. So if

$$\Delta y = (x + \Delta x)^n - x^n$$

$$= x^n + nx^{n-1}(\Delta x) + \frac{n(n-1)}{2!}x^{n-2}(\Delta x)^2$$

$$+ \frac{n(n-1)(n-2)}{3!}x^{n-3}(\Delta x)^3 + \cdots + nx(\Delta x)^{n-1} + (\Delta x)^n - x^n$$

then

$$\frac{\Delta y}{\Delta x} = nx^{n-1} + \frac{n(n-1)}{2!}x^{n-2}(\Delta x) + \frac{n(n-1)(n-2)}{3!}x^{n-3}(\Delta x)^2 + \cdots$$

$$+ nx(\Delta x)^{n-2} + (\Delta x)^{n-1}$$

We then have

$$\frac{dy}{dx} = \lim_{\Delta x \to 0} \frac{\Delta y}{\Delta x} = nx^{n-1}$$

Note that every term but the first term has a factor of Δx, which will make each of these other terms approach 0 as Δx approaches 0. Thus,

$$\frac{d}{dx}x^n = nx^{n-1}$$

EXAMPLE 3

Find the derivative of $y = x^{32}$. Since $n = 32$,

$$\frac{dy}{dx} = 32x^{32-1}$$

$$= 32x^{31}$$

We now make the following observation:

$$\frac{d}{dx}[cf(x)] = c\frac{d}{dx}[f(x)]$$

This formula is derived as follows:

$$\frac{d}{dx}[cf(x)] = \lim_{\Delta x \to 0} \frac{c[f(x + \Delta x)] - c[f(x)]}{\Delta x}$$

$$= \lim_{\Delta x \to 0} \frac{c[f(x + \Delta x) - f(x)]}{\Delta x}$$

$$= c \lim_{\Delta x \to 0} \frac{f(x + \Delta x) - f(x)}{\Delta x}$$

$$= c \frac{d}{dx}[f(x)]$$

EXAMPLE 4

Find the derivative of $y = -5x^{12}$.

$$\frac{dy}{dx} = \frac{d}{dx}(-5x^{12})$$

$$= -5\frac{d}{dx}(x^{12})$$

$$= -5(12x^{12-1})$$

$$= -60x^{11}$$

We can now differentiate functions of the form $y = cx^n$, where n is a positive integer, by use of a simple formula. We now develop formulas to differentiate other functions.

If $h(x) = f(x) + g(x)$, the sum of two functions, then

$$\frac{d}{dx}h(x) = \frac{d}{dx}[f(x) + g(x)]$$

$$= \lim_{\Delta x \to 0} \frac{[f(x + \Delta x) + g(x + \Delta x)] - [f(x) + g(x)]}{\Delta x}$$

$$= \lim_{\Delta x \to 0} \frac{[f(x + \Delta x) - f(x)] + [g(x + \Delta x) - g(x)]}{\Delta x}$$

$$= \lim_{\Delta x \to 0} \left\{ \frac{[f(x + \Delta x) - f(x)]}{\Delta x} + \frac{[g(x + \Delta x) - g(x)]}{\Delta x} \right\}$$

$$= \lim_{\Delta x \to 0} \frac{[f(x + \Delta x) - f(x)]}{\Delta x} + \lim_{\Delta x \to 0} \frac{[g(x + \Delta x) - g(x)]}{\Delta x}$$

$$= \frac{d}{dx}[f(x)] + \frac{d}{dx}[g(x)]$$

That is, the derivative of a sum of functions is the sum of the derivatives of the functions:

$$\frac{d}{dx}[f(x) + g(x)] = \frac{d}{dx}[f(x)] + \frac{d}{dx}[g(x)]$$

Similarly,

$$\frac{d}{dx}[f(x) - g(x)] = \frac{d}{dx}[f(x)] - \frac{d}{dx}[g(x)]$$

That is, the derivative of a difference of functions is the difference of the derivatives of the functions.

We now have the formulas we need to differentiate polynomials.

EXAMPLE 5

Differentiate $y = 7x^5 - 2x^3 + x^2 - 8$.

$$\frac{dy}{dx} = \frac{d}{dx}(7x^5 - 2x^3 + x^2 - 8)$$

$$= \frac{d}{dx}(7x^5) - \frac{d}{dx}(2x^3) + \frac{d}{dx}(x^2) - \frac{d}{dx}(8)$$

$$= 7\frac{d}{dx}(x^5) - 2\frac{d}{dx}(x^3) + \frac{d}{dx}(x^2) - \frac{d}{dx}(8)$$

$$= 7 \cdot 5x^{5-1} - 2 \cdot 3x^{3-1} + 2x^{2-1} - 0$$

$$= 35x^4 - 6x^2 + 2x$$

EXAMPLE 6

Find the equation of the tangent line to the curve $y = 5x^3 - 2x^2 + 3$ at the point $(1, 6)$.

The slope of the tangent line, $m_{\tan}$, is the derivative of $y = 5x^3 - 2x^2 + 3$ at $x = 1$.

$$\frac{dy}{dx} = \frac{d}{dx}(5x^3 - 2x^2 + 3)$$

$$= 5 \cdot 3x^{3-1} - 2 \cdot 2x^{2-1} + 0$$

$$= 15x^2 - 4x$$

Thus the derivative $\dfrac{dy}{dx}$ at $x = 1$ is $15(1)^2 - 4(1) = 11$. So, $m_{\tan} = 11$. The equation of the tangent line written in point-slope form is

$$y - y_1 = m(x - x_1)$$

$$y - 6 = 11(x - 1)$$

$$y = 11x - 5$$

In this example we needed to evaluate the derivative of a function after applying the differentiation formulas. To show that the derivative is to be evaluated at $x = a$, we usually write

$$\frac{dy}{dx}\bigg|_{x=a} \quad \text{or} \quad f'(a)$$

So, in Example 6 we write

$$m_{\tan} = \frac{dy}{dx}\bigg|_{x=1} = 15(1)^2 - 4(1) = 11 \quad \text{or} \quad m_{\tan} = f'(1) = 15(1)^2 - 4(1) = 11$$

Using a calculator, we have

F3   1   5x^3−2x^2+3,x)   ENTER   right arrow | x=1   ENTER

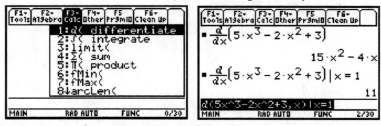

Note that the "with" key | is located directly to the left of **7** on the TI-89.

For examples of numerical derivatives on the TI-83 Plus, see Appendix C, Section C.11.

EXAMPLE 7

Find the instantaneous velocity v of an object falling freely from a building 100 ft tall after 2 s. The position of this free-falling object is given by $s = -16t^2 + 100$ (measured in feet).

v is the derivative of $s = -16t^2 + 100$ at $t = 2$. So

$$v = \frac{ds}{dt}\bigg|_{t=2} = \frac{d}{dt}(-16t^2 + 100)\bigg|_{t=2}$$

$$= (-32t + 0)|_{t=2}$$

$$= -32(2) = -64 \text{ ft/s}$$

Note: The negative sign indicates that the velocity of the object is in the negative direction (downward). A positive velocity would indicate motion in the positive direction (upward).

While we showed that $\frac{d}{dx}(x^n) = nx^{n-1}$ based on n being a positive integer, in fact n can be any real number.

EXAMPLE 8

Find the derivative of $y = \sqrt{x}$.

Since $y = \sqrt{x} = x^{1/2}$, then

$$\frac{dy}{dx} = \tfrac{1}{2}x^{(1/2)-1}$$

$$= \tfrac{1}{2}x^{-1/2}$$

$$= \frac{1}{2\sqrt{x}}$$

EXAMPLE 9

Find the derivative of $y = 1/x^3$.

$$y = \frac{1}{x^3} = x^{-3}$$

$$\frac{dy}{dx} = -3x^{-3-1}$$

$$= -3x^{-4}$$

$$= -\frac{3}{x^4}$$

EXAMPLE 10

Find the derivative of $y = 3/\sqrt{x}$.

$$y = \frac{3}{\sqrt{x}} = 3x^{-1/2}$$

$$\frac{dy}{dx} = \frac{d}{dx}(3x^{-1/2})$$

$$= 3\frac{d}{dx}(x^{-1/2})$$

$$= 3\left(-\frac{1}{2}x^{-(1/2)-1}\right)$$

$$= -\frac{3}{2}x^{-3/2}$$

Exercises 2.5

Find the derivative of each polynomial function.

1. $y = 32$ **2.** $y = -100$ **3.** $y = x^5$

4. $y = x^{16}$ **5.** $y = 4x + 1$ **6.** $y = 6x - 2$

7. $y = 1 - 3x$ **8.** $y = x$ **9.** $y = 5x^2$

10. $y = -3x^2$ **11.** $y = x^2 - 3x$ **12.** $y = x^2 - 4x + 2$

13. $y = 4x^2 - 3x - 2$ **14.** $y = 9x^2 + 8x - 7$ **15.** $y = 1 - 8x^2$

16. $y = 4 - 6x - 5x^2$ **17.** $y = 3x^3 + 2x^2 - 6x$ **18.** $y = 13x^4 - \dfrac{7x^2}{2} + 2$

19. $y = 4x^5 - 2x^3 + x + 3$ **20.** $y = 5x^6 - 3x^4 + 2x^3 - 8x^2 + 4x - 7$

21. $y = \frac{5}{2}x^8 - \frac{6}{5}x^5 + \frac{15}{2}x^4 - x^3 + \sqrt{2}$ **22.** $y = \frac{8}{3}x^6 - \frac{7}{3}x^5 + 4x^4 - 3x^3 - 7x + \pi$

23. $y = \sqrt{7}x^4 - \sqrt{5}x^3 - \sqrt{3}x + \sqrt{7}$ **24.** $y = \sqrt{10}x^{10} - \sqrt{7}x^7 + \sqrt{5}x^5 - \sqrt{3}$

Find $f'(a)$ for each function.

25. $y = 3x^2 + 2x - 1;\ a = -1$ **26.** $y = 4x^2 + 6x;\ a = 2$

27. $y = 2x^3 - 6x^2 + 2x + 9;\ a = -3$ **28.** $y = 6x^3 - 5x + 3;\ a = -2$

29. $y = 4x^5 + 3x^2 - 2;\ a = 1$ **30.** $y = 5x^4 - 2x^2 + 18;\ a = 2$

31. $y = 5x^4 + 8x^3 + 2x - 1;\ a = 0$ **32.** $y = 9x^6 + 6x^5 - 7x^4 + 2;\ a = 0$

33. $y = 1 - 8x^2 - 5x^3 + 5x^6;\ a = 3$ **34.** $y = 3 - 4x^2 - 6x^4 + 5x^9;\ a = -2$

35. Find the equation of the tangent line to the curve $y = x^3 + 4x^2 - x + 2$ at $(-2, 12)$.

36. Find the equation of the tangent line to the curve $y = x^{100} + 5$ at $(-1, 6)$.

37. Given that $p = Ri^2$, find the rate of change dp/di of the power p in a 30-ohm (Ω) resistor when $i = 2$ amperes (A).

38. An object is falling according to $h = 5000 - 3.28t^2$, where h is in metres and t is in seconds. Find the speed (*instantaneous velocity*) of the object after 5 s.

39. Given that $V = ir$, find the rate of change dV/dr of the voltage drop for a 0.4-A current when $r = 4\ \Omega$.

40. In an electric circuit the voltage V varies according to $V = t^4$, where t is time in seconds. Find dV/dt when $t = 3$ s.

Find the derivative of each function.

41. $y = x^{3/2}$ **42.** $y = \sqrt[3]{x}$ **43.** $y = \dfrac{1}{x^4}$ **44.** $y = \dfrac{4}{x^3}$

45. $y = 6x^{20}$ **46.** $y = 35x^{10}$ **47.** $y = \dfrac{14}{x^8}$ **48.** $y = \dfrac{52}{x^{13}}$

49. $y = \dfrac{5}{\sqrt[3]{x}}$ **50.** $y = \dfrac{2}{x\sqrt{x}}$

51. Given that $V = ir$, find the (instantaneous) rate of change dV/dr of the voltage drop V with respect to r (measured in ohms) for a 0.5-A current.

52. Given that $p = Ri^2$, find the rate of change dp/di of the power p in a 20-Ω resistor, where p is in watts (W) and i is in amperes (A).

2.6   DERIVATIVES OF PRODUCTS AND QUOTIENTS

We need to differentiate products and quotients of functions. For example, the techniques developed so far would not apply to $y = (x^2 + 4x)\sqrt{x - 1}$ or $y = \dfrac{32x^2 - 9}{5x^5 - 7x^2}$. We would be forced to find the derivative $\dfrac{dy}{dx}$ by using the limit process method of Section 2.4. Fortunately, we can develop formulas to do such examples more efficiently.

> **DERIVATIVE OF A PRODUCT**
>
> If $y = f(x)$ can be written as the product of two functions $u = g(x)$ and $v = h(x)$, then we can write
>
> $$y = g(x) \cdot h(x)$$
>
> or
>
> $$y = u \cdot v$$
>
> In Section 2.9 we show that
>
> $$\frac{dy}{dx} = u\frac{dv}{dx} + v\frac{du}{dx}$$
>
> That is, *the derivative of a product of two functions is the product of the first function and the derivative of the second function plus the product of the second function and the derivative of the first function.*

EXAMPLE 1

Find $\dfrac{d}{dx}[(4x + 3)(7x - 1)]$.

Let $u = 4x + 3$, $v = 7x - 1$, and $y = u \cdot v$.

$$\frac{dy}{dx} = u\frac{dv}{dx} + v\frac{du}{dx}$$

$$= (4x + 3)\frac{d}{dx}(7x - 1) + (7x - 1)\frac{d}{dx}(4x + 3)$$

$$= (4x + 3)(7) + (7x - 1)(4)$$

$$= 28x + 21 + 28x - 4$$

$$= 56x + 17$$

EXAMPLE 2

Find $\dfrac{d}{dx}[(3x^2 - 4)(5x^3 - 7)]$.

Let $u = 3x^2 - 4$, $v = 5x^3 - 7$, and $y = u \cdot v$.

$$\frac{dy}{dx} = u\frac{dv}{dx} + v\frac{du}{dx}$$

$$= (3x^2 - 4)\frac{d}{dx}(5x^3 - 7) + (5x^3 - 7)\frac{d}{dx}(3x^2 - 4)$$

$$= (3x^2 - 4)(15x^2) + (5x^3 - 7)(6x)$$

$$= 45x^4 - 60x^2 + 30x^4 - 42x$$

$$= 75x^4 - 60x^2 - 42x$$

DERIVATIVE OF A QUOTIENT

If $y = f(x)$ can be written as the quotient of two functions $u = g(x)$ and $v = h(x)$, then we can write

$$y = \frac{g(x)}{h(x)}$$

or

$$y = \frac{u}{v}$$

In Section 2.9 we show that

$$\frac{d}{dx}\left(\frac{u}{v}\right) = \frac{v\dfrac{du}{dx} - u\dfrac{dv}{dx}}{v^2}$$

That is, *the derivative of a quotient of two functions is the denominator times the derivative of the numerator minus the numerator times the derivative of the denominator all divided by the square of the denominator.*

EXAMPLE 3

Find $\dfrac{d}{dx}\left(\dfrac{5x + 3}{4x^2 - 7}\right)$.

Here $u = 5x + 3$ and $v = 4x^2 - 7$. Then

$$\frac{d}{dx}\left(\frac{u}{v}\right) = \frac{v\dfrac{du}{dx} - u\dfrac{dv}{dx}}{v^2}$$

$$= \frac{(4x^2 - 7)\dfrac{d}{dx}(5x + 3) - (5x + 3)\dfrac{d}{dx}(4x^2 - 7)}{(4x^2 - 7)^2}$$

$$= \frac{(4x^2 - 7)(5) - (5x + 3)(8x)}{(4x^2 - 7)^2}$$

$$= \frac{20x^2 - 35 - 40x^2 - 24x}{(4x^2 - 7)^2}$$

$$= \frac{-20x^2 - 24x - 35}{(4x^2 - 7)^2}$$

EXAMPLE 4

Find $\dfrac{dy}{dx}$ if $y = \dfrac{32x^2 - 9}{5x^5 - 7x^2}$.

$$\frac{dy}{dx} = \frac{d}{dx}\left(\frac{32x^2 - 9}{5x^5 - 7x^2}\right)$$

$$= \frac{(5x^5 - 7x^2)(64x) - (32x^2 - 9)(25x^4 - 14x)}{(5x^5 - 7x^2)^2}$$

$$= \frac{320x^6 - 448x^3 - 800x^6 + 225x^4 + 448x^3 - 126x}{(5x^5 - 7x^2)^2}$$

$$= \frac{-480x^6 + 225x^4 - 126x}{(5x^5 - 7x^2)^2}$$

Using a calculator, we have

2nd 8 (32x^2-9)/(5x^5-7x^2),x) **ENTER**

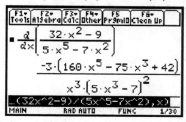

Show that the two results are equivalent.

Exercises 2.6

*Find the derivative of each function (**a**) by finding the derivative of the product as given using the formula for the derivative of a product and (**b**) by first multiplying the given expression, then finding the derivative of the resulting polynomial.*

1. $y = x^2(2x + 1)$ **2.** $y = x^3(3x^2 + 2x - 1)$

3. $y = 2x(4x^2 + 3x - 5)$ **4.** $y = 4x^2(5 - 6x - 3x^2)$

5. $y = (2x + 3)(5x - 4)$ **6.** $y = (6x - 2)(4x - 3)$

7. $y = (4x + 7)(x^2 - 1)$ **8.** $y = (3x^3 - 1)(2x - 1)$

Find the derivative of each product.

9. $y = (x^2 + 3x + 4)(x^3 - 4x)$ **10.** $y = (x^3 + 2x - 7)(x^2 + 4x - 2)$

11. $y = (x^4 - 3x^2 - x)(2x^3 - 4x)$ **12.** $y = (x^2 - 3x + 8)(1 - 3x^4)$

Find the derivative of each quotient.

13. $y = \dfrac{x}{2x + 5}$ **14.** $y = \dfrac{3x}{x - 4}$ **15.** $y = \dfrac{1}{x^2 + x}$

16. $y = \dfrac{3}{x^2 - 1}$ **17.** $y = \dfrac{3x - 1}{2x + 4}$ **18.** $y = \dfrac{5x - 1}{3x + 2}$

19. $y = \dfrac{x^2}{2x + 1}$ **20.** $y = \dfrac{4x^2}{3x^2 - 1}$ **21.** $y = \dfrac{x - 1}{x^2 + x + 1}$

22. $y = \dfrac{3x - 7}{x^2 - 2}$ **23.** $y = \dfrac{4x^2 + 9}{3x^3 - 4x^2}$ **24.** $y = \dfrac{4x^3 - 1}{6x^2 + 3}$

25. Find $f'(2)$ when $f(x) = (x^2 - 4x + 3)(x^3 - 5x)$.

26. Find $f'(2)$ when $f(x) = (3x^2 - 1)(x^4 - 6x)$.

27. Find $f'(-1)$ when $f(x) = \dfrac{3x - 4}{x + 2}$.   **28.** Find $f'(3)$ when $f(x) = \dfrac{x - 2}{x^2 + 5}$.

29. Find the slope of the tangent line to the curve $y = \dfrac{x - 3}{2 - 5x}$ at $\left(2, \dfrac{1}{8}\right)$.

30. Find the slope of the tangent line to the curve $y = \dfrac{2x^2 + 1}{x - 2}$ at $x = 1$.

31. Find the equation of the tangent line to the curve $y = \dfrac{x + 3}{x - 2}$ at $x = 3$.

32. Find the equation of the tangent line to the curve $y = \dfrac{1}{x + 3}$ at $x = -1$.

33. Given $V = ir$, the voltage across a resistor, find $\dfrac{dV}{dt}$ at $t = 3$ s if the current $i = 6 + 0.02t^3$ A and the resistance $r = 20 - 0.05t$ Ω.

34. Given $i = V/r$, find di/dt at $t = 10$ s if $V = 40 + 0.1t^2$ V and $r = 60 - 0.01t$ Ω.

2.7   THE DERIVATIVE OF A POWER

If $y = (3x + 2)^{50}$, $\dfrac{dy}{dx}$ could be found by applying the product formula repeatedly, but this would be quite a long process. Also, we need to be able to differentiate such functions as $y = \sqrt{3x + 2}$. We now use a formula for such powers.

We show in Section 2.9 that if $y = u^n$, where $u = f(x)$, then the following holds:

> **POWER RULE**
>
> $$\frac{dy}{dx} = \frac{d}{dx}(u^n) = nu^{n-1}\frac{du}{dx}$$

The power rule should not be confused with the formula in Section 2.5,

$$\frac{d}{dx}(x^n) = nx^{n-1}$$

Note that the formula for $\dfrac{d}{dx}(u^n)$ involves an additional factor $\dfrac{du}{dx}$. This is because u itself is a function of x. Be sure to keep this distinction in mind. For example, if $y = u^3$ and $u = x$, then

$$y = x^3$$
$$\frac{dy}{dx} = 3x^{3-1} = 3x^2$$

But if $u = x^2 + 1$, then

$$y = (x^2 + 1)^3 = u^3$$
$$\frac{dy}{dx} = 3u^{3-1}\frac{du}{dx}$$
$$= 3(x^2 + 1)^2\frac{d}{dx}(x^2 + 1)$$
$$= 3(x^2 + 1)^2(2x)$$
$$= 6x(x^2 + 1)^2$$

Thus, only when $u = x$ are the formulas the same, for then the additional factor $\frac{du}{dx} = 1$.

EXAMPLE 1

Find $\frac{dy}{dx}$ if $y = (3x + 2)^{50}$.

$$\frac{dy}{dx} = \frac{d}{dx}(3x + 2)^{50}$$

$$= 50(3x + 2)^{50-1}\frac{d}{dx}(3x + 2)$$

$$= 50(3x + 2)^{49}(3)$$

$$= 150(3x + 2)^{49}$$

Compare this result with the following example.

EXAMPLE 2

Find $\frac{dy}{dx}$ if $y = x^{50}$.

$$\frac{dy}{dx} = 50x^{50-1} = 50x^{49}$$

The formula $\frac{d}{dx}(u^n) = nu^{n-1}\frac{du}{dx}$ is also valid for n any real number.

A **composite function** is a function of another function. For example,

$$y = (3x - 2)^4$$

may be written as

$$y = u^4, \qquad \text{where} \quad u = 3x - 2$$

Here y is a function of u, and u is a function of x. So y is a function of a function of x.
   More generally, let

$$y = f(g(x))$$

or

$$y = f(u), \qquad \text{where} \quad u = g(x)$$

be any composite function. Then

$$\frac{dy}{dx} = \lim_{\Delta x \to 0}\frac{\Delta y}{\Delta x}$$

$$= \lim_{\Delta x \to 0}\left(\frac{\Delta y}{\Delta u} \cdot \frac{\Delta u}{\Delta x}\right) \qquad (\Delta u \neq 0)$$

$$= \lim_{\Delta x \to 0}\frac{\Delta y}{\Delta u} \cdot \lim_{\Delta x \to 0}\frac{\Delta u}{\Delta x}$$

$$= \lim_{\Delta u \to 0}\frac{\Delta y}{\Delta u} \cdot \lim_{\Delta x \to 0}\frac{\Delta u}{\Delta x} \qquad (\textit{Note: } \Delta u \to 0 \text{ as } \Delta x \to 0.)$$

$$= \frac{dy}{du} \cdot \frac{du}{dx}$$

Thus we have the following result:

CHAIN RULE

For a function $y = f(g(x))$ where $u = g(x)$,

$$\frac{dy}{dx} = \frac{dy}{du} \cdot \frac{du}{dx}$$

The power rule is a special case of the *chain rule*. The chain rule is used to find derivatives of a function that is a function of another function. The chain rule is used extensively beginning with the transcendental functions in Chapter 4.

Using the chain rule to find the derivative of $y = (3x - 2)^4$, let

$$y = u^4 \quad \text{and} \quad u = 3x - 2$$

$$\frac{dy}{du} = 4u^3 \qquad \frac{du}{dx} = 3$$

Then

$$\frac{dy}{dx} = \frac{dy}{du} \cdot \frac{du}{dx}$$
$$= (4u^3)(3)$$
$$= 12(3x - 2)^3$$

EXAMPLE 3

Find $\dfrac{dy}{dx}$ if $y = \sqrt{3x^2 + 5}$.

$$\frac{dy}{dx} = \frac{d}{dx}(\sqrt{3x^2 + 5})$$

$$= \frac{d}{dx}[(3x^2 + 5)^{1/2}]$$

$$= \frac{1}{2}(3x^2 + 5)^{(1/2)-1}\frac{d}{dx}(3x^2 + 5) \qquad \left(n = \frac{1}{2}\right)$$

$$= \frac{1}{2}(3x^2 + 5)^{-1/2}(6x)$$

$$= \frac{3x}{\sqrt{3x^2 + 5}}$$

EXAMPLE 4

Find $\dfrac{dy}{dx}$ if $y = \dfrac{1}{(3x^2 - 2)^5}$

First, rewrite the expression as a power:

$$y = \frac{1}{(3x^2 - 2)^5} = (3x^2 - 2)^{-5}$$

Then

$$\frac{dy}{dx} = \frac{d}{dx}(3x^2 - 2)^{-5}$$

$$= -5(3x^2 - 2)^{-6}\frac{d}{dx}(3x^2 - 2)$$

$$= -5(3x^2 - 2)^{-6}(6x)$$

$$= \frac{-30x}{(3x^2 - 2)^6}$$

EXAMPLE 5

Find $\dfrac{dy}{dx}$ if $y = (8x + 1)^{1/4}(6x^2 + 2)$.

Using the derivative of a product form, we have

$$\frac{dy}{dx} = (8x + 1)^{1/4}\frac{d}{dx}(6x^2 + 2) + (6x^2 + 2)\frac{d}{dx}(8x + 1)^{1/4}$$

Note: The factor $(8x + 1)^{1/4}$ is in the form $u^{1/4}$, where $u = 8x + 1$. Using the chain rule on this factor, we have

$$\frac{1}{4}u^{-3/4}\frac{du}{dx} = \frac{1}{4}(8x + 1)^{-3/4}(8)$$

$$\frac{dy}{dx} = (8x + 1)^{1/4}(12x) + (6x^2 + 2)\left(\frac{1}{4}\right)(8x + 1)^{-3/4}(8)$$

$$= 12x(8x + 1)^{1/4} + (12x^2 + 4)(8x + 1)^{-3/4}$$

$$= (8x + 1)^{-3/4}[12x(8x + 1) + (12x^2 + 4)] \qquad \text{(Factor out the power}$$
$$\qquad\qquad\qquad\qquad\qquad\qquad\qquad\qquad\qquad\qquad \text{with a negative exponent.)}$$

$$= \frac{96x^2 + 12x + 12x^2 + 4}{(8x + 1)^{3/4}}$$

$$= \frac{108x^2 + 12x + 4}{(8x + 1)^{3/4}}$$

EXAMPLE 6

Find $\dfrac{dy}{dx}$ if $y = \dfrac{(2x - 3)^3}{(3x + 1)^4}$.

Using the derivative of a quotient form, we have

$$\frac{dy}{dx} = \frac{(3x + 1)^4\dfrac{d}{dx}(2x - 3)^3 - (2x - 3)^3\dfrac{d}{dx}(3x + 1)^4}{[(3x + 1)^4]^2}$$

$$= \frac{(3x + 1)^4(3)(2x - 3)^2(2) - (2x - 3)^3(4)(3x + 1)^3(3)}{[(3x + 1)^4]^2}$$

$$= \frac{6(3x + 1)^3(2x - 3)^2[(3x + 1) - 2(2x - 3)]}{(3x + 1)^8} \qquad \text{(Factor.)}$$

$$= \frac{6(2x - 3)^2(-x + 7)}{(3x + 1)^5}$$

EXAMPLE 7

Find $\dfrac{dy}{dx}$ if $y = \dfrac{(3x + 1)^{2/3}}{(2x - 3)^{1/2}}$.

$$\frac{dy}{dx} = \frac{(2x - 3)^{1/2}(\frac{2}{3})(3x + 1)^{-1/3}(3) - (3x + 1)^{2/3}(\frac{1}{2})(2x - 3)^{-1/2}(2)}{[(2x - 3)^{1/2}]^2}$$

$$= \frac{2(2x - 3)^{1/2}(3x + 1)^{-1/3} - (3x + 1)^{2/3}(2x - 3)^{-1/2}}{2x - 3}$$

Next, factor the negative exponent factors in the numerator as follows:

$$= \frac{(3x + 1)^{-1/3}(2x - 3)^{-1/2}[2(2x - 3) - (3x + 1)]}{(2x - 3)^1}$$

$$= \frac{4x - 6 - 3x - 1}{(3x + 1)^{1/3}(2x - 3)^{3/2}}$$

$$= \frac{x - 7}{(3x + 1)^{1/3}(2x - 3)^{3/2}}$$

EXAMPLE 8

Find $\dfrac{dy}{dx}$ if $y = (2x + 1)^{1/2}(4x - 5)^{3/4}$.

$$\frac{dy}{dx} = (2x + 1)^{1/2}(\tfrac{3}{4})(4x - 5)^{-1/4}(4) + (4x - 5)^{3/4}(\tfrac{1}{2})(2x + 1)^{-1/2}(2)$$

$$= 3(2x + 1)^{1/2}(4x - 5)^{-1/4} + (4x - 5)^{3/4}(2x + 1)^{-1/2}$$

Next, factor the negative exponent factors as follows:

$$= (4x - 5)^{-1/4}(2x + 1)^{-1/2}[3(2x + 1) + (4x - 5)]$$

$$= (4x - 5)^{-1/4}(2x + 1)^{-1/2}[6x + 3 + 4x - 5]$$

$$= \frac{10x - 2}{(4x - 5)^{1/4}(2x + 1)^{1/2}}$$

Exercises 2.7

Find the derivative of each function.

1. $y = (4x + 3)^{40}$

2. $y = 5(x^2 - 7)^{16}$

3. $y = (3x^2 - 7x + 4)^5$

4. $y = (x^4 - 3x^2 + 1)^6$

5. $y = \dfrac{1}{(x^3 + 3)^4}$

6. $y = \dfrac{1}{(3x^4 - 2x + 3)^3}$

7. $y = \sqrt{5x^2 - 7x + 2}$

8. $y = \sqrt{4x^3 + 2x^2 - x}$

9. $y = (8x^3 + 3x)^{2/3}$

10. $y = (6x^4 - 5x + 2)^{3/8}$

11. $y = (2x + 3)^{-3/4}$

12. $y = (4x^2 - 1)^{-1/2}$

13. $y = 3x(4x + 5)^4$

14. $y = 2x^2(3 - x^2)^5$

15. $y = x^3(x^3 - x)^3$

16. $y = 2x(x^2 - 4)^4$

17. $y = (2x + 1)^2(x^2 + 1)^2$

18. $y = (x^2 - 2)^3(3x - 4)^2$

19. $y = (x^2 + 1)\sqrt{9x^2 - 2x}$

20. $y = (x + 1)^{3/2}x^4$

21. $y = (3x + 4)^{3/4}(4x^2 + 8)$

22. $y = (3x - 1)^{2/3}\sqrt{4x + 5}$

23. $y = \dfrac{1}{x^4} - (2x + 1)^4$

24. $y = (5x - 2)^3 - (1 - x)^4$

25. $y = \dfrac{5x^2}{(3x - 1)^2}$

26. $y = \dfrac{10x^3}{(1 - 5x^2)^2}$

27. $y = \dfrac{(x^3 + 2)^4}{4x^2 - 3x}$

28. $y = \dfrac{8x^2 + 2}{\sqrt{1 - x}}$

29. $y = \dfrac{(3x + 2)^5}{(2x - 1)^3}$

30. $y = \dfrac{(4x^2 - 1)^3}{(3x + 4)^5}$

31. $y = \dfrac{(3x - 1)^{2/3}}{\sqrt{4x + 3}}$

32. $y = \dfrac{\sqrt[4]{8x^2 + 4x}}{(3x^2 + 1)^{5/3}}$

33. $y = \left(\dfrac{1 + x}{1 - x}\right)^4$

34. $y = \left(\dfrac{1 + x^2}{1 - x^2}\right)^5$

35. Find the velocity of an object after 3 s of travel where the distance s (in metres) traveled by the object is given by $s = \dfrac{t + 1}{\sqrt{t^2 + 1}}$.

2.8   IMPLICIT DIFFERENTIATION

Often a function $y = f(x)$ is defined *implicitly*. That is, y is not directly expressed in terms of x. Such a function is called an *implicit function* of x. For example, the relation $y^2 = x$ actually defines two implicit functions of x:

$$y = f(x) = \sqrt{x} \quad \text{and} \quad y = g(x) = -\sqrt{x}$$

since both $[f(x)]^2 = x$ and $[g(x)]^2 = x$ (see Fig. 2.11). In this example, we were able to determine the two functions of x defined by the relation $y^2 = x$. Often it is not possible or at least not easy to determine directly the functions defined implicitly by a given relation, say $2y^3 + 3x^2y - 8x^3 + 2x - y = 0$. That is, could you solve this equation for y in terms of x?

It is still possible, however, to obtain an expression for the derivative $\dfrac{dy}{dx}$. The general procedure is to differentiate both sides of the given equation with respect to the independent variable.

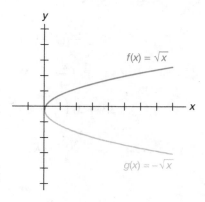

Figure 2.11

EXAMPLE 1

Find $\dfrac{dy}{dx}$ if $y^2 = x$.

$$\frac{d}{dx}(y^2) = \frac{d}{dx}(x)$$

$$2y^{2-1}\frac{d}{dx}(y) = 1 \qquad \text{(Use the power or chain rule.)}$$

$$2y\frac{dy}{dx} = 1 \qquad \left(\text{Solve for } \frac{dy}{dx}.\right)$$

$$\frac{dy}{dx} = \frac{1}{2y}$$

This process is called *implicit differentiation*.

EXAMPLE 2

Find $\dfrac{dy}{dx}$ if $2y^3 + 3x^2y - 8x^3 + 2x - y = 0$ defines y as an implicit function of x.

$$\frac{d}{dx}(2y^3 + 3x^2y - 8x^3 + 2x - y) = \frac{d}{dx}(0) \qquad \text{(Use product rule on second term.)}$$

$$6y^2\frac{dy}{dx} + 3x^2\frac{dy}{dx} + 6xy - 24x^2 + 2 - \frac{dy}{dx} = 0 \qquad \left(\text{Solve for } \frac{dy}{dx}.\right)$$

$$6y^2\frac{dy}{dx} + 3x^2\frac{dy}{dx} - \frac{dy}{dx} = -6xy + 24x^2 - 2$$

$$(6y^2 + 3x^2 - 1)\frac{dy}{dx} = -6xy + 24x^2 - 2 \quad \text{(Factor.)}$$

$$\frac{dy}{dx} = \frac{-6xy + 24x^2 - 2}{6y^2 + 3x^2 - 1}$$

Note: When differentiating the term $3x^2y$, we must consider this term as the product of two functions of x: $u = 3x^2$ and $v = y$. Then we apply the product formula for differentiation.

EXAMPLE 3

Find $\dfrac{dy}{dx}$ if $(y + 3)^3 = (5x^2 - 4)^2$.

$$\frac{d}{dx}[(y + 3)^3] = \frac{d}{dx}[(5x^2 - 4)^2]$$

$$3(y + 3)^{3-1}\frac{d}{dx}(y + 3) = 2(5x^2 - 4)^{2-1}\frac{d}{dx}(5x^2 - 4)$$

$$3(y + 3)^2\left(\frac{dy}{dx} + 0\right) = 2(5x^2 - 4)(10x)$$

$$3(y + 3)^2\frac{dy}{dx} = 20x(5x^2 - 4) \qquad \left(\text{Solve for } \frac{dy}{dx}.\right)$$

$$\frac{dy}{dx} = \frac{20x(5x^2 - 4)}{3(y + 3)^2}$$

EXAMPLE 4

Find $\dfrac{dy}{dx}$ if $(2y^3 + 1)^4 = 8x^2 + 4y^2$.

Note that the left side of the equation is in the form u^4, where $u = 2y^3 + 1$. Using the chain rule on this term, we have

$$4u^3\frac{du}{dx} = 4(2y^3 + 1)^3\left(6y^2\frac{dy}{dx}\right)$$

So,

$$\frac{d}{dx}(2y^3 + 1)^4 = \frac{d}{dx}(8x^2 + 4y^2)$$

$$4(2y^3 + 1)^3\left(6y^2\frac{dy}{dx}\right) = 16x + 4\left(2y\frac{dy}{dx}\right)$$

$$24y^2(2y^3 + 1)^3\frac{dy}{dx} = 16x + 8y\frac{dy}{dx}$$

$$24y^2(2y^3 + 1)^3\frac{dy}{dx} - 8y\frac{dy}{dx} = 16x$$

$$[24y^2(2y^3 + 1)^3 - 8y]\frac{dy}{dx} = 16x$$

$$\frac{dy}{dx} = \frac{16x}{24y^2(2y^3 + 1)^3 - 8y} = \frac{2x}{3y^2(2y^3 + 1)^3 - y}$$

Exercises 2.8

Find the derivative of each expression using implicit differentiation.

1. $4x + 3y = 7$
2. $10y - 8x = 4$
3. $x^2 - y^2 = 9$
4. $3x^2 + 4y^2 = 12$
5. $x^2 + y^2 + 4y = 0$
6. $x^2 - y^2 + 8x = 0$
7. $3x^2 - y^3 - 3xy = 0$
8. $y^3 = 3x^2y - 4$
9. $y^4 - y^2x + x^2 = 0$
10. $y^2 - 2xy + x^3 = 0$
11. $y^4 - 2y^2x^2 + 3x^2 = 0$
12. $3x^2y^2 + 4y^5 + 8x^2y^3 + xy = 5$
13. $(y^2 + 2)^2 = (x^3 - 4x)^3$
14. $(y + 4)^4 = (2x^2 - 3x + 2)^5$
15. $(x + y)^3 = (x - y + 4)^2$
16. $(x^2 + y^2)^2 = 3x^2 + 4y^2$
17. $\dfrac{x + y}{x - y} = y^2$
18. $(x + y)^{2/3} = x^2$

Find the slope of the tangent line to each curve at the given point.

19. $4x^2 + 5y^2 = 36;\ (2, -2)$
20. $x^2 - y^2 = 16;\ (5, 3)$
21. $x^2 + y^2 - 6x - 2y = 0;\ (2, 4)$
22. $y^2 + 3x - 8y + 3 = 0;\ (4, 3)$

Find the equation of the tangent line to each curve at the given point.

23. $y = 3x^2 + 4x + 9;\ (0, 9)$
24. $y = \dfrac{(x + 2)^2}{\sqrt{3x^2 + 1}};\ (0, 4)$
25. $y^2 + 3xy = 4;\ (1, -4)$
26. $xy + y^2 = 6;\ (1, 2)$

Find $\dfrac{dy}{dx}$ at the given point by (a) solving the given equation for y and finding the derivative explicitly, and (b) using implicit differentiation.

27. $x^2 + 2y = 7$ at $(1, 3)$
28. $4x^2 - 3y + 3 = 0$ at $(6, 49)$
29. $y^2 = x - 2$ at $(11, 3)$
30. $y^2 = 3x + 1$ at $(1, 2)$

2.9   PROOFS OF DERIVATIVE FORMULAS

Derivative of a Product

In Section 2.6 we claimed that if $y = f(x) = g(x) \cdot h(x)$ then

$$\frac{dy}{dx} = u\frac{dv}{dx} + v\frac{du}{dx}$$

where $u = g(x)$ and $v = h(x)$. We will now demonstrate this result.
   Using the notation of increments, we have that

$$\Delta u = g(x + \Delta x) - g(x)$$
$$\Delta v = h(x + \Delta x) - h(x)$$

and

$$\Delta y = g(x + \Delta x)h(x + \Delta x) - g(x)h(x)$$

Thus

$$\frac{dy}{dx} = \lim_{\Delta x \to 0} \frac{\Delta y}{\Delta x} = \lim_{\Delta x \to 0} \frac{g(x + \Delta x)h(x + \Delta x) - g(x)h(x)}{\Delta x}$$

$$= \lim_{\Delta x \to 0} \frac{g(x + \Delta x)h(x + \Delta x) - g(x + \Delta x)h(x) + g(x + \Delta x)h(x) - g(x)h(x)}{\Delta x}$$

Note: $-g(x + \Delta x)h(x) + g(x + \Delta x)h(x)$, which is zero, is added to the numerator.

$$= \lim_{\Delta x \to 0} \frac{g(x + \Delta x)[h(x + \Delta x) - h(x)] + h(x)[g(x + \Delta x) - g(x)]}{\Delta x}$$

$$= \lim_{\Delta x \to 0} \left[g(x + \Delta x) \frac{h(x + \Delta x) - h(x)}{\Delta x} + h(x) \frac{g(x + \Delta x) - g(x)}{\Delta x} \right]$$

$$= \lim_{\Delta x \to 0} \left[g(x + \Delta x) \frac{h(x + \Delta x) - h(x)}{\Delta x} \right]$$

$$+ \lim_{\Delta x \to 0} \left[h(x) \frac{g(x + \Delta x) - g(x)}{\Delta x} \right] \qquad \text{[By limit formula (1), Section 2.2.]}$$

$$= \left[\lim_{\Delta x \to 0} g(x + \Delta x) \right] \left[\lim_{\Delta x \to 0} \frac{h(x + \Delta x) - h(x)}{\Delta x} \right]$$

$$+ \left[\lim_{\Delta x \to 0} h(x) \right] \left[\lim_{\Delta x \to 0} \frac{g(x + \Delta x) - g(x)}{\Delta x} \right] \qquad \text{[By limit formula (4), Section 2.2.]}$$

$$= g(x) \frac{dv}{dx} + h(x) \frac{du}{dx}$$

Note: $h(x)$ is not affected by Δx and so is constant as we apply the limit as $\Delta x \to 0$.

$$= u \frac{dv}{dx} + v \frac{du}{dx}$$

or

$$\frac{d}{dx} [g(x)h(x)] = g(x) \frac{d}{dx} [h(x)] + h(x) \frac{d}{dx} [g(x)]$$

Derivative of a Quotient

The formula for $\dfrac{d}{dx} \left(\dfrac{u}{v} \right)$ from Section 2.6 can be found as follows:

Let $y = f(x) = \dfrac{g(x)}{h(x)}$, where $y = g(x)$ and $v = h(x)$. Using the same increment notation as before, we have

$$\Delta u = g(x + \Delta x) - g(x)$$
$$\Delta v = h(x + \Delta x) - h(x)$$

and

$$\Delta y = \frac{g(x + \Delta x)}{h(x + \Delta x)} - \frac{g(x)}{h(x)}$$

Then,

$$\frac{dy}{dx} = \lim_{\Delta x \to 0} \frac{\Delta y}{\Delta x} = \lim_{\Delta x \to 0} \frac{\dfrac{g(x + \Delta x)}{h(x + \Delta x)} - \dfrac{g(x)}{h(x)}}{\Delta x}$$

$$= \lim_{\Delta x \to 0} \frac{h(x)g(x + \Delta x) - h(x + \Delta x)g(x)}{\Delta x \, h(x)h(x + \Delta x)}$$

$$= \lim_{\Delta x \to 0} \frac{\dfrac{h(x)g(x + \Delta x) - h(x + \Delta x)g(x)}{\Delta x}}{h(x)h(x + \Delta x)}$$

$$= \lim_{\Delta x \to 0} \frac{\dfrac{h(x)g(x + \Delta x) - h(x)g(x) + h(x)g(x) - h(x + \Delta x)g(x)}{\Delta x}}{h(x)h(x + \Delta x)}$$

Note: $-h(x)g(x) + h(x)g(x)$, which is zero, is added to the numerator.

$$= \lim_{\Delta x \to 0} \frac{h(x)\left[\dfrac{g(x + \Delta x) - g(x)}{\Delta x}\right] - g(x)\left[\dfrac{h(x + \Delta x) - h(x)}{\Delta x}\right]}{h(x)h(x + \Delta x)}$$

$$= \frac{\left[\lim_{\Delta x \to 0} h(x)\right]\left[\lim_{\Delta x \to 0}\dfrac{g(x + \Delta x) - g(x)}{\Delta x}\right] - \left[\lim_{\Delta x \to 0} g(x)\right]\left[\lim_{\Delta x \to 0}\dfrac{h(x + \Delta x) - h(x)}{\Delta x}\right]}{\left[\lim_{\Delta x \to 0} h(x)\right]\left[\lim_{\Delta x \to 0} h(x + \Delta x)\right]}$$

[By limit formulas (1), (4), and (5), Section 2.2.]

$$= \frac{h(x)\dfrac{du}{dx} - g(x)\dfrac{dv}{dx}}{h(x)h(x)}$$

$$= \frac{v\dfrac{du}{dx} - u\dfrac{dv}{dx}}{v^2}$$

Derivative of a Power

In Section 2.7 we introduced the formula $\dfrac{d}{dx}u^n = nu^{n-1}\dfrac{du}{dx}$. To show this result, let $u = f(x)$ and $y = u^n$, where n is a positive integer. Then

$$\Delta y = (u + \Delta u)^n - u^n$$

$$= u^n + nu^{n-1}(\Delta u) + \frac{n(n - 1)}{2}u^{n-2}(\Delta u)^2 + \cdots + (\Delta u)^n - u^n$$

$$= nu^{n-1}(\Delta u) + \frac{n(n - 1)}{2}u^{n-2}(\Delta u)^2 + \cdots + (\Delta u)^n$$

$$= nu^{n-1}(\Delta u)$$
$$+ \left[\frac{n(n - 1)}{2}u^{n-2} + \text{(other terms involving both } u \text{ and } \Delta u) + (\Delta u)^{n-2}\right](\Delta u)^2$$

So,

$$\frac{\Delta y}{\Delta x} = nu^{n-1}\frac{\Delta u}{\Delta x}$$
$$+ \left[\frac{n(n - 1)}{2}u^{n-2} + \text{(other terms involving both } u \text{ and } \Delta u) + (\Delta u)^{n-2}\right]\left(\frac{\Delta u}{\Delta x}\right)(\Delta u)$$

Then, as $\Delta x \to 0$, all terms except $nu^{n-1}\dfrac{\Delta u}{\Delta x}$ approach 0 since

$$\lim_{\Delta x \to 0}\left(\frac{\Delta u}{\Delta x} \cdot \Delta u\right) = \lim_{\Delta x \to 0}\frac{\Delta u}{\Delta x} \cdot \lim_{\Delta x \to 0} \Delta u$$

$$= \frac{du}{dx} \cdot \lim_{\Delta x \to 0} [f(x + \Delta x) - f(x)]$$

$$= \frac{du}{dx} \cdot 0$$

$$= 0$$

and $\left(\dfrac{\Delta u}{\Delta x} \cdot \Delta u \right)$ is a factor of all the remaining terms. So,

$$\frac{dy}{dx} = \lim_{\Delta x \to 0} \frac{\Delta y}{\Delta x}$$

$$= \lim_{\Delta x \to 0} nu^{n-1} \frac{\Delta u}{\Delta x}$$

$$= nu^{n-1} \cdot \lim_{\Delta x \to 0} \frac{\Delta u}{\Delta x}$$

$$= nu^{n-1} \frac{du}{dx}$$

2.10   HIGHER DERIVATIVES

The derivative of a function is also a function. For example, given

$$f(x) = 5x^4$$

then

$$f'(x) = 20x^3$$

Since $f'(x)$ is a function, its derivative (if it exists) is also a function. This result, called the second derivative of $f(x)$, is written $f''(x)$. Thus

$$f''(x) = 60x^2$$

Continuing, we have

$$f'''(x) = 120x$$
$$f^{(4)}(x) = 120$$
$$f^{(5)}(x) = 0$$
$$f^{(6)}(x) = 0$$

and so forth.

Some of the various notations used for derivatives are given below.

First derivative	Second derivative	Third derivative	Fourth derivative
$f'(x)$	$f''(x)$	$f'''(x)$	$f^{(4)}(x)$
y'	y''	y'''	$y^{(4)}$
$\dfrac{dy}{dx}$	$\dfrac{d^2y}{dx^2}$	$\dfrac{d^3y}{dx^3}$	$\dfrac{d^4y}{dx^4}$
$\dfrac{d}{dx}f(x)$	$\dfrac{d^2}{dx^2}f(x)$	$\dfrac{d^3}{dx^3}f(x)$	$\dfrac{d^4}{dx^4}f(x)$
Dy	D^2y	D^3y	D^4y
$Df(x)$	$D^2f(x)$	$D^3f(x)$	$D^4f(x)$

EXAMPLE 1

Find the first four derivatives for $y = x^6 - 8x^4 + 3x^3 - 2$.

$$\frac{dy}{dx} = 6x^5 - 32x^3 + 9x^2$$

$$\frac{d^2y}{dx^2} = 30x^4 - 96x^2 + 18x$$

$$\frac{d^3y}{dx^3} = 120x^3 - 192x + 18$$

$$\frac{d^4y}{dx^4} = 360x^2 - 192$$

EXAMPLE 2

Find the first three derivatives of $y = x^2 + x^{1/2}$.

$$y' = 2x + \frac{1}{2}x^{-1/2} = \frac{4x^{3/2} + 1}{2\sqrt{x}}$$

$$y'' = 2 - \frac{1}{4}x^{-3/2} = \frac{8x^{3/2} - 1}{4x^{3/2}}$$

$$y''' = \frac{3}{8}x^{-5/2} = \frac{3}{8x^{5/2}}$$

Using a calculator, we have

2nd 8 x^2+x^(1/2),x) **ENTER**   right arrow left arrow **, 2 ENTER**   right arrow left arrow ← **3 ENTER**

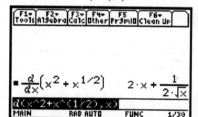   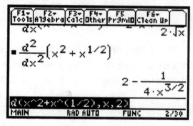   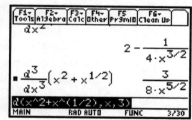

The second derivative of an implicit function may be found as shown in the following example.

EXAMPLE 3

Given $y^2 - xy = 5$, find $\frac{d^2y}{dx^2}$.

First, find y' as shown in Section 2.8.

$$2yy' - xy' - y = 0$$

Then solve for y'.

$$(2y - x)y' = y$$

$$y' = \frac{y}{2y - x}$$

Next, find y'' using the quotient formula.

$$y'' = \frac{(2y - x)y' - y(2y' - 1)}{(2y - x)^2}$$

$$= \frac{2yy' - xy' - 2yy' + y}{(2y - x)^2}$$

$$= \frac{-xy' + y}{(2y - x)^2} \quad \text{(Next, substitute for } y' \text{ and simplify.)}$$

$$= \frac{-x\left(\dfrac{y}{2y - x}\right) + y}{(2y - x)^2} \cdot \left(\frac{2y - x}{2y - x}\right) \quad \text{(Simplify the complex fraction.)}$$

$$= \frac{-xy + 2y^2 - xy}{(2y - x)^3}$$

$$= \frac{2y^2 - 2xy}{(2y - x)^3}$$

$$= \frac{2(y^2 - xy)}{(2y - x)^3}$$

$$= \frac{2(5)}{(2y - x)^3} \quad (\textit{Note: From the original equation } y^2 - xy = 5.)$$

$$= \frac{10}{(2y - x)^3}$$

Recall that *velocity* is the instantaneous rate of change of displacement with respect to time. That is,

VELOCITY

$$v = \frac{ds}{dt}$$

Acceleration is the instantaneous rate of change of velocity with respect to time. So, acceleration is the first derivative of velocity with respect to time and the second derivative of displacement (distance) with respect to time. That is,

ACCELERATION

$$a = \frac{dv}{dt} = \frac{d^2s}{dt^2}$$

EXAMPLE 4

The displacement of an object (in metres) is given by $s = 5t^4 - 6t^3 + 8t + 3$. Find the equation that describes the acceleration of the object. Find its acceleration at $t = 2$ s.

First, find the velocity equation:

$$v = \frac{ds}{dt} = 20t^3 - 18t^2 + 8$$

Then find the acceleration equation:

$$a = \frac{dv}{dt} = 60t^2 - 36t$$

At $t = 2$ s,

$$a = 60(2)^2 - 36(2) = 168 \text{ m/s}^2$$

Exercises 2.10

Find the first four derivatives of each function.

1. $y = x^5 + 3x^2$　　　　　**2.** $y = 3x^6 - 8x^3 + 2$　　　**3.** $y = 5x^5 + 2x^3 - 8x$

4. $y = 3x^2 + 4x - 7$

Find the indicated derivative.

5. $y = \dfrac{1}{x}; \dfrac{d^3y}{dx^3}$　　　　**6.** $y = \dfrac{3}{x^2}; y'''$　　　　**7.** $y = (3x - 5)^3; y'''$

8. $y = (4x^2 - 2)^4; \dfrac{d^2y}{dx^2}$　　**9.** $y = \sqrt{3x + 2}; \dfrac{d^4y}{dx^4}$　　**10.** $y = (2x + 1)^{3/2}; \dfrac{d^4y}{dx^4}$

11. $y = \dfrac{1}{x^2 + 1}; y''$　　　**12.** $y = \dfrac{4}{(x^2 + 5)^2}; y''$　　**13.** $y = \dfrac{x + 1}{x - 1}; \dfrac{d^2y}{dx^2}$

14. $y = \dfrac{3x + 1}{2x - 4}; \dfrac{d^2y}{dx^2}$

Find y' and y'' implicitly and express the result in terms of x and y.

15. $x^2 + y^2 = 1$　　　　**16.** $(x - 3)^2 + y^2 = 9$　　**17.** $x^2 - xy + y^2 = 1$

18. $y^2 + xy = 1$　　　　**19.** $\sqrt{x} + \sqrt{y} = 1$　　　**20.** $x + \dfrac{x}{y} = 8$

21. $\dfrac{1}{x} - \dfrac{1}{y} = 1$　　　**22.** $x = \dfrac{y + 1}{y - 1}$　　　　**23.** $x = (1 + y)^2$

24. $\sqrt{1 + y^2} = x$

Each equation describes the displacement of an object. Find the equation that describes the acceleration of the object.

25. $s = 0.5t^4 - 6t^3 - 4t^2 - 1$　　**26.** $s = \dfrac{4}{2t + 1}$

27. $s = \sqrt{6t - 4}$　　　　　**28.** $s = \dfrac{8t + 3}{5 - 4t}$

29. The curve $x^2 - xy + y^2 = 7$ has two tangents at $x = 1$. Find their equations.

30. Show that the tangent to the parabola $y^2 = 4cx$ at (x_0, y_0) is $y_0 y = 2c(x + x_0)$.

31. Show that the tangent to the ellipse $\dfrac{x^2}{a^2} + \dfrac{y^2}{b^2} = 1$ at (x_0, y_0) is $\dfrac{x_0 x}{a^2} + \dfrac{y_0 y}{b^2} = 1$.

32. Show that the tangent to the hyperbola $\dfrac{x^2}{a^2} - \dfrac{y^2}{b^2} = 1$ at (x_0, y_0) is $\dfrac{x_0 x}{a^2} - \dfrac{y_0 y}{b^2} = 1$.

CHAPTER 2 SUMMARY

1. *Average velocity:*

$$\bar{v} = \frac{\text{change in distance}}{\text{change in time}} = \frac{\Delta s}{\Delta t} = \frac{f(t + \Delta t) - f(t)}{\Delta t}$$

2. *Limit:* If $f(x) \to L$ as $x \to a$, then L is called the "limit of the function as $x \to a$." This is written

$$\lim_{x \to a} f(x) = L$$

and read "the limit of f of x as x approaches a equals L."

3. *Instantaneous velocity:*

$$v = \lim_{\Delta t \to 0} \frac{f(t + \Delta t) - f(t)}{\Delta t} \quad \text{or} \quad v = \frac{ds}{dt}$$

4. *Limit formulas* $\left[\lim_{x \to a} f(x) \text{ and } \lim_{x \to a} g(x) \text{ must both exist}\right]$:

(a) $\lim_{x \to a} [f(x) \pm g(x)] = \lim_{x \to a} f(x) \pm \lim_{x \to a} g(x)$

(b) $\lim_{x \to a} [k \cdot f(x)] = k \cdot \lim_{x \to a} f(x)$, where k is a constant

(c) $\lim_{x \to a} k = k$, where k is a constant

(d) $\lim_{x \to a} [f(x) \cdot g(x)] = \lim_{x \to a} f(x) \cdot \lim_{x \to a} g(x)$

(e) $\lim_{x \to a} \dfrac{f(x)}{g(x)} = \dfrac{\lim\limits_{x \to a} f(x)}{\lim\limits_{x \to a} g(x)}$, where $\lim_{x \to a} g(x) \neq 0$

5. *Continuity:*

(a) A function is continuous at $x = a$ if
   (i) $f(a)$ is defined,
   (ii) $\lim_{x \to a} f(x)$ exists, and
   (iii) $\lim_{x \to a} f(x) = f(a)$.

(b) If a function is continuous at all points in a given interval, it is continuous on that interval.

6. *Slope of a tangent line to* $y = f(x)$:

$$m_{\text{tan}} = \lim_{\Delta x \to 0} \frac{\Delta y}{\Delta x} = \lim_{\Delta x \to 0} \frac{f(x + \Delta x) - f(x)}{\Delta x}$$

7. *Derivative:* The derivative of the function $f(x)$ is

$$\frac{dy}{dx} = \lim_{\Delta x \to 0} \frac{\Delta y}{\Delta x} = \lim_{\Delta x \to 0} \frac{f(x + \Delta x) - f(x)}{\Delta x}$$

8. *Basic differentiation formulas:*

(a) $\dfrac{d}{dx}(c) = 0$

(b) $\dfrac{d}{dx}(x) = 1$

(c) $\dfrac{d}{dx}(x^n) = nx^{n-1}$

(d) $\dfrac{d}{dx}(cu) = c\dfrac{du}{dx}$

(e) $\dfrac{d}{dx}(u + v) = \dfrac{du}{dx} + \dfrac{dv}{dx}$

(f) $\dfrac{d}{dx}(u - v) = \dfrac{du}{dx} - \dfrac{dv}{dx}$

(g) $\dfrac{d}{dx}(uv) = u\dfrac{dv}{dx} + v\dfrac{du}{dx}$

(h) $\dfrac{d}{dx}\left(\dfrac{u}{v}\right) = \dfrac{v\dfrac{du}{dx} - u\dfrac{dv}{dx}}{v^2} \qquad (v \neq 0)$

(i) $\dfrac{d}{dx}(u^n) = nu^{n-1}\dfrac{du}{dx}$

9. *Acceleration:*

$$a = \frac{dv}{dt} = \frac{d^2s}{dt^2}$$

CHAPTER 2 REVIEW

Find (a) Δs and (b) $\bar{v}$ for each function expressing distance s in terms of t and Δt.

1. $s = 3t^2 + 4$ **2.** $s = 5t^2 - 6$ **3.** $s = t^2 - 3t + 5$

4. $s = 3t^2 - 6t + 8$

Find $\bar{v}$ for each function $s = f(t)$ at the values of t and Δt (s is measured in metres and t in seconds).

5. $s = 3t^2 - 7, t = 2, \Delta t = 5$ **6.** $s = 5t^2 - 3, t = 1, \Delta t = 2$

7. $s = 2t^2 - 4t + 7, t = 2, \Delta t = 3$ **8.** $s = 4t^2 - 7t + 2, \ t = 3, \Delta t = 4$

9–12. Find the instantaneous velocity v for the functions given in Exercises 5 through 8 at the values of t.

Find each limit.

13. $\lim\limits_{x \to 3} (2x^2 - 5x + 1)$ **14.** $\lim\limits_{x \to -2} (x^2 + 4x - 7)$ **15.** $\lim\limits_{x \to -2} \dfrac{x^2 - 4}{x + 2}$

16. $\lim\limits_{x \to 5} \dfrac{25 - x^2}{5 - x}$ **17.** $\lim\limits_{x \to 2} \sqrt{3 - 4x}$ **18.** $\lim\limits_{x \to -3} \sqrt{6 + x^2}$

19. $\lim\limits_{x \to 2} \dfrac{5x^2 + 2}{3x^2 - 2x + 1}$ **20.** $\lim\limits_{x \to -3} \dfrac{2x^2 - 4x + 7}{x^3 - x}$

21. $\lim\limits_{x \to -3} (x^2 - 4x + 3)(2x^2 + 5x + 4)$ **22.** $\lim\limits_{x \to 2} (x^3 + x - 2)(x^3 + x^2 + x)$

23. $\lim\limits_{h \to 0} \dfrac{\dfrac{1}{2 + h} - \dfrac{1}{2}}{h}$ **24.** $\lim\limits_{h \to 0} \dfrac{\sqrt{1 + h} - 1}{h}$

25. $\lim\limits_{x \to \infty} \dfrac{5x^2 - 2x + 3}{2x^2 - 4}$ **26.** $\lim\limits_{x \to \infty} \dfrac{7x^3 - 4x + 2}{10x^3 - x^2 + 5}$

In Exercises 27 through 32, use Fig. 2.12.

27. Find $\lim\limits_{x \to a} f(x)$ if it exists.

28. Find $\lim\limits_{x \to d} f(x)$ if it exists.

29. Find $\lim\limits_{x \to +\infty} f(x)$ if it exists.

30. Find $\lim\limits_{x \to -\infty} f(x)$ if it exists.

31. Is the function continuous at $x = a$?

32. Is the function continuous at $x = d$?

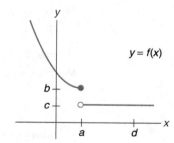

Figure 2.12

Find the slope and equation of the tangent line to each curve at the given point.

33. $y = 3x^2 - 4x + 5; (-1, 12)$ **34.** $y = x^2 - 5x - 12; (2, -18)$

35. $y = 2x^2 + 2x + 7; (3, 31)$ **36.** $y = 4x^2 - 8x + 3; (-2, 35)$

37. An object is moving along a straight-line path according to the equation $s = 3/t^2$, where s is measured in centimetres. Find its velocity after 5 s.

38. An object is falling freely according to the equation $s = 150 - 16t^2$, where s is measured in feet. Find its velocity after 2 s.

Find each derivative dy/dx:

39. $y = 5x^4 - 3x^3 + 2x^2 + 5x - 9$ **40.** $y = x^{100} + 80x^5 + 16$

41. $y = (x^3 + 4)(x^3 - x + 1)$ **42.** $y = (3x^2 - 5)(x^5 + x^2 - 4x)$

43. $y = \dfrac{x^2 + 1}{3x - 4}$ 　　　　　　**44.** $y = \dfrac{2x - x^2}{3x^4 + 2}$ 　　　　**45.** $y = (3x^2 - 8)^5$

46. $y = (x^4 + 2x^3 + 7)^{3/4}$ 　　　**47.** $y = \dfrac{1}{(3x + 5)^4}$ 　　　**48.** $y = \dfrac{\sqrt{7x^2 - 5}}{(x + 3)^2}$

49. $y = \dfrac{x\sqrt{2 - 3x}}{x + 5}$ 　　　　　**50.** $x^2 - 4xy^3 + y^2 = 0$ 　　**51.** $y^4 - y^2 = 2xy$

52. $(y^2 + 1)^3 = 4x^2 + 3$ 　　　　**53.** $(y + 2)^4 = (2x^3 - 3)^3$

Find $f'(a)$ for each.

54. $f(x) = (x^2 + 2)^3(x + 1);\ a = -2$ 　　**55.** $f(x) = \dfrac{x^2 - 8}{x + 3};\ a = -4$

56. $f(x) = \dfrac{x^2 + 3x - 2}{x - 2};\ a = 3$ 　　　**57.** $f(x) = \dfrac{\sqrt{3x^2 - 1}}{x + 5};\ a = 1$

Find the equation of the tangent line to each curve at the given point.

58. $y = 3x^2 + x - 2$ at $(-2, 8)$ 　　　**59.** $y = x^3 - x + 8$ at $(-3, -16)$

60. $y = \dfrac{x^2 - 2}{\sqrt{x - 3}}$ at $(4, 14)$ 　　　**61.** $y = \dfrac{\sqrt{x^2 + 7}}{x - 2}$ at $(3, 4)$

Find the instantaneous velocity of an object moving along a straight line according to each function $s = f(t)$ at the given time t (s is measured in metres and t in seconds).

62. $s = 3t^2 - 8t + 4;\ t = 2$ 　　　　**63.** $s = t^3 - 9t^2 + 3;\ t = -2$

64. $s = \dfrac{t^2 - 5}{\sqrt{t + 1}};\ t = 3$ 　　　　　**65.** $s = \dfrac{\sqrt{t^2 - 3}}{t + 5};\ t = 4$

66. Find the equation of the tangent line to the curve $y = \dfrac{x^2 - 6}{x + 3}$ at $(-4, -10)$.

67. The instantaneous current $i = dq/dt$ at any point in an electric circuit, where q is the charge in coulombs (C) and t is the time in seconds. Find i in amperes (A) where $q = 1000t^3 + 50t$ when $t = 0.01$ s.

68. The specific heat c of a gas as a function of the temperature T is given by

$$c = 8.40 + 0.5T + 0.000006T^2$$

Find the rate of change of the specific heat with respect to temperature dc/dT.

69. The resonant frequency of a series ac circuit is given by

$$f = \dfrac{1}{2\pi\sqrt{LC}}$$

where L and C are the inductance and capacitance in the circuit, respectively. Find the rate of change f with respect to C, assuming L remains constant.

70. Find the first four derivatives of $y = 4x^6 - 8x^4 + 9x^3 - 6x + 9$.

Find the indicated derivative.

71. $y = \sqrt{2x - 3};\ y''$ 　　　　　　**72.** $y = \dfrac{3}{2x^2 + 1};\ \dfrac{d^2y}{dx^2}$

Find y' and y'' implicitly and express the result in terms of x and y.

73. $y^2 + 2xy = 4$ 　　　　　　　**74.** $\dfrac{1}{\sqrt{x}} - \dfrac{1}{\sqrt{y}} = 1$

75. The equation $s = (2t + 3)^{1/4}$ describes the displacement of an object. Find the equation that describes its acceleration.

3

Applications
of the Derivative

INTRODUCTION

Many problems require the use of a derivative for their solutions. With derivatives, we can determine the shape of a container that will give maximum volume using a fixed amount of material, we can find the right combination of materials to produce a product that meets specifications but costs as little as possible, and we can calculate the rate at which the radius of a balloon is changing as it is being inflated. Problems such as these are discussed in this chapter.

Objectives

- Find relative maximum and minimum values of a function.
- Determine intervals in which a curve is concave upward and concave downward.
- Use derivatives to sketch curves.
- Improve the accuracy of estimated solutions using Newton's method.
- Solve maximum and minimum application problems.
- Solve related-rate problems.

3.1 CURVE SKETCHING

In this course, as well as in your other technical courses, you will find it most helpful to sketch quickly the graph of an equation without plotting several points. In this section you will be given a series of graphing aids, each designed to give you valuable information about the graph, that will enable you to sketch quickly the graph of an equation.

Intercepts

The intercepts are those points where the graph crosses or touches either the x-axis or the y-axis.

1. To find the x-intercepts, substitute $y = 0$ into the given equation and solve for x. Each resulting value of x is an x-intercept.
2. To find the y-intercepts, substitute $x = 0$ into the given equation and solve for y. Each resulting value of y is a y-intercept.

EXAMPLE 1

Find the intercepts for the graph of $y = (x - 1)(x + 3)^2$.

Step 1: To find the x-intercepts, substitute $y = 0$ and solve for x:

$$y = (x - 1)(x + 3)^2$$
$$0 = (x - 1)(x + 3)^2$$
$$x - 1 = 0 \quad \text{or} \quad (x + 3)^2 = 0$$
$$x = 1 \quad \text{and} \quad x = -3 \quad \text{are } x\text{-intercepts}$$

Step 2: To find the y-intercepts, substitute $x = 0$ and solve for y:

$$y = (x - 1)(x + 3)^2$$
$$y = (0 - 1)(0 + 3)^2$$
$$y = -9 \quad \text{is the } y\text{-intercept}$$

Location of the Curve Above and Below the x-Axis

Knowing in which regions the curve is above and below the x-axis can be most important information. If the expression can be factored, this information can be quickly found as follows:

1. Solve the given equation for y.
2. Factor the result from Step 1 as much as possible. [If this is a rational (fractional) expression, factor both the numerator and the denominator as much as possible.]
3. Set each factor from Step 2 equal to zero. These solutions are called *points of division* because they divide the number line (x-axis) into regions where the graph is above or below the x-axis. Plot each solution on the x-axis.
4. Find the sign of y in each region by choosing a test point. Substitute this test point value into each factor of the given equation and determine whether each factor is positive or negative in the region. Determine the sign of y by using the rules for multiplication and/or division of signed numbers. If the sign of y is *positive*, the curve is *above* the x-axis in this region. If the sign of y is *negative*, the curve is *below* the x-axis in the region.

EXAMPLE 2

Determine where the graph of $y = (x - 1)(x + 3)^2$ is above and below the x-axis.
From Example 1, the points of division are 1 and -3. Plot them on the x-axis.

| Signs of factors in each interval: | $(x - 1)$ | $-$ | | $-$ | $+$ |
| | $(x + 3)^2$ | $+$ | | $+$ | $+$ |

| Sign of y in each interval: | | $-$ | $-$ | $+$ |
| | | (below) | (below) | (above) |

As you can see, we have three regions:

For $x > 1$, the product is *positive*, which means the curve is *above* the x-axis.

For $-3 < x < 1$, the product is *negative*, which means the curve is *below* the x-axis.

For $x < -3$, the product is *negative*, which means the curve is *below* the x-axis.

From the information gained from these first two graphing aids, we can now make a quick sketch of the graph of the equation in Fig. 3.1. We will be able to refine this procedure even more as we progress through the chapter.

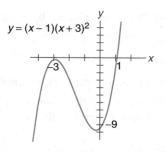

$y = (x - 1)(x + 3)^2$

Figure 3.1

Symmetry

Another graphing aid or characteristic that is helpful in sketching a curve is *symmetry*. We consider two kinds of symmetry: symmetry about a line and symmetry about a point.

A curve is symmetric about a line if one half of the curve is the mirror image of the other half on opposite sides of the given line. That is, for every point P on the curve on one side of the given line, there is a point P' on the curve on the opposite side of the line so that PP' is perpendicular to the given line and bisected by it. For example, the graph of $y = 1/x^2$ is symmetric about the y-axis (see Fig. 3.2).

A curve is symmetric about a point, say O, if for every other point $P \neq O$ on the curve, there is a point P' on the curve so that PP' is bisected by point O. For example, the graph of $y = 1/x$ is symmetric about the origin (see Fig. 3.3).

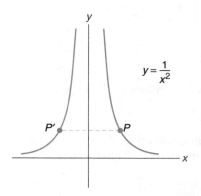

$y = \dfrac{1}{x^2}$

Figure 3.2 Symmetry about the y-axis.

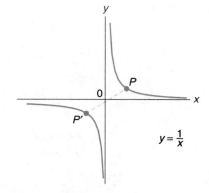

$y = \dfrac{1}{x}$

Figure 3.3 Symmetry about the origin.

Of the many possible lines and points of symmetry, we shall present the three most common: symmetry about the y-axis, symmetry about the x-axis, and symmetry about the origin.

1. A curve is symmetric about the y-axis if for every point $P(x, y)$ on the curve, there is a point $P'(-x, y)$ on the curve. This symmetry can be tested as follows:

SYMMETRY ABOUT THE y-AXIS

The graph of an equation is symmetric about the y-axis if replacement of x by $-x$ in the original equation results in an equivalent equation.

Note that if we replace x by $-x$ in the earlier equation $y = 1/x^2$, we get

$$y = \frac{1}{(-x)^2}$$

which is equivalent to the original equation.

2. A curve is symmetric about the x-axis if for every point $P(x, y)$ on the curve, there is a point $P'(x, -y)$ on the curve. This symmetry can be tested as follows:

SYMMETRY ABOUT THE x-AXIS

The graph of an equation is symmetric about the x-axis if replacement of y by $-y$ in the original equation results in an equivalent equation.

Note that if we replace y by $-y$ in the equation $x = y^2$, we get

$$x = (-y)^2$$

which is equivalent to the original equation (see Fig. 3.4).

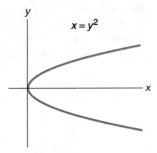

Figure 3.4 Symmetry about the x-axis.

3. A curve is symmetric about the origin if for every point $P(x, y)$ on the curve, there is a point $P'(-x, -y)$ on the curve. This symmetry can be tested as follows:

SYMMETRY ABOUT THE ORIGIN

The graph of an equation is symmetric about the origin if replacement of both x by $-x$ and y by $-y$ in the original equation results in an equivalent equation.

Note that if we replace x by $-x$ and y by $-y$ in the earlier equation

$$y = \frac{1}{x}$$

we get

$$-y = \frac{1}{-x}$$

which is equivalent to the original equation.

If any two of these three symmetry tests are satisfied, then the graph contains all three symmetries. Do you see why?

Asymptotes

An *asymptote* to a curve is a line that the curve approaches (gets closer to) as the distance from the origin increases without bound.

A *rational function* is an equation in the form

$$y = f(x) = \frac{g(x)}{h(x)}$$

where $g(x)$ and $h(x)$ are polynomials. Such rational functions may have asymptotes. We will present three possible asymptotes. In all cases, first solve the given equation for y in terms of x.

1. *Vertical asymptotes:* Set the denominator equal to zero and solve for x. These solutions give the points where the vertical asymptotes cross the x-axis. For example, if $x = a$ is a solution, one vertical asymptote crosses the x-axis at a and $x = a$ is the equation of the vertical asymptote.

2. *Horizontal asymptotes:* If $\lim_{x \to +\infty} f(x) = b$ or $\lim_{x \to -\infty} f(x) = b$, then $y = b$ is a horizontal asymptote. We have two cases:

   (a) If the degree of the numerator is less than the degree of the denominator, then $y = 0$ is a horizontal asymptote.

   Given the equation $y = 1/x^2$, do you see that as $x \to \infty$, $y \to 0$?

   (b) If the rational function is in the form

   $$f(x) = \frac{a_n x^n + \cdots + a_0}{b_n x^n + \cdots + b_0} \qquad (b_n \neq 0)$$

   then $y = \dfrac{a_n}{b_n}$ is a horizontal asymptote. That is, if the numerator and the denominator are of the same degree, the horizontal asymptote is the ratio of the coefficients of the terms of highest degree.

   Given the equation

   $$y = \frac{3x^2 - 10x - 8}{x^2 + 3x - 10}$$

   divide numerator and denominator by x^2, which is the largest power of x:

   $$\lim_{x \to \infty} \frac{3 - \dfrac{10}{x} - \dfrac{8}{x^2}}{1 + \dfrac{3}{x} - \dfrac{10}{x^2}} = 3$$

   So $y = 3$ is a horizontal asymptote.

3. *Slant asymptotes:* If the degree of the numerator is one greater than the degree of the denominator, there may be a slant asymptote. To find it, divide the numerator by the denominator using polynomial division and drop the remainder. Then $y = \textit{the quotient}$ is the equation of the slant asymptote.

   Given the equation

   $$y = \frac{x^2 - 1}{x - 2}$$

divide the numerator by the denominator:

$$x - 2 \overline{\smash{)}\begin{matrix} x + 2 + \dfrac{3}{x-2} \\ x^2 - 1 \end{matrix}}$$

$$\begin{array}{r} x + 2 + \dfrac{3}{x-2} \\ x-2\,)\overline{x^2 - 1} \\ \underline{x^2 - 2x} \\ 2x - 1 \\ \underline{2x - 4} \\ 3 \end{array}$$

The slant asymptote is $y = x + 2$.

Do you see that as $x \to \infty$, the remainder, $\dfrac{3}{x-2}$, approaches zero?

Restricted Domains

Some equations have restricted domains by the nature of their definitions. For example, the domain of

$$y = \sqrt{3 - x}$$

is $x \le 3$ since the square root of a negative number is not real. The domain of

$$y = \log_{10}(x + 2)$$

is $x > -2$ since the logarithm of only a positive number is defined.

These graphing aids will now be illustrated with the following examples. You will find it most helpful to follow a consistent pattern of applying each aid.

EXAMPLE 3

Graph $y = x^2(x^2 - 9)$.

    Factor: $y = x^2(x + 3)(x - 3)$

    Intercepts: If $y = 0$, then $x = 0, 3, -3$.

              If $x = 0$, then $y = 0$.

Plot points of division on the x-axis:

Signs of factors	x^2	+	+	+	+
in each interval:	$(x + 3)$	−	+	+	+
	$(x - 3)$	−	−	−	+

$$\xleftarrow{}\!\!\underset{\substack{}}{\overline{}}\!\!\!\!\!\!\underset{-3}{/}\!\!\!\!\!\!\underset{0}{/}\!\!\!\!\!\!\underset{3}{/}\!\!\!\!\!\!\xrightarrow{} x$$

Sign of y in each interval:	+	−	−	+
	(above)	(below)	(below)	(above)

Symmetry: y-axis   (Replacement of x by $-x$ results in an equivalent equation.)
Asymptotes: None
Restricted domain: None
(See Fig. 3.5.)

EXAMPLE 4

Graph $y = \dfrac{3}{(x + 1)^2}$.

    Intercepts: Note that $y \ne 0$ because $\dfrac{3}{(x + 1)^2} \ne 0$; therefore, there is no x-intercept.

              If $x = 0$, then $y = 3$.

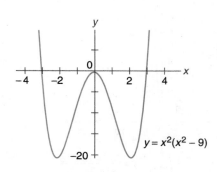

$y = x^2(x^2 - 9)$

Figure 3.5

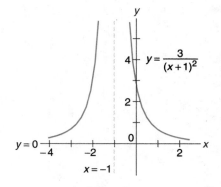

$y = \dfrac{3}{(x+1)^2}$

$y = 0$

$x = -1$

Figure 3.6

Points of division on the *x*-axis:
Signs of factor in
each interval: $(x + 1)^2$ +   +

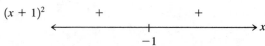

-1

Note: *y* is always positive; therefore, this curve is always above the
x-axis.

Symmetry: None
Asymptotes:
   Vertical: $x = -1$ [*Note:* $(x + 1)^2 = 0$ when $x = -1$.]
   Horizontal: $y = 0$ (Degree of numerator is less than degree of denominator.)
   Slant: None
Restricted domain: None except $x \neq -1$.
(See Fig. 3.6.)

EXAMPLE 5

Graph $y = \dfrac{3x^2 - 10x - 8}{x^2 + 3x - 10}$.

Factor: $y = \dfrac{(3x + 2)(x - 4)}{(x + 5)(x - 2)}$

Intercepts: If $y = 0$, then $x = -\frac{2}{3}, 4$.
               If $x = 0$, then $y = \frac{4}{5}$.

Plot points of division on the *x*-axis (set each factor equal to zero):

Signs of factors	$(3x + 2)$	$-$	$-$	$+$	$+$	$+$
in each interval:	$(x - 4)$	$-$	$-$	$-$	$-$	$+$
	$(x + 5)$	$-$	$+$	$+$	$+$	$+$
	$(x - 2)$	$-$	$-$	$-$	$+$	$+$

$\xleftarrow{\qquad\quad -5 \qquad -2/3 \qquad\quad 2 \qquad\quad 4 \qquad\quad}\rightarrow x$

Sign of *y* in
each interval: $+$ $-$ $+$ $-$ $+$
                     (above)   (below)   (above)   (below)   (above)

Symmetry: None
Asymptotes:
   Vertical: $x = -5, x = 2$ (Set the denominator equal to zero.)
   Horizontal: $y = 3$.   (Degree of numerator equals degree of denominator;
                            the ratio of coefficients of highest degree is 3/1 or 3.)
   Slant: None
Restricted domain: None except $x \neq -5, 2$.
(See Fig. 3.7.)

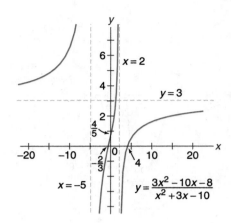

Figure 3.7

(In the figure: $x = 2$, $y = 3$, $x = -5$, $y = \dfrac{3x^2 - 10x - 8}{x^2 + 3x - 10}$)

EXAMPLE 6

Graph $y = \dfrac{x^2 - 1}{x - 2}$.

Factor: $y = \dfrac{(x + 1)(x - 1)}{x - 2}$

Intercepts: If $y = 0$, then $x = -1, 1$.
  If $x = 0$, then $y = \frac{1}{2}$.

Plot points of division on the x-axis:

Signs of factors $(x + 1)$ $-$ $+$ $+$ $+$
in each interval: $(x - 1)$ $-$ $-$ $+$ $+$
               $(x - 2)$ $-$ $-$ $-$ $+$

$$\xleftarrow{\hspace{2cm}} \underset{-1}{|} \quad \underset{1}{|} \quad \underset{2}{|} \xrightarrow{\hspace{1cm}} x$$

Sign of y in $-$ $+$ $-$ $+$
each interval:
           (below)   (above)   (below)   (above)

Symmetry: None

Asymptotes:
   Vertical: $x = 2$
   Horizontal: None
   Slant: $y = x + 2$ (Degree of numerator is one greater than degree of denominator. Divide the numerator by the denominator as shown on page 136.)

Restricted domain: None except $x \neq 2$.
(See Fig. 3.8.)

EXAMPLE 7

Graph $y = \sqrt{\dfrac{x + 4}{1 - x}}$.

Intercepts: If $y = 0$, then $x = -4$.
  If $x = 0$, then $y = 2$.

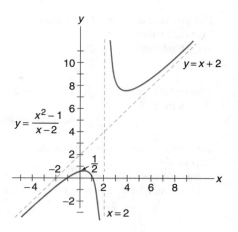

Figure 3.8

Plot points of division on the *x*-axis:

| Signs of factors | $(x + 4)$ | − | + | + |
| in each interval: | $(1 - x)$ | + | + | − |

Sign under radical
in each interval:

| | − | + | − |

$$-4 \qquad 1 \qquad\qquad x$$

Note: This function has a *restricted domain* of $-4 \le x < 1$ and the graph is never below the *x*-axis.

Symmetry: None
Asymptotes:
  Vertical: $x = 1$
(See Fig. 3.9.)

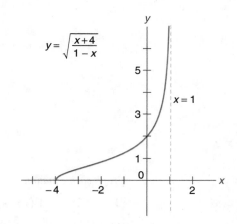

Figure 3.9

EXAMPLE 8

Graph $y^2 = \dfrac{x^2}{x^2 - 4}$.

Solve for *y* and factor: $y = \pm \sqrt{\dfrac{x^2}{(x + 2)(x - 2)}}$

Intercepts: If $y = 0$, then $x = 0$.
    If $x = 0$, then $y = 0$.

Plot points of division on the x-axis:

Signs of factors x^2 $\quad\quad$ + $\quad\quad$ + $\quad\quad$ + $\quad\quad$ +
in each interval: $(x + 2)$ $\quad\quad$ − $\quad\quad$ + $\quad\quad$ + $\quad\quad$ +
$\quad\quad\quad\quad\quad\quad\quad$ $(x - 2)$ $\quad\quad$ − $\quad\quad$ − $\quad\quad$ − $\quad\quad$ +

Sign under radical
in each interval: $\quad\quad$ + $\quad\quad\quad$ − $\quad\quad\quad$ − $\quad\quad\quad$ +

Note: This equation has a *restricted domain* of $x < -2$, $x > 2, x = 0$.

Symmetry: y-axis, x-axis, and origin.

Asymptotes:

$\quad$ Vertical: $\quad x = 2, x = -2$.

$\quad$ Horizontal: $\quad y = 1, y = -1$ $\quad\quad$ (Divide numerator and denominator of the given

$$\text{equation by } x^2 \colon y^2 = \frac{1}{1 - \dfrac{4}{x^2}}. \text{ Do you see that}$$

$$y^2 \to 1 \text{ as } x \to \infty?)$$

(See Fig. 3.10.)

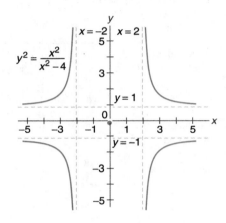

Figure 3.10

Exercises 3.1

Graph each equation.

1. $y = 2x(x + 1)(x - 4)$
2. $y = (x + 2)(x - 3)(x + 4)$
3. $y = (x - 1)(x - 3)(x + 5)$
4. $y = (3 - x)(x^2 - 4)$
5. $y = x^3 + 2x^2 - 15x$
6. $y = x^3 - 10x^2 + 24x$
7. $y = x^2(x + 1)(3 - 2x)$
8. $y = x(x + 4)(x - 1)^2$
9. $y = x^4 - 13x^2 + 36$
10. $y = (x + 1)^3(x - 7)^2(x + 2)$
11. $y = x^2(x - 2)^2(x + 4)^2$
12. $y = (x - 3)(2x + 1)(x - 2)^2$
13. $y = \dfrac{3}{2x + 1}$
14. $y = \dfrac{2}{(x - 4)^2}$
15. $y = \dfrac{2x}{(x + 1)(x - 3)}$
16. $y = \dfrac{2x - 1}{(x - 2)(x - 4)}$
17. $y = \dfrac{3}{x^2 + 4}$
18. $y = \dfrac{4x}{x^2 - 9}$
19. $y = \dfrac{4x}{x - 2}$
20. $y = \dfrac{3x}{1 - 2x}$
21. $y = \dfrac{3x^2}{x^2 - 4}$

22. $y = \dfrac{x - 5}{x + 2}$

23. $y = \dfrac{x^2 - 6}{x + 2}$

24. $y = \dfrac{2x^2 - 11x + 12}{x - 1}$

25. $y = \dfrac{2x^2 - x - 3}{x - 4}$

26. $y = \dfrac{x^2 - x}{x + 3}$

27. $y = \sqrt{x + 4}$

28. $y = \sqrt{1 - 2x}$

29. $y = \sqrt{\dfrac{x}{x - 3}}$

30. $y = -\sqrt{\dfrac{9}{x + 4}}$

31. $y^2 = x + 9$

32. $y^2 = (x + 1)(x - 3)$

33. $y^2 = \dfrac{x}{x + 4}$

34. $y^2 = \dfrac{x}{(x + 1)(x - 3)}$

35. $y^2 = \dfrac{x^2}{x^2 + 4}$

36. $y^2 = \dfrac{x^2}{(1 - x)(x + 2)}$

3.2   USING DERIVATIVES IN CURVE SKETCHING

The concept of a derivative is very useful in curve sketching. We can obtain information about the curve $y = f(x)$ that would be unavailable without the use of differentiation. From the derivative of a function $y = f(x)$, we can determine where a function is increasing and where it is decreasing.

INCREASING AND DECREASING FUNCTIONS

A function $y = f(x)$ is *increasing* on an interval if $f(x_2) > f(x_1)$ for any two points $x_2 > x_1$ in the interval.
A function $y = f(x)$ is *decreasing* on an interval if $f(x_2) < f(x_1)$ for any two points $x_2 > x_1$ in the interval.

In Fig. 3.11 the function is increasing for $x < a$ and for $x > b$. The function is decreasing for $a < x < b$.

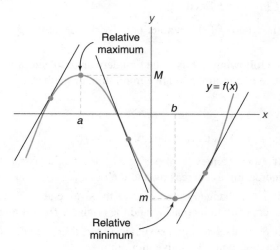

Figure 3.11

Observe that $f'(x)$, the slope of the tangent line at x, is positive when $f(x)$ is increasing and negative when $f(x)$ is decreasing. That is,

$f(x)$ is increasing when $f'(x) > 0$ and $f(x)$ is decreasing when $f'(x) < 0$

Observe also in Fig. 3.11 that at $x = a$ the function changes from increasing to decreasing. At such a point the value of the function $f(a) = M$ is called a *relative maximum* (or *local maximum*). At $x = b$ the function changes from decreasing to increasing. The value of the function $f(b) = m$ is called a *relative minimum* (or *local minimum*).

In Fig. 3.11 note that at both $x = a$ and $x = b$ the derivative of $y = f(x)$ is zero. That is, $f'(a) = 0$ and $f'(b) = 0$. Note that if the function $y = f(x)$ is to change smoothly from increasing to decreasing or from decreasing to increasing, then the derivative $f'(x)$ must be zero at that point.

A relative maximum or relative minimum can also occur at a point x where the curve has undefined slope (the derivative does not exist). In Fig. 3.12, $y = f(x)$ has a relative maximum at $x = a$, but there is no derivative.

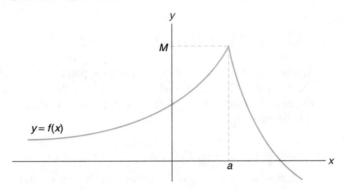

Figure 3.12   A critical point at $x = a$.

CRITICAL POINTS

Critical points are points of continuity $(x, f(x))$ on $y = f(x)$ where

(a) $f'(x) = 0$ or
(b) $f'(x)$ is undefined.

That is, where $f'(x)$ is neither positive nor negative.

The following test uses the first derivative to determine whether a given critical point is a relative maximum, a relative minimum, or neither.

FIRST DERIVATIVE TEST

Given $(c, f(c))$ is a critical point on $y = f(x)$.

(a) If $f'(x)$ changes from positive to negative at $x = c$, then $f(x)$ is changing from increasing to decreasing and the point $(c, f(c))$ is a relative maximum.
(b) If $f'(x)$ changes from negative to positive at $x = c$, then $f(x)$ is changing from decreasing to increasing and the point $(c, f(c))$ is a relative minimum.
(c) If $f'(x)$ does not change sign at $x = c$, then the point $(c, f(c))$ is neither a relative maximum nor a relative minimum.

EXAMPLE 1

Find any relative maximum or minimum values of the function $f(x) = x^3 - 3x$ and sketch the curve.

$$f'(x) = 3x^2 - 3 = 3(x^2 - 1)$$

so

$$f'(x) = 0 \quad \text{when} \quad 3(x^2 - 1) = 0$$
$$3(x + 1)(x - 1) = 0$$
$$x = -1 \quad \text{or} \quad x = 1$$

So $x = -1$ and $x = 1$ are critical points. Check to see if the function has relative maximums or minimums at these points. Observe that

if $x < -1$	$f'(x) = 3(x + 1)(x - 1) > 0$
if $-1 < x < 1$	$f'(x) = 3(x + 1)(x - 1) < 0$
if $x > 1$	$f'(x) = 3(x + 1)(x - 1) > 0$

Note: The following diagram can help determine the sign of the derivative. In this example, the expression for the derivative involves two factors. Determine the sign of each factor for each interval determined by the critical points. Applying the rule of signs for multiplication, determine the sign of the derivative:

Sign of factor $3(x + 1)$ $-$ $+$ $+$
in each interval: $(x - 1)$ $-$ $-$ $+$

Sign of $f'(x)$: $+$ -1 $-$ 1 $+$
Function is: (increasing)   (decreasing)   (increasing)

Thus the function $f(x) = x^3 - 3x$ is

increasing for $x < -1$

decreasing for $-1 < x < 1$

increasing for $x > 1$

We conclude that $f(-1) = (-1)^3 - 3(-1) = 2$ or $(-1, 2)$ is a relative maximum and $f(1) = (1)^3 - 3(1) = -2$ or $(1, -2)$ is a relative minimum (see Fig. 3.13).

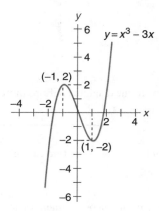

Figure 3.13

Note: When the *original equation factors easily,* we may use the discussion in Section 3.1 to determine where the curve is above and below the *x*-axis:

$$f(x) = x^3 - 3x = x(x^2 - 3) = x(x + \sqrt{3})(x - \sqrt{3})$$

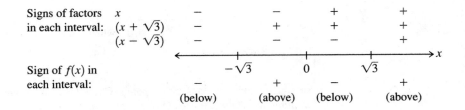

Signs of factors in each interval:					
x	$-$	$-$	$+$	$+$	
$(x + \sqrt{3})$	$-$	$+$	$+$	$+$	
$(x - \sqrt{3})$	$-$	$-$	$-$	$+$	

Sign of $f(x)$ in each interval:

$-$ (below) $+$ (above) $-$ (below) $+$ (above)

critical points at $-\sqrt{3}$, 0, $\sqrt{3}$ along the x-axis

EXAMPLE 2

Find any relative maximum or minimum values of $f(x) = x^3$ and sketch the curve.

$$f'(x) = 3x^2$$

so

$$f'(x) = 0 \quad \text{when} \quad 3x^2 = 0$$
$$x = 0$$

We find that $x = 0$ is the only critical point. But since $f'(x) = 3x^2$ is never negative, the function $f(x) = x^3$ is always increasing. Thus, there is no relative maximum or minimum. Observe, however, in Fig. 3.14 that although the curve is always increasing, there is a difference in the shape of the curve for $x < 0$ and for $x > 0$.

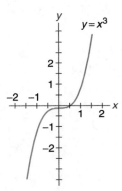

Figure 3.14

The number line diagram confirms this discussion.

Sign of $f'(x)$: $3x^2$ $+$ $+$

Function is: (increasing)   (increasing)

with 0 marked on the x-axis

EXAMPLE 3

Find any relative maximum or minimum values of the function $f(x) = x^4 + \frac{8}{3}x^3$ and sketch the curve.

$$f'(x) = 4x^3 + 8x^2 = 4x^2(x + 2) = 0$$

when

$$x = 0 \quad \text{or} \quad x = -2$$

Using the number line diagram, we have:

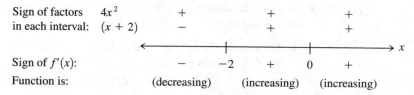

We conclude that $f(-2) = (-2)^4 + \frac{8}{3}(-2)^3 = 16 - \frac{64}{3} = -\frac{16}{3}$ or $(-2, -\frac{16}{3})$ is a relative minimum, and that $x = 0$ or $(0, 0)$ is neither a relative maximum nor a relative minimum (see Fig. 3.15).

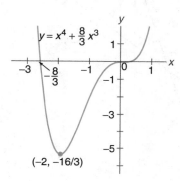

Figure 3.15

Exercises 3.2

Find any relative maximum or minimum values of each function and sketch the curve.

1. $f(x) = x^2 + 6x - 16$

2. $f(x) = 3x^2 + 12x + 9$

3. $f(x) = 4 - 4x - 3x^2$

4. $f(x) = 24 + 4x - 4x^2$

5. $f(x) = x^3 + 3x^2 + 4$

6. $f(x) = x^3 - 3x - 6$

7. $f(x) = \frac{1}{3}x^3 - 9x - 4$

8. $f(x) = \frac{5}{3}x^3 + 10x^2 + 8$

9. $f(x) = 3x^5 - 5x^3$

10. $f(x) = x^4 - 4x^2 + 3$

11. $f(x) = (x - 2)^5$

12. $f(x) = (x + 1)^4$

13. $f(x) = (x^2 - 1)^4$

14. $f(x) = (x^2 - 4)^3$

15. $f(x) = \dfrac{x^2}{x - 4}$

16. $f(x) = \dfrac{x^2}{x + 9}$

17. $f(x) = \dfrac{x}{x + 1}$

18. $f(x) = \dfrac{x}{x - 3}$

19. $f(x) = x + (1/x)$

20. $f(x) = 4x + (16/x)$

21. $f(x) = \sqrt{x}$

22. $f(x) = \sqrt[3]{x}$

23. $f(x) = x^{2/3}$

24. $f(x) = x^{-1/3}$

3.3 MORE ON CURVE SKETCHING

The derivative of a function $f(x)$ tells us where that function increases and where it decreases. So, $f''(x)$, the derivative of $f'(x)$, will tell us where $f'(x)$ increases or decreases [just as $f'(x)$ has told us where $f(x)$ increases or decreases].

As with any derivative, those values of x where $f''(x) = 0$ are possible points where the function $f'(x)$ can change from increasing to decreasing or from decreasing to increasing.

For example, if $y = x^3$, $f''(x) = 6x$.

1. For $x < 0$, $f''(x) = 6x < 0$. (This corresponds to the observation in Fig. 3.16 that the derivative is decreasing for $x < 0$.)

2. For $x > 0$, $f''(x) = 6x > 0$. (This tells us that the derivative is increasing as shown in Fig. 3.17.)

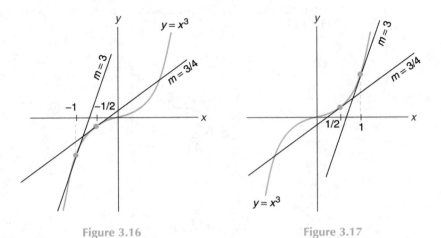

Figure 3.16   Figure 3.17

The curve $y = f(x)$ is *concave upward* (opens up) where the derivative $f'(x)$ is increasing, that is, where $f''(x) > 0$. The curve is *concave downward* (opens down) where the derivative $f'(x)$ is decreasing, that is, where $f''(x) < 0$. Any point $(x, f(x))$ where the curve changes from concave upward to concave downward or from concave downward to concave upward is called a *point of inflection*.

So $y = x^3$ is concave downward for $x < 0$ and concave upward for $x > 0$ and $(0, 0)$ is a point of inflection.

The curve in Fig. 3.18 is concave upward (opens up) for $a < x < b$. This curve is concave downward (opens down) for $b < x < c$.

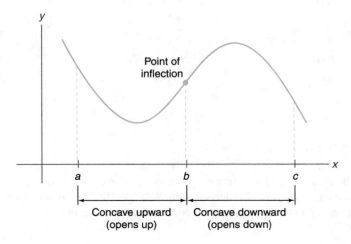

Figure 3.18

EXAMPLE 1

Find the concavity of the function $y = x^3 - 3x$.

$$f'(x) = 3x^2 - 3 \quad \text{so} \quad f''(x) = 6x$$

As in $y = x^3$, the function is concave downward for $x < 0$, concave upward for $x > 0$, and $(0, 0)$ is a point of inflection. The sketch of the curve appears in Fig. 3.13 in Section 3.2.

The following method is used to aid us in sketching a curve $y = f(x)$:

CURVE SKETCHING

1. Find any x- and y-intercepts. The curve crosses or touches the x-axis at an x-intercept. That is, an x-intercept is a point where $y = 0$. The curve crosses or touches the y-axis at a y-intercept. That is, a y-intercept is a point where $x = 0$. If the original equation factors easily, you may use the discussion in Section 3.1 to determine where the curve is above and below the x-axis.

2. Find all critical points for $y = f(x)$. That is, find all values of x where $f'(x) = 0$ or where $f'(x)$ is undefined.

3. Knowing the critical points, determine where the function is increasing and where it is decreasing.

$$y = f(x) \quad \text{is increasing where} \quad f'(x) > 0$$
$$y = f(x) \quad \text{is decreasing where} \quad f'(x) < 0$$

4. Find the relative maximum and minimum values. That is, find all values of x where $f'(x) = 0$ or is undefined. Check these critical points for possible relative maximums and relative minimums using the information obtained in Step 3.

5. Find the x-coordinate of each possible point of inflection. That is, find all values of x where $f''(x) = 0$ or is undefined.

6. From the possible points of inflection, determine the concavity of $y = f(x)$.

$$y = f(x) \quad \text{is concave upward where} \quad f''(x) > 0$$
$$y = f(x) \quad \text{is concave downward where} \quad f''(x) < 0$$

7. Find which points from Step 5 are points of inflection using the information obtained in Step 6. Note that it is possible for the second derivative to be zero at $x = a$ and $f''(a) = 0$, while $f(x)$ does not have a point of inflection at $x = a$. That is, the curve does not necessarily change concavity where $f''(x) = 0$. This must be checked in Step 6.

8. Sketch the curve.

EXAMPLE 2

Find the maximum and minimum values of the function $y = 3x^2 - 2x^3$. Determine the concavity and sketch the curve.

Step 1: Setting $y = 0$, we have

$$3x^2 - 2x^3 = 0$$
$$x^2(3 - 2x) = 0$$

so that $x = 0$ and $x = \frac{3}{2}$ are x-intercepts.
Setting $x = 0$, we have $y = 0$ as the only y-intercept.

To find where the curve is above and below the x-axis:

Signs of factors x^2 $\quad + \quad\quad + \quad\quad +$
in each interval: $(3 - 2x)$ $\quad + \quad\quad + \quad\quad -$

$$\longleftarrow \quad\quad\quad \overset{\displaystyle |}{0} \quad\quad \overset{\displaystyle |}{\tfrac{3}{2}} \quad\quad \longrightarrow \; x$$

Sign of y in
each interval: $\quad\quad\quad\quad + \quad\quad + \quad\quad -$
Function is: $\quad\quad\quad\quad$ (above) (above) (below)

Step 2: Setting $f'(x) = 0$, we have

$$f'(x) = 6x - 6x^2 = 0$$
$$6x(1 - x) = 0$$

so that $x = 0$ and $x = 1$ are the critical points.

Step 3: $f'(x) = 6x(1 - x)$

To find where the curve is increasing and decreasing:

Signs of factors $6x$ $\quad\quad - \quad\quad\quad + \quad\quad\quad +$
in each interval: $(1 - x)$ $\quad\quad + \quad\quad\quad + \quad\quad\quad -$

$$\longleftarrow \quad\quad \overset{\displaystyle |}{0} \quad\quad\quad \overset{\displaystyle |}{1} \quad\quad \longrightarrow \; x$$

Sign of $f'(x)$: $\quad\quad\quad\quad - \quad\quad\quad + \quad\quad\quad -$
Function is: $\quad\quad$ (decreasing) (increasing) (decreasing)

So, $y = f(x)$ is increasing for $0 < x < 1$ and decreasing for $x < 0$ and for $x > 1$.

Step 4: Since $y = f(x)$ changes from decreasing to increasing at $x = 0, f(0) = 0$ is a relative minimum. Since $y = f(x)$ changes from increasing to decreasing at $x = 1, f(1) = 1$ is a relative maximum.

Step 5: Setting $f''(x) = 0$, we have

$$f''(x) = 6 - 12x = 0$$

so that $x = \frac{1}{2}$ will give us a possible point of inflection.

Step 6: $f''(x) = 6 - 12x$

To find where the curve is concave upward and concave downward:

Sign of $f''(x)$
in each interval: $(6 - 12x)$ $\quad\quad\quad + \quad\quad\quad\quad\quad -$

$$\longleftarrow \quad\quad\quad\quad \overset{\displaystyle |}{} \quad\quad\quad\quad \longrightarrow x$$

Function is: $\quad\quad\quad \left(\begin{matrix} \text{concave} \\ \text{up} \end{matrix} \right) \quad \tfrac{1}{2} \quad \left(\begin{matrix} \text{concave} \\ \text{down} \end{matrix} \right)$

So, $y = f(x)$ is concave upward for $x < \frac{1}{2}$ and concave downward for $x > \frac{1}{2}$.

Step 7: Since $y = f(x)$ changes concavity at $x = \frac{1}{2}$, and $f(\frac{1}{2}) = 3(\frac{1}{2})^2 - 2(\frac{1}{2})^3 = \frac{1}{2}, (\frac{1}{2}, \frac{1}{2})$ is a point of inflection.

Step 8: The curve is sketched in Fig. 3.19.

From Fig. 3.19 note that the curve is concave downward at a relative maximum and concave upward at a relative minimum. We can use this information to distinguish relative minimums from relative maximums in place of the first derivative test. This procedure uses the second derivative to test critical points and is known as the *second derivative test*:

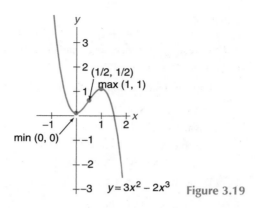

$y = 3x^2 - 2x^3$ **Figure 3.19**

In Example 2, we saw that $f''(x) = 6 - 12x$. At $x = 0$, $f''(0) = 6 > 0$, so $0 = f(0)$ is a relative minimum (as already determined by first derivative test). At $x = 1$, $f''(1) = -6$, so that $1 = f(1)$ is a relative maximum.

EXAMPLE 3

Find any relative maximum and minimum values for $y = x^4 - 2x^2$.

$$f'(x) = 4x^3 - 4x = 4x(x + 1)(x - 1)$$

Setting $f'(x) = 0$, we have $4x(x + 1)(x - 1) = 0$, so that $x = 0, x = -1$, and $x = 1$ are critical points.

$$f''(x) = 12x^2 - 4$$

Since $f''(0) = -4 < 0, f(0) = 0$ is a relative maximum.

Since $f''(-1) = 8 > 0, f(-1) = -1$ is a relative minimum.

Since $f''(1) = 8 > 0, f(1) = -1$ is a relative minimum.

(See Fig. 3.20.)

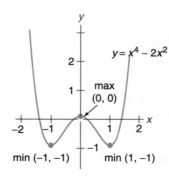

Figure 3.20

EXAMPLE 4

Find any relative maximum and minimum values for $y = \dfrac{2x + 1}{x - 3}$. Determine the concavity and sketch the curve.

Using techniques from Section 3.1:

Symmetry: None

Asymptotes:

  Vertical: $x = 3$

  Horizontal: $y = 2$ (Degree of numerator equals degree of denominator.)

Using the curve sketching outline in this section:

Step 1: Setting $y = 0$, we have

$$\frac{2x + 1}{x - 3} = 0$$

so that $x = -\frac{1}{2}$ is the x-intercept.

Setting $x = 0$, we have $y = -\frac{1}{3}$ as the y-intercept.
To find where the curve is above and below the x-axis:

Signs of factors	$(2x + 1)$	$-$	$+$	$+$
in each interval:	$(x - 3)$	$-$	$-$	$+$

Sign of y in			
each interval:	$+$	$-$	$+$
Function is:	(above)	(below)	(above)

Step 2: $f'(x) = \dfrac{(x - 3)(2) - (2x + 1)(1)}{(x - 3)^2} = \dfrac{2x - 6 - 2x - 1}{(x - 3)^2} = \dfrac{-7}{(x - 3)^2}$

Note that $f'(x)$ cannot equal 0 and that $x = 3$ makes $f'(x)$ undefined because $f(3)$ is undefined. Thus, there are no critical points.

Step 3: To find where the curve is increasing or decreasing:

Sign of $f'(x)$ in
each interval: $-$ $-$

Function is: (decreasing)   (decreasing)

So $y = f(x)$ is decreasing on the intervals $x < 3$ and $x > 3$.

Step 4: There is no relative maximum or minimum.

Step 5: $f''(x) = \dfrac{(x - 3)^2(0) - (-7)(2)(x - 3)(1)}{(x - 3)^4} = \dfrac{14(x - 3)}{(x - 3)^4} = \dfrac{14}{(x - 3)^3}$

Since the second derivative cannot equal 0, there are no points of inflection.

Step 6: Since the second derivative is undefined at $x = 3$, we need to check the concavity of $f(x)$ as follows:

Sign of $f''(x)$ in
each interval: $-$ $+$

Function is: (concave down)   (concave up)

The curve is sketched in Fig. 3.21.

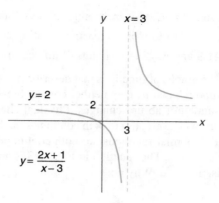

Figure 3.21

Figure 3.22 compares the curve $y = f(x)$ with its first derivative $y' = f'(x)$ and its second derivative $y'' = f''(x)$.

From A to B, $y = f(x)$ is decreasing and $y' = f'(x) < 0$.

From B to D, y is increasing and $y' > 0$.

From D to E, y is decreasing and $y' < 0$.

At B, $y' = 0$ and $y'' > 0$ (relative minimum).

At D, $y' = 0$ and $y'' < 0$ (relative maximum).

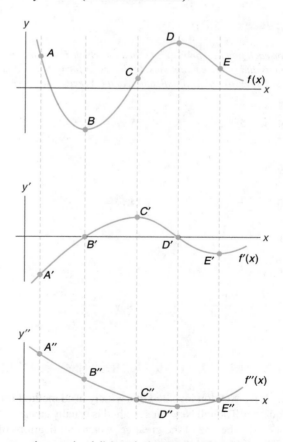

Figure 3.22   Compare the graph of $f(x)$ with the graphs of its first and second derivatives.

From A to C, y' is increasing, $y'' > 0$, and y is concave upward.

From C to E, y' is decreasing, $y'' < 0$, and y is concave downward.

At C and E, $y'' = 0$ (points of inflection).

The graphs of functions that describe most physical relationships are both continuous and "smooth"; that is, they neither contain breaks (missing points or displaced points) nor make sudden or abrupt changes. Physical changes are most often smooth and gradual. Functions whose graphs are both continuous and smooth are differentiable at each and every point. Polynomial functions are both continuous and smooth, and the derivative exists at every value of x. The function in Fig. 3.23 is not smooth at $x = a$, and the derivative does not exist at $x = a$. Why not?

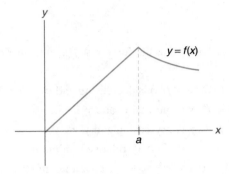

Figure 3.23

Exercises 3.3

For each function find (a) intervals for which $f(x)$ is increasing and decreasing, (b) relative maximums and relative minimums, (c) intervals for which $f(x)$ is concave upward and concave downward, and (d) points of inflection, and (e) sketch the curve.

1. $y = x^2 - 4x$ 2. $y = x^2 - x - 2$ 3. $y = x^4$

4. $y = 5 - x^2$ 5. $y = 3x - x^3$ 6. $y = 3x^4 - 4x^3$

7. $y = -x^2 + 4x - 1$ 8. $y = x^4 - 18x^2 + 40$ 9. $y = x^4 - 8x^2 + 5$

10. $y = x^7$ 11. $y = \dfrac{1}{x^2}$ 12. $y = \dfrac{1}{x^3}$

13. $y = \dfrac{x}{x + 2}$ 14. $y = \dfrac{x}{x - 1}$ 15. $y = \dfrac{-1}{(x + 1)^3}$

16. $y = \dfrac{1}{(x - 2)^2}$ 17. $y = \dfrac{x}{x^2 + 1}$ 18. $y = \dfrac{x^2 + 1}{x}$

19. $y = \dfrac{x - 2}{x + 3}$ 20. $y = \dfrac{x + 3}{x - 2}$ 21. $y = \dfrac{4}{x^2 + 4}$

22. $y = \dfrac{4}{x^2 - 4}$ 23. $y = \dfrac{x - 1}{x^2}$ 24. $y = \dfrac{x + 4}{x^2}$

3.4 NEWTON'S METHOD FOR IMPROVING ESTIMATED SOLUTIONS

Sir Isaac Newton invented this widely used method for improving estimated solutions to an equation. Though Newton's method is usually categorized as a *numerical* procedure, it is considered to be one of the great *geometric* applications of calculus. Newton's insight was that *x*-intercepts of tangent lines can be used to successively approximate an *x*-intercept of the original curve. The method starts with an equation in a form where one side is zero, so that solutions of the equation correspond to the *x*-intercepts of the graph of the function on the other side. Recall that the tangent line is an excellent local approximation of a curve near the point of tangency. It follows that the *x*-intercept of the tangent line might give an excellent approximation of the *x*-intercept of the original curve! Our knowledge that the tangent line does its best approximation of the original curve *near* the point of tangency suggests that the method will work best if we use a point of tangency that is already *near* the curve's *x*-intercept. Thus, it will be important to find reasonably good initial estimates, using a graph or a table of values. Wild guesses are *not* encouraged.

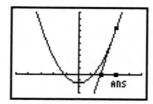

Let *Ans* represent an estimated solution of the equation $f(x) = 0$. Newton's method constructs the point $(Ans, f(Ans))$ and uses the *x*-intercept of its tangent line as the next estimate. Using the point-slope equation of the tangent line at $(Ans, f(Ans))$, we write

$$y - y_1 = m(x - x_1)$$
$$y - f(Ans) = f'(Ans)(x - Ans)$$ [Note that $f'(Ans)$ is the *slope* of the tangent line.]
$$0 - f(Ans) = f'(Ans)(x - Ans)$$ (Set $y = 0$ to find the *x*-intercept.)
$$-\frac{f(Ans)}{f'(Ans)} = x - Ans$$
$$Ans - \frac{f(Ans)}{f'(Ans)} = x$$

Thus each successive iteration of Newton's method will correct the present estimate of the *x*-intercept by subtracting a fraction composed of its function value divided by its derivative value, that is, the height divided by the slope. As the function value (the numerator of the fraction) gets close to zero, this correction term will generally become very small, causing the estimates to rapidly converge to a solution of the equation. In the cases that are best suited to Newton's method, this correction term can literally double the number of accurate digits with each successive use!

EXAMPLE 1

Use the initial estimate $x = 2$ to find a solution of the equation $x^2 - 6 = 0$, accurate to 10 significant digits. Note that this problem is equivalent to estimating $\sqrt{6}$.

Since our equation must be of the form $f(x) = 0$, it follows that

$$f(x) = x^2 - 6$$
$$f'(x) = 2x$$

The iteration formula is

$$Ans - \frac{f(Ans)}{f'(Ans)} = Ans - \frac{Ans^2 - 6}{2Ans}$$

Starting with $Ans = 2$, our next estimates will be

$$2 - \frac{2^2 - 6}{2(2)} = 2.5$$

$$2.5 - \frac{2.5^2 - 6}{2(2.5)} = 2.45$$

$$2.45 - \frac{2.45^2 - 6}{2(2.45)} = 2.449489796$$

$$2.449489796 - \frac{2.449489796^2 - 6}{2(2.449489796)} = 2.449489743$$

$$2.449489743 - \frac{2.449489743^2 - 6}{2(2.449489743)} = 2.449489743$$

Since the final estimate, 2.449489743, was unchanged by the formula, we conclude that all 10 digits are accurate, so $x = 2.449489743$ is an approximate solution of the equation $x^2 - 6 = 0$. Equivalently, we have found that $\sqrt{6} \cong 2.449489743$. Note that by starting with an estimate like $Ans = -2$, we could approximate this equation's other solution, $x = -\sqrt{6}$, in a similar way.

Using a graphing calculator to perform Newton's method involves using the calculator's simple but powerful **Ans** feature, which is just a location in the calculator's memory containing the most recent answer displayed on the calculator's screen. The value of **Ans** is updated automatically every time that **ENTER** is pressed. To use **Ans** in a formula, you must press **2nd ANS** (press **2nd** followed by the sign change key). To begin Newton's method, place the initial estimate in **Ans** by pressing **2** then **ENTER**, then type the iteration formula in terms of **Ans** and press **ENTER** *repeatedly*. Note that the TI-89 and TI-83 Plus display the results in a different format, but use keystrokes that are essentially the same. Note also that the TI-89 prints **ans(1)** on the command line when you press **2nd ANS**, while the TI-83 Plus displays **Ans** for those same keystrokes.

2 **ENTER 2nd ANS -(2nd ANS** ^2-6)/(2 **2nd ANS**) **green diamond ENTER ENTER ENTER ENTER ENTER**

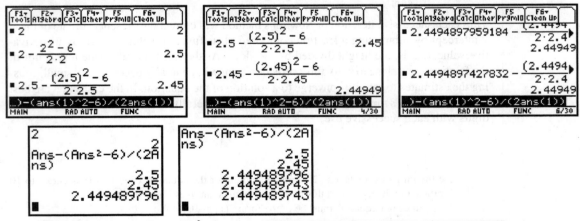

2 **ENTER 2nd ANS -(2nd ANS x²** -6)/(2 **2nd ANS**) **ENTER ENTER ENTER ENTER ENTER**

The approximate solution from the TI-83 Plus is $x = 2.449489743$. All of the digits shown in the TI-89 result, $x = 2.4494897427832$, are also accurate!

EXAMPLE 2

Find the real solution of the equation $x^3 - 4x + 5 = 0$.

To find a good initial estimate, graph $f(x) = x^3 - 4x + 5$ and visually approximate its x-intercept.

green diamond Y =   **F2   6**

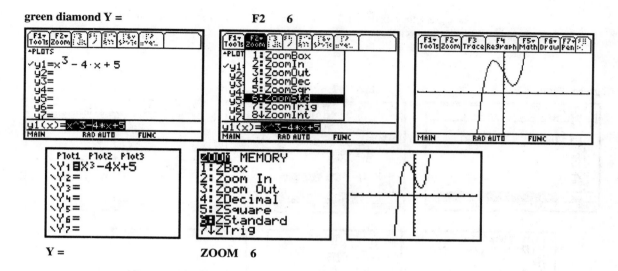

Y =   **ZOOM   6**

It looks like the x-intercept is close to $x = -2.5$, so use that as the initial estimate of the solution.

$$f(x) = x^3 - 4x + 5$$
$$f'(x) = 3x^2 - 4$$
$$Ans - \frac{f(Ans)}{f'(Ans)} = Ans - \frac{Ans^3 - 4\,Ans + 5}{3\,Ans^2 - 4}$$

-2.5 ENTER 2nd ANS -(2nd ANS ^3-4 2nd ANS +5)/(3 2nd ANS ^2-4) ENTER ENTER ENTER ENTER

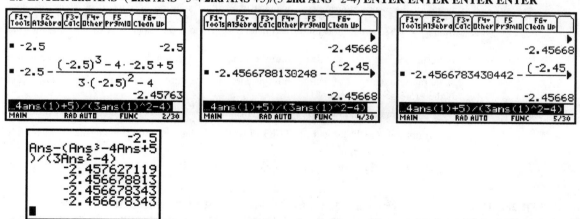

-2.5 ENTER 2nd ANS -(2nd ANS MATH 3 -4 2nd ANS +5)/(3 2nd ANS x² -4) ENTER ENTER ENTER ENTER

The approximate solution is $x = -2.456678343$.

The previous two examples illustrate how specific iteration formulas can be coded for each individual use of Newton's method. The next example shows that your calculator is also capable of using a generalized form of the iteration formula.

EXAMPLE 3

Use Newton's method to approximate the solutions of the trigonometric equation $\sin^2 x = 2 \cos x$ for $0 \le x < 2\pi$.

First, set one side of the equation equal to zero:

$$\sin^2 x - 2 \cos x = 0$$

Then, graph the function $f(x) = \sin^2 x - 2 \cos x$ to find good initial estimates of its x-intercepts that lie between 0 and 2π.

green diamond Y=   **F2   7**

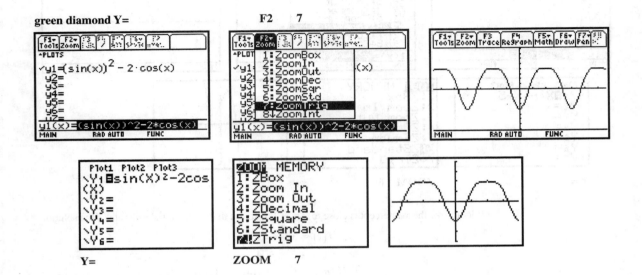

Y=   **ZOOM   7**

For $0 \le x < 2\pi$, we look only at the right-hand side of the graph, recalling that each scale mark on the x-axis represents a distance of $\dfrac{\pi}{2}$. One solution appears to be somewhat less than $\dfrac{\pi}{2} \cong 1.57$, so use the initial estimate $x = 1.1$, and the other appears to be somewhat more than $\dfrac{3\pi}{2} \cong 4.71$, so use the initial estimate $x = 5.1$. On the TI-89, note that the fourth scale mark to the right of the origin represents 2π. The third x-intercept lies beyond that, and is therefore being ignored.

The generalized iteration formula, $Ans - \dfrac{f(Ans)}{f'(Ans)}$, can be coded (in slightly different ways) on both the TI-89 and the TI-83 Plus. Recall that we will be using the estimates 1.1 and 5.1.

1.1 ENTER 2nd ANS -y1(x)/ 2nd 8 y1(x),x)|x= 2nd ANS ENTER ENTER ENTER ENTER

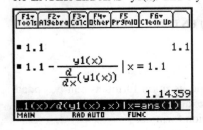  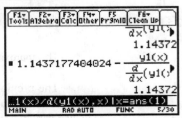

green diamond COPY F1 8 5.1 **ENTER green diamond PASTE ENTER ENTER ENTER ENTER**

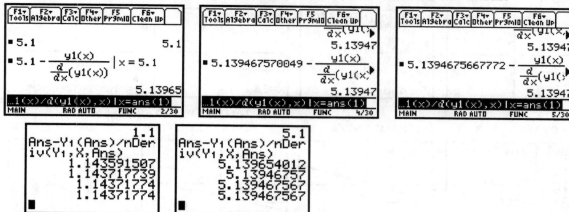

1.1 **ENTER 2nd ANS - VARS** right arrow **1 1 (2nd ANS)/MATH 8 VARS** right arrow **1 1 ,x, 2nd ANS)**
ENTER ENTER ENTER ENTER 5.1 **ENTER 2nd ENTRY 2nd ENTRY ENTER ENTER ENTER ENTER**

The approximate solutions are $x = 1.14371774$ and $x = 5.139467567$.

Remember that Newton's method doesn't "solve" equations in the algebraic sense. Instead, it focuses on numerically improving an *estimated* solution. However, it is possible for Newton's method to make an estimate worse instead of better. This often happens when the initial estimate is rough and the slopes of nearby tangent lines are close to zero. As shown in the following example, a better initial estimate can usually fix this problem. In some cases, you may even want to use your calculator's **TRACE** feature to get a *very* accurate initial estimate of the *x*-intercept.

EXAMPLE 4

In solving the equation $\arctan(x - \sqrt{2}) = 0$, show that Newton's method is unsuccessful if $x = 3$ is used as the initial estimate. Also show that the more accurate initial estimate $x = 1.5$ is highly successful.

Y =   **ZOOM**   **4**   3 **ENTER 2nd ANS - VARS** right arrow **1 1 (2nd ANS)/**
MATH 8 VARS right arrow **1 1 ,x, 2nd ANS) ENTER ENTER**

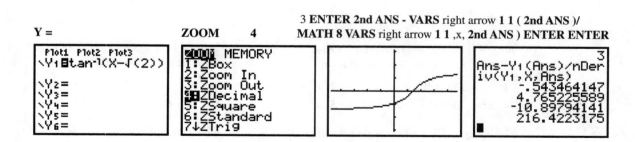

Note that when we use $x = 3$ as the initial guess, the estimates fluctuate wildly and do not converge to a solution. In fact, a division-by-zero error will be encountered if **ENTER** is pressed a few more times. To understand this problem geometrically, use the **(2nd) DRAW Tangent** feature to plot the tangent line at $x = 3$ and at the next estimate, $x = -0.543464147$:

GRAPH   **2nd DRAW**   **5**   **3 ENTER**

```
DRAW POINTS STO
1:ClrDraw
2:Line(
3:Horizontal
4:Vertical
5:Tangent(
6:DrawF
7↓Shade(
```

```
Y1=tan-1(X-f(2))



X=3
```

```
X=3
y=.2845178471X+.1546252_
```

2nd DRAW   **5**   **-.543464147 ENTER**

2nd QUIT 1.5 ENTER 2nd ENTRY
2nd ENTRY ENTER ENTER ENTER ENTER

```
DRAW POINTS STO
1:ClrDraw
2:Line(
3:Horizontal
4:Vertical
5:Tangent(
6:DrawF
7↓Shade(
```

```
Y1=tan-1(X-f(2))



X=-.543464147
```

```
X=-.543464
y=.2069321744SX+-.98607_
```

```
                    1.5
Ans-Y1(Ans)/nDer
iv(Y1,X,Ans)
         1.413793266
         1.414213563
         1.414213562
         1.414213562
```

Note that the tangent line at $x = 3$ has a slope close to zero, thus its x-intercept lies far to the left, at $x = -0.543464147$. The tangent line at $x = -0.543464147$ has an even smaller slope, so its x-intercept lies even farther to the right than our initial estimate. The estimates thus get worse and worse until the derivative (which is in the denominator of the iteration formula) is numerically so small that it causes a division-by-zero error on the calculator. The last frame shows that a more accurate initial estimate, $x = 1.5$, results in the rapid convergence that we usually associate with Newton's method.

The fact that the derivative occupies the denominator in the iteration formula $Ans - \dfrac{f(Ans)}{f'(Ans)}$ means that we may also encounter difficulties with Newton's method when we try to find a zero of the original function which is a zero of its derivative as well. Common cases of this include polynomial equations at a solution of multiplicity greater than one and trigonometric equations at a point where the graph just touches, rather than crosses, the x-axis; for example, $x = \dfrac{\pi}{2}$ as a solution of $2 \cos^2 x + \sin x - 1 = 0$. In such cases, the derivative can get very close to zero as the desired solution is approached. Just as a zero denominator would make the iteration formula undefined, a denominator very close to zero can cause difficulties with numeric accuracy.

Exercises 3.4

In each of the following exercises, an equation is given along with an initial estimate of one of its solutions. Use Newton's method to improve this estimate to at least six significant digits.

1. $x^2 - 150 = 0, x = 12$ **2.** $x^2 - 90 = 0, x = 10$ **3.** $x^3 - 5 = 0, x = 1.7$

4. $x^3 - 20 = 0, x = 2.7$ **5.** $x^3 + 5x - 7 = 0, x = 1$ **6.** $x^5 - 30 = 0, x = 2$

Use a graph to find estimates for the real solutions of each equation, then use Newton's method to improve your estimates to at least six significant digits. For the trigonometric equations, be sure that your calculator is set in radians.

7. $x^3 + x^2 - 5x + 2 = 0$ **8.** $x^3 - 5x^2 + 2x + 7 = 0$

9. $2x^3 + 1 = 5x^2 - x$ **10.** $3x^3 + 2x = 7x^2 - 1$

11. $\sin 2x - \cos x - 1 = 0, 0 \le x < 2\pi$ **12.** $\cos^2 x - 2 \sin x + 1 = 0, 0 \le x < 2\pi$

13. $\sin x = 2 \cos x, 0 \le x < 2\pi$ **14.** $\sin 2x = 3 \cos x - 1, 0 \le x < 2\pi$

15. Note that the solutions to Exercises 1 and 3 were estimates of $\sqrt{150}$ and $\sqrt[3]{5}$, respectively. Use Newton's method to estimate $\sqrt[4]{23}$ to at least six significant digits.

16. In solving the equation $0.7 - \sqrt[3]{x} = 0$, show that Newton's method does not converge to a solution if $x = 2$ is used as the initial estimate. Also show that the more accurate initial estimate $x = 0.3$ rapidly converges to the solution $x = 0.343$.

3.5 MAXIMUM AND MINIMUM PROBLEMS

Many applications involve finding the maximum or minimum values of a variable quantity under given conditions. If we can express this quantity as a function of some other variable, then we can use the techniques of the last two sections to locate the possible relative maximum or relative minimum values.

In addition to the techniques developed in those sections, we must:

1. Translate the information of a stated word problem into a mathematical function.

2. Determine that maximum (or minimum) value which is the largest (or smallest) value that the quantity can attain.

EXAMPLE 1

Find the largest possible rectangular area that can be enclosed using 120 m of fencing.

The area of a rectangle is given by $A = xy$, where x is the length of one side and y is the length of the other side (see Fig. 3.24). The perimeter P of a rectangle is given by

$$P = 2x + 2y$$

which in this case must be 120 m.

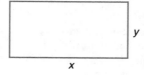

y

x **Figure 3.24**

Possible choices for x and y are $x = 10$ and $y = 50$, where $A = xy = (10)(50) = 500$ m^2 or $x = 20$ and $y = 40$ where $A = xy = (20)(40) = 800$ m^2. But what is the maximum area A? To find the maximum area we will use the techniques of the previous sections. We must express A as a function of one variable only. To do this, solve for x in $2x + 2y = P$ where $P = 120$:

$$2x + 2y = 120$$
$$2x = 120 - 2y$$
$$x = 60 - y$$

and substitute for x in the formula for area,

$$A = xy$$
$$A = (60 - y)y = 60y - y^2$$

The area is now expressed as a function of one variable y. Using the techniques of the last sections, locate the maximum value:

$$\frac{dA}{dy} = \frac{d}{dy}(60y - y^2)$$
$$= 60 - 2y$$

Setting $\dfrac{dA}{dy} = 0$, we have

$$0 = 60 - 2y$$
$$2y = 60$$
$$y = 30$$

Since $\dfrac{d^2A}{dy^2} = -2$, the curve $A = 60y - y^2$ is always concave downward.

So $y = 30$ is a relative maximum and the maximum area is obtained when $y = 30$ m. To find the maximum area, find the corresponding value of x when $y = 30$ m:

$$x = 60 - y$$
$$= 60 - (30)$$
$$= 30 \text{ m}$$

The maximum area occurs when the rectangle is a square and its value is

$$A = xy$$
$$= (30 \text{ m})(30 \text{ m})$$
$$= 900 \text{ m}^2$$

When an expression that is to be maximized or minimized is given in more than one other variable, a formula, the Pythagorean theorem, or similar triangles may be used to eliminate a variable. In Example 1 it was necessary to combine the formula for perimeter with the formula for area. Only then could the area be expressed in terms of one variable.

If there is only one critical point, the information contained in the problem will often make it clear whether the critical point corresponds to a maximum or a minimum (without using the standard tests).

EXAMPLE 2

Each side of a square piece of metal is 12 cm. A small square is to be cut from each corner and the metal folded to form a box without a top. Determine the dimensions of the box that will have the largest volume.

If a square with dimension s cm is cut out from each corner, the resulting box will have a square base with each side $12 - 2s$ cm and a height of s cm (see Fig. 3.25). The volume of the box will be

$$V = (12 - 2s)^2 s$$

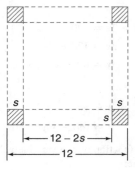
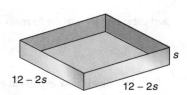

Figure 3.25

From the given conditions, the maximum value will occur when $0 \leq s \leq 6$ (since $2s \leq 12$). Differentiating, we obtain

$$\frac{dV}{ds} = (12 - 2s)^2(1) + s(2)(12 - 2s)(-2)$$

$$= (12 - 2s)[(12 - 2s) - 4s]$$

$$= (12 - 2s)(12 - 6s)$$

$$= 12(6 - s)(2 - s)$$

Alternatively, since $V = (12 - 2s)^2 s = 144s - 48s^2 + 4s^3$,

$$\frac{dV}{ds} = 144 - 96s + 12s^2$$

$$= 12(12 - 8s + s^2)$$

$$= 12(6 - s)(2 - s)$$

Setting $\frac{dV}{ds} = 12(6 - s)(2 - s) = 0$, we have $s = 6$ or $s = 2$. When $s = 6$ cm, the volume is $V = 0$ cm³ (an obvious minimum). When $s = 2$ cm, from $\frac{d^2V}{ds^2} = -96 + 24s$, we obtain

$$\left.\frac{d^2V}{ds^2}\right|_{s=2} = -96 + 24(2) = -48$$

While our intuition indicates that there must be a maximum volume, the second derivative test guarantees a relative maximum at $s = 2$. So indeed, the maximum volume must occur when $s = 2$ cm. That is,

$$V = [12 - 2(2)]^2(2)$$

$$= 128 \text{ cm}^3$$

Note that the second derivative test cannot be used in finding a maximum or a minimum if the value of the second derivative is zero or undefined at a critical point. Should this occur, the first derivative test must be used.

SOLVING MAXIMUM AND MINIMUM PROBLEMS

1. Make a sketch of the conditions given in the problem whenever possible.
2. Label appropriate quantities and assign symbols for variable quantities.
3. Determine which variable quantity is to be maximized or minimized.
4. Write an equation that expresses the quantity identified in Step 3 as a function of one variable. You may need to combine different equations to obtain the desired function of one variable. These equations are obtained either from given conditions or from your understanding of the relationship between quantities involved in the problem.
5. Differentiate the function obtained in Step 4.
6. Set the derivative from Step 5 equal to zero. Solve for the values of the variable that make the derivative zero or undefined.
7. Determine which values of the variable from Step 6 provide the desired maximum or minimum.

EXAMPLE 3

The height of a bullet fired vertically upward is given by $s = 1200t - 16t^2$ with initial velocity 1200 ft/s. Find the maximum height that the bullet will rise (neglect air resistance).

Differentiate and set $\frac{ds}{dt} = 1200 - 32t = 0$.

$$t = 37.5$$

Since $\dfrac{d^2s}{dt^2} = -32$, there is a relative maximum at $t = 37.5$ s. The maximum height is then

$$s = 1200(37.5) - 16(37.5)^2$$
$$= 45{,}000 - 22{,}500 = 22{,}500 \text{ ft}$$

EXAMPLE 4

For a cylindrical can made of 24π cm^2 of metal, find the dimensions of the can that give the maximum volume (see Fig. 3.26).

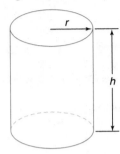

Figure 3.26

The volume of a cylinder is given by

$$V = \pi r^2 h$$

The lateral surface area of a cylinder is given by $A = 2\pi rh$. The sum of the areas of the two circular bases or ends is $2\pi r^2$. The total surface area is then

$$A = 2\pi rh + 2\pi r^2$$

To maximize the volume while the total surface area is held constant, we must express the volume as a function of only one variable. So, substitute $A = 24\pi$ into

$$A = 2\pi rh + 2\pi r^2$$
$$24\pi = 2\pi rh + 2\pi r^2$$

and solve for h. First, divide both sides of this equation by 2π:

$$12 = rh + r^2$$
$$12 - r^2 = rh$$
$$\frac{12 - r^2}{r} = h$$

Then, substitute for h into the volume formula:

$$V = \pi r^2 h$$
$$V = \pi r^2 \left(\frac{12 - r^2}{r}\right)$$
$$V = \pi r(12 - r^2)$$
$$V = \pi(12r - r^3)$$

Then, differentiate and set $\dfrac{dV}{dr} = 0$:

$$\frac{dV}{dr} = \pi(12 - 3r^2) = 0$$
$$12 - 3r^2 = 0$$
$$12 = 3r^2$$
$$4 = r^2$$
$$\pm 2 = r$$

Since $r > 0$, $r = 2$. Then, substitute into

$$h = \frac{12 - r^2}{r}$$

$$h = \frac{12 - 2^2}{2} = \frac{12 - 4}{2} = \frac{8}{2} = 4$$

Thus, $r = 2$ cm and $h = 4$ cm give the maximum volume.
Using a calculator, we have

F2 1 F3 1 $\pi(12r-r^3),r)=0,r)$ **ENTER F3 1** $\pi(12r-r^3),r,2)|r=2$ **ENTER**

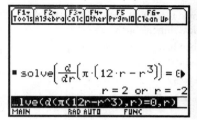   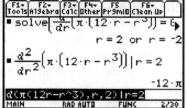

Finding the critical values   The second derivative test indicates a maximum when $r = 2$.

Exercises 3.5

1. The sum of two positive numbers is 56. Find the two numbers if their product is to be a maximum.

2. Find a positive number such that the sum of this number and its reciprocal is a minimum.

3. An open box is to be made from a square piece of aluminum, 3 cm on a side, by cutting equal squares from each corner and then folding up the sides. Determine the dimensions of the box that will have the largest volume.

4. An open rectangular box is to be made from a rectangular piece of metal 16 in. by 10 in. by cutting equal squares from each corner and then folding up the sides. Determine the maximum volume of the box.

5. A man wishes to fence in a rectangular plot lying next to a river. No fencing is required along the river bank. If he has 800 m of fence and he wishes the maximum area to be fenced, find the dimensions of the desired enclosed plot.

6. A long rectangular sheet of metal 12 in. wide is to be made into a trough by turning up two sides to form right angles. Find the dimensions of the trough that give it maximum capacity.

7. Find the maximum area of a rectangle whose perimeter is 36 cm.

8. A rancher wants to fence in two rectangular corrals, equal in area, using an inner fence as shown in Fig. 3.27. If 300 ft of fencing are used, find the maximum area of the combined corrals.

9. A farmer wants to fence in 80,000 m^2 of land and then divide it into three plots of equal area as shown in Fig. 3.28. Find the minimum amount of fence needed.

10. Four neighbors want to fence in an 8100-ft^2 garden plot into equal plots as shown in Fig. 3.29. Find the minimum amount of fence needed.

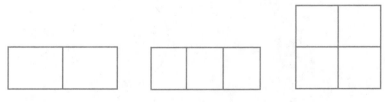

Figure 3.27   Figure 3.28   Figure 3.29

11. Find the maximum area of the rectangle with two vertices on the parabola $y = 36 - x^2$ and the remaining two vertices on the x-axis.

12. Find the dimensions of the largest rectangle that can be inscribed in a semicircle of radius 4.

13. Find the area of the largest rectangle that can be inscribed in the ellipse $x^2 + 9y^2 = 16$.

14. The charge transmitted through a circuit varies according to $q = \dfrac{4t}{t^2 + 1}$ coulombs (C). Find the maximum charge at time t in milliseconds (ms).

15. The power P in watts (W) in a circuit with resistance R in ohms (Ω) varies according to

$P = \dfrac{36R}{(R + 4)^2}$. Find the resistance that gives the maximum power.

16. A rectangular area 24,300 ft^2 is bounded on three sides by a fence that costs \$6/ft and in the front by a fence that costs \$10/ft. Find the most economical dimensions.

17. Show that the rectangle of largest area that can be inscribed in a given circle is a square.

18. Find the minimum slope of a tangent line to the curve $y = 4x^2 + 8x^3$.

19. Find the maximum slope of a tangent line to the curve $y = 3x^2 - 2x^3$.

20. The work done by a solenoid in moving an armature varies according to $w = 2t^2 - 3t^4$ joules (J).
Find the greatest power in watts (W) developed in t seconds $\left(\text{power } p = \dfrac{dw}{dt} \right)$.

21. The charge transmitted through a circuit varies according to $q = t^4 - 4t^3$ coulombs (C). Find the time t in seconds when the current i in amperes (A), $i = \dfrac{dq}{dt}$, reaches a minimum.

22. Find the greatest current in a capacitor with capacitance C equal to $\frac{4}{3} \times 10^{-6}$ farad (F) if the applied voltage is given by $V = 250t^2 - 200t^3$ volts (V) $\left(i = C \dfrac{dV}{dt} \right)$.

23. A rectangular box, open at the top, with a square base is to have a volume of 4000 cm^3. Find the dimensions if the box is to contain the least amount of material.

24. If the box in Exercise 23 has a closed top, find its dimensions.

25. The total cost C of making x units of a commodity is given by $C = 0.005x^3 + 0.45x^2 + 12.75x$. All units made are sold at \$36.75 per unit. The profit P is then given by $P = 36.75x - C$. Find the number of units to make to maximize profit.

26. Find the volume of the largest right circular cylinder that can be inscribed in a sphere of radius 3 in.

27. A cylindrical can with one end is to be made with 24π cm^2 of metal. Find the dimensions of the can that give the maximum volume.

28. The current I in a cell is given by $I = \dfrac{E}{R + r}$, where E is the electromotive force, R is the external resistance, and r is the internal resistance. In a given cell, E and r are fixed and determined by the cell. The power developed is $P = RI^2$. Show that P is a maximum when $R = r$.

29. The strength S of a rectangular beam is proportional to the product of its width w and the square of its depth d, that is, $S = kwd^2$, where k is a constant. Find the dimensions of the strongest wooden beam that can be cut from a circular log of radius r in Fig. 3.30.

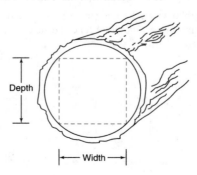

Figure 3.30

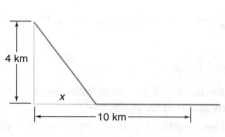

Figure 3.31   **Figure 3.32**

30. A person is in a boat 4 km off a straight coast. The person needs to reach a point 10 km down and along the coast in the least possible time. If the person can row at 6 km/h and run at 8 km/h, how far, x, down the coast should he land the boat? (See Fig. 3.31.)

31. Two ships are anchored off a straight coast as shown in Fig. 3.32. A boat from ship A is to land a passenger and then proceed to ship B in the shortest distance. Find x.

32. Show that any cylindrical can with two ends made with a given amount of material has a maximum volume when the height equals the diameter.

3.6   RELATED RATES

If an equation relates two or more variables, the rate at which one variable changes will affect the rates of change of the remaining variables. Problems involving variables whose rates of change are related by some equation are called *related-rate* problems. In such problems, one or more rates are given and another rate is to be found.

EXAMPLE 1

A hot air balloon (spherical) is being inflated at the rate of 3 m^3/s. Find the rate at which the radius is increasing when the radius is 10 m.

First determine the relationship between the volume of the balloon and its radius. The volume of a sphere is given by $V = \frac{4}{3}\pi r^3$. Differentiate each side of the equation with respect to time.

$$\frac{dV}{dt} = \frac{d}{dt}\left(\frac{4}{3}\pi r^3\right)$$

$$= \frac{4}{3}\pi \frac{d}{dt}(r^3)$$

$$= \frac{4}{3}\pi\left(3r^2\frac{dr}{dt}\right) \quad \text{(Note that } r \text{ is a function of time.)}$$

$$= 4\pi r^2 \frac{dr}{dt}$$

$\dfrac{dV}{dt}$ is given as 3 m^3/s, and we wish to find $\dfrac{dr}{dt}$ when $r = 10$ m. Substituting, we obtain

$$3 \text{ m}^3/\text{s} = 4\pi(10 \text{ m})^2 \frac{dr}{dt}$$

$$3 \text{ m}^3/\text{s} = (400\pi \text{ m}^2) \frac{dr}{dt}$$

$$\frac{3 \text{ m}^3/\text{s}}{400\pi \text{ m}^2} = \frac{dr}{dt}$$

$$\frac{dr}{dt} = \frac{3}{400\pi} \text{ m/s} \quad \text{or} \quad 0.00239 \text{ m/s} \quad \text{or} \quad 2.39 \text{ mm/s}$$

SOLVING RELATED-RATE PROBLEMS

1. Determine the equation for the variables whose rates are related. This equation may or may not be directly stated in the problem.
2. Differentiate each side of the resulting equation with respect to time (or other desired variable).
3. *After* differentiating in Step 2, substitute all given rates and given values of variables into the equation.
4. Solve for the unknown rate-of-change quantity.

EXAMPLE 2

Two airplanes pass each other in flight at 9:00 A.M. One is traveling east at 90 mi/h. The other is traveling south at 180 mi/h. How fast are they separating at 11:00 A.M.?

Step 1: Relate the distance that each plane has traveled with the distance traveled since separation at 9:00 A.M. From Fig. 3.33 note that the distances are related as the sides of a right triangle. The Pythagorean theorem provides the relationship:

$$x^2 + y^2 = z^2$$

where x is the distance traveled by A, y is the distance traveled by B, and z is the distance of separation.

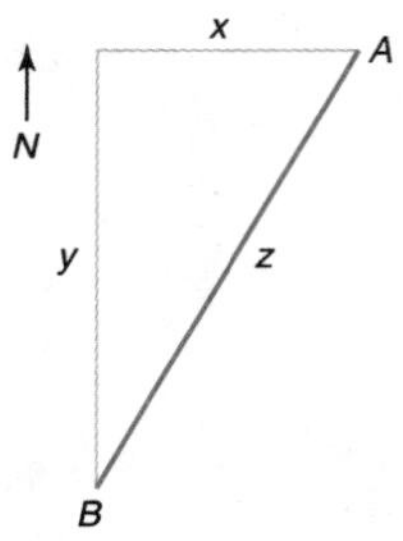

Step 2:
$$\frac{d}{dt}(x^2 + y^2) = \frac{d}{dt}(z^2)$$

$$2x\frac{dx}{dt} + 2y\frac{dy}{dt} = 2z\frac{dz}{dt}$$

$$x\frac{dx}{dt} + y\frac{dy}{dt} = z\frac{dz}{dt}$$

Step 3: We are given that $\frac{dx}{dt} = 90$ mi/h and $\frac{dy}{dt} = 180$ mi/h.

After 2 h of travel,

$$x = (90 \text{ mi/h})(2 \text{ h}) = 180 \text{ mi} \quad (d = rt)$$
$$y = (180 \text{ mi/h})(2 \text{ h}) = 360 \text{ mi}$$

So, again from the Pythagorean theorem,

$$z = \sqrt{x^2 + y^2} = \sqrt{(180 \text{ mi})^2 + (360 \text{ mi})^2} = 402 \text{ mi}$$

Step 4:
$$\frac{dz}{dt} = \frac{x\dfrac{dx}{dt} + y\dfrac{dy}{dt}}{z} \quad \text{(from step 2)}$$

$$= \frac{(180 \text{ mi})(90 \text{ mi/h}) + (360 \text{ mi})(180 \text{ mi/h})}{402 \text{ mi}}$$

$$= 201 \text{ mi/h}$$

Figure 3.33

EXAMPLE 3

The electric resistance of a resistor is given by $R = 6 + 0.002T^2$ in ohms (Ω), where T is the temperature (in °C). If the temperature is increasing at the rate of 0.2°C/s, find how fast the resistance is changing when $T = 120$°C.

Step 1: The relationship is given:

$$R = 6 + 0.002T^2$$

Step 2: $\dfrac{dR}{dt} = 2(0.002T)\dfrac{dT}{dt}$

$$= 0.004T\dfrac{dT}{dt}$$

Step 3: $\dfrac{dR}{dt} = 0.004(120)(0.2)$

Step 4: $\dfrac{dR}{dt} = 0.096 \ \Omega/\text{s}$

Exercises 3.6

1. Given $y = 3x^2$ and $\dfrac{dx}{dt} = 2$ at $x = 3$. Find $\dfrac{dy}{dt}$.

2. Given $y = 4x^3 + 2x^2$ and $\dfrac{dx}{dt} = \dfrac{1}{2}$ at $x = 1$. Find $\dfrac{dy}{dt}$.

3. Given $x^2 + y^2 = 25$ and $\dfrac{dy}{dt} = \dfrac{9}{2}$ at $y = 4 (x > 0)$. Find $\dfrac{dx}{dt}$.

4. Given $x^2 + y^2 = z^2$, $\dfrac{dx}{dt} = \dfrac{1}{2}$, and $\dfrac{dy}{dt} = 4$ at $x = 6$ and $y = 8 \ (z > 0)$. Find $\dfrac{dz}{dt}$.

5. The electric resistance of a resistor is given by $R = 3 + 0.001T^2$ in ohms (Ω), where T is the temperature in °C. If the temperature is increasing at the rate of 0.3°C/s, find how fast the resistance is changing when $T = 100$°C.

6. A man begins walking due north at 3 mi/h. From the same place at the same time a woman begins walking east at 4 mi/h. Find the rate of change of the distance between them after 1 h of walking.

7. A square plate is being heated so that the length of a side increases at a rate of 0.08 cm/min. How fast is the area increasing when the length of a side is 12 cm?

8. A circular plate is being heated. Find the rate of increase in the area of the plate as it expands if the radius is increasing by 0.2 cm/h, when the radius is 5 cm.

9. The side of a cube due to heating is increasing at the rate of 0.1 cm/min. Find how fast the volume of the container is changing when a side measures 12 cm.

10. A stone is dropped into a lake and causes ripples of concentric circles of increasing radii. Find the rate at which the area of one of these circles is increasing when its radius is 3 ft and when its radius is increasing at the rate of 0.5 ft/s.

11. The sides of an equilateral triangular plate being cooled are decreasing at a rate of 0.04 cm/min. At what rate is the area changing when the sides are 8 cm in length? The area of an equilateral triangle is given by $A = \dfrac{\sqrt{3}}{4}s^2$, where s is the length of a side.

12. The area of an equilateral triangular plate being heated is increasing at a rate of 150 mm²/min. At what rate is the length of a side changing when the sides are 250 mm long?

13. Mineral waste is falling into a conical pile at the rate of 5 m³/min. The height is equal to $\frac{3}{4}$ the radius of the base. Find how fast the radius is changing when the pile is 10 m high.

14. The relation between the voltage V that produces a current i in a wire of radius r is given by $V = 0.02\, i/r^2$. Find the rate at which the voltage is increasing when the current is increasing at the rate of 0.04 A/s in a wire of radius 0.02 in.

15. The power in a circuit is given by $P = I^2R$. Find how fast the power changes in W/s when the current is 8 A and decreasing at a rate of 0.4 A/s, and the resistance is 75 Ω and increasing at a rate of 5 Ω/s.

16. Boyle's law states that at constant temperature the pressure of a gas varies inversely as its volume. If the initial volume of a gas is 800 cm^3 at a pressure of 250 kilopascals (kPa) and is decreased at a rate of 20 cm^3/min, how is the pressure changing when the volume is 500 cm^3?

17. A cylinder with an inside radius of 75 mm is sealed at one end and a piston is at the other end. At what rate is the piston moving if fluid is being pumped into the cylinder at the rate of 90 cm^3/s?

18. A man on a dock throws a rope to a woman in a boat, who fastens the rope to the boat. The man then pulls the boat in. If the man's hands are 8 ft above the water and if he hauls the rope in at 2 ft/s, find how fast the boat is approaching the base of the dock when there are still 10 ft of rope remaining to be pulled in.

19. A 5-m ladder is leaning against a wall. Its upper end is sliding down the wall at a rate of 1 m/s. Find how fast the bottom end of the ladder is moving at the point 3 m from the wall.

20. The work W done by an electromagnet varies according to $W = 36t^3 - t^2$. Find the power $\dfrac{dW}{dt}$ at $t = \dfrac{1}{4}$ s.

21. When a gas is compressed adiabatically (with no loss or gain of heat), its behavior is described by $PV^{1.4} = k$, where P is the pressure, V is the volume, and k is a constant. At a given instant, the pressure is 60 lb/in^2 and the volume is 56 in^3 and decreasing at a rate of 8 in^3/min. At what rate is the pressure changing?

22. In Exercise 21, find the rate at which the volume is changing when the volume is 5600 cm^3, the pressure is 400 kilopascals (kPa), and the pressure is increasing at a rate of 50 kPa/min.

23. The equivalent resistance R of a parallel circuit with two resistances R_1 and R_2 is given by

$$R = \frac{R_1 R_2}{R_1 + R_2}$$

If R_1 is a constant 120 Ω and R_2 is decreasing at a rate of 15 Ω/s, find the rate at which R is changing when R_2 is 180 Ω.

24. In Exercise 23, assume that R_1 is 150 Ω and increasing at 15 Ω/s while R_2 is 300 Ω and decreasing at 25 Ω/s. Find the rate at which R is changing.

25. The power P in watts in a circuit varies according to $P = Ri^2$, where R is the resistance in ohms and i is the current in amperes. Find the rate of change, namely $\dfrac{dP}{di}$, in a 30-Ω resistor when the current $i = 4$ A.

26. Given $P = Ri^2$. If $R = 100$ Ω and i varies according to $i = t^2 + 3t$, find the rate of change of the power with respect to time when $t = 2$ s.

27. A voltage $V = 0.02i/r^2$ produces a current i in a wire of radius r. Find the rate at which the voltage is increasing when the current is increasing at the rate of 0.04 A/s in a wire of radius 0.01 in.

28. A light inside a garage is 10 ft above the floor and 6 ft from the door opening. If the overhead garage door opener lets the door down at a rate of 1 ft/s, at what rate is the door's shadow approaching the garage when the bottom of the door is 2 ft above the floor? Assume that the bottom of the garage door stays in the same vertical plane as the door opening.

29. A tank is in the shape of an inverted cone with height 8 m and radius 2 m. Water is being pumped in at a rate of 2π m^3/min. How fast is the depth of the water changing when the depth is (a) 2 m and (b) 6 m? (*Hint:* Use similar triangles to express the volume in terms of the depth only.)

30. The weight in pounds of an object varies according to

$$W = W_e\left(1 + \frac{r}{3960}\right)^{-2}$$

where W_e is the object's weight on the earth's surface and r is the distance above the earth's surface in miles. Find the rate at which a person's weight is decreasing in a space shuttle 500 miles above the earth when its altitude is increasing at 16 mi/s. The person's weight on earth is 175 lb.

3.7 DIFFERENTIALS AND LINEAR APPROXIMATIONS

Up to now, we have defined and treated dy/dx as the limit:

$$\frac{dy}{dx} = \lim_{\Delta x \to 0} \frac{\Delta y}{\Delta x}$$

Now we need to discuss separate meanings of dy and dx.

First, solve the expression $\dfrac{dy}{dx} = f'(x)$ for dy.

> **DIFFERENTIAL**
>
> $$dy = f'(x)\,dx$$

The differential of y, denoted dy, is defined as $dy = f'(x)\,dx$, where $y = f(x)$ and dx is taken to represent a change in the value of x. Figure 3.34 shows the geometric relationships between dy, dx, Δy, and Δx. Note that L_1 is the line tangent to the curve at point $P(x, y)$ and L_2 is a secant line through point P and a second point "close" to point P. Note that

1. $f'(x)$ is the slope of the tangent line L_1 to $y = f(x)$.

2. $\dfrac{dy}{dx}$ is the instantaneous rate of change of the function $y = f(x)$.

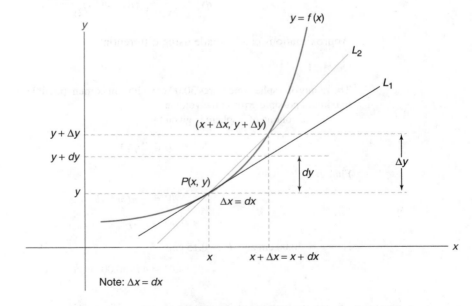

Figure 3.34 Geometric relationships between dy, dx, Δy, and Δx.

3. $\dfrac{\Delta y}{\Delta x}$ is the slope of the secant line and the rate of change of the function between the points (x, y) and $(x + \Delta x, y + \Delta y)$.

4. dx and Δx are each the amount of change in x.

5. Δy is the amount of change in y as measured along the secant line.

6. dy is the amount of change in y as measured along the tangent line.

7. If Δx is "small," dy is approximately equal to Δy, that is, $|dy - \Delta y|$ is approximately zero.

To find the differential dy of a function, simply find the derivative $\dfrac{dy}{dx}$ and then multiply both sides of the equation by dx.

EXAMPLE 1

Given $y = 8x^3 - 4x + 2$, find dy.

$$y = 8x^3 - 4x + 2$$

$$\frac{dy}{dx} = 24x^2 - 4$$

$$dy = (24x^2 - 4)\,dx$$

EXAMPLE 2

Given $y = \dfrac{8x + 4}{2x - 1}$, find dy.

$$y = \frac{8x + 4}{2x - 1}$$

$$\frac{dy}{dx} = \frac{(2x - 1)(8) - (8x + 4)(2)}{(2x - 1)^2}$$

$$\frac{dy}{dx} = \frac{-16}{(2x - 1)^2}$$

$$dy = \frac{-16}{(2x - 1)^2}\,dx \quad \text{or} \quad \frac{-16\,dx}{(2x - 1)^2}$$

Approximations can be made using differentials.

EXAMPLE 3

The radius of a sphere measures 30.00 cm with a maximum possible error of 0.15 cm. Find the maximum possible error in the volume.

The volume of a sphere is given by

$$V = \frac{4}{3}\pi r^3$$

Find dV:

$$dV = \frac{4}{3}\pi (3r^2)\,dr$$

$$dV = 4\pi r^2\,dr$$

Here $r = 30.00$ cm and $dr = 0.15$ cm:

$$dV = 4\pi (30.00 \text{ cm})^2 (0.15 \text{ cm})$$

$$= 1696.46 \text{ cm}^3$$

which is the differential approximation of the maximum possible error.

Note: $\Delta V = \frac{4}{3}\pi(30.15 \text{ cm})^3 - \frac{4}{3}\pi(30.00 \text{ cm})^3 = 1704.96 \text{ cm}^3$, which is the calculated maximum possible error by substitution into the volume formula. That is, when Δr or dr is small, $|dV - \Delta V|$ is small.

An expression that better describes some approximations is relative error or percentage error.

$$\text{relative error in } x = \frac{\text{error in } x}{x} = \frac{dx}{x}$$

$$\text{percentage error in } x = \frac{\text{error in } x}{x} \cdot 100\% = \frac{dx}{x} \cdot 100\%$$

EXAMPLE 4

Find the percentage error in Example 3.

$$\frac{dV}{V} \cdot 100\% = \frac{4\pi r^2 \, dr}{\frac{4}{3}\pi r^3} \cdot 100\%$$

$$= \frac{3 \, dr}{r} \cdot 100\%$$

$$= \frac{3(0.15 \text{ cm})}{30.00 \text{ cm}} \cdot 100\%$$

$$= 1.5\%$$

EXAMPLE 5

The current in a circuit changes according to $i = (3t + 2)^{1/3}$. Find the approximate change in current using differentials as t changes from 2.00 s to 2.05 s.

First, find the differential di:

$$i = (3t + 2)^{1/3}$$

$$di = \frac{1}{3}(3t + 2)^{-2/3}(3) \, dt$$

$$= (3t + 2)^{-2/3} \, dt$$

$$= [3(2.00) + 2]^{-2/3}(0.05) \qquad\qquad (\textit{Note: } dt = 0.05.)$$

$$= \left(\frac{1}{4}\right)(0.05) = 0.0125 \text{ A} \quad \text{or} \quad 12.5 \text{ mA}$$

Exercises 3.7

Find the differential for each expression.

1. $y = 5x^2 - 8x^3$

2. $y = 4t^5 - 6\sqrt{t} + 7$

3. $y = \dfrac{x + 3}{2x - 1}$

4. $s = \dfrac{2t + 1}{t + 6}$

5. $y = (2t^2 + 1)^4$

6. $i = 4t^2(t^2 + 1)^3$

7. $s = (t^4 - t^{-2})^{-2}$

8. $m = \left(3t - \dfrac{1}{3t}\right)^{-3}$

Find dy for each expression.

9. $x^2 + 4y^2 = 6$

10. $y^2 + 4xy = x$

11. $(x + y)^3 = \sqrt{x} + \sqrt{y}$

12. $(x^2 + y^2)^{1/2} = x + y$

Using a differential expression, find the change in each expression for the given change in the given independent variable.

13. $y = 8x^4$ from $x = 3.00$ to 3.05

14. $y = 4t^{2/3}$ from $t = 8.0$ to 8.1

15. $v = r^3 - 3r^2$ from $r = 4.00$ to 4.05

16. $y = (x - 2)^3$ from $x = 5.0$ to 5.1

17. $V = \frac{4}{3}\pi r^3$ from $r = 15.00$ to 15.10

18. $A = 4\pi r^2$ from $r = 21.0$ to 21.5

19. The side of a square measures 12.00 cm with a maximum possible error of 0.05 cm. **(a)** Find the maximum possible error in the area using differentials. **(b)** Find the maximum possible error by substituting into the formula for the area of a square. **(c)** Find the percentage error.

20. The side of a cube measures 12.00 cm with a maximum possible error of 0.05 cm. **(a)** Find the maximum possible error in the volume using differentials. **(b)** Find the maximum possible error by substituting into the formula for the volume of a cube. **(c)** Find the percentage error.

21. Suppose you want to build a spherical water tower with an inner diameter of 26.00 m and sides of thickness 4.00 cm. **(a)** Find the approximate volume of steel needed using differentials. **(b)** If the density of steel is 7800 kg/m³, find the approximate amount of steel used.

22. The current in a resistor varies according to $i = 0.08t^6 - 0.04t^2$. Find the approximate change in current using differentials as t changes from 2.00 s to 2.10 s.

23. The horsepower of an internal combustion engine is given by $p = nd^2$, where n is the number of cylinders and d is the diameter of each bore. Find the approximate increase in horsepower using differentials for an engine with eight cylinders when the bore of each cylinder is increased from 3.750 in. to 3.755 in.

24. A freely falling body drops according to $s = \frac{1}{2}gt^2$, where s is the distance in metres, $g = 9.80$ m/s², and t is the time in seconds. Approximate the distance ds that an object falls from $t = 10.00$ s to $t = 10.03$ s.

25. The voltage V in volts varies according to $V = 10P^{2/3}$, where P is the power in watts. Find the change dV when the power changes from 125 W to 128 W.

26. The impedance Z in an ac circuit varies according to $Z = \sqrt{R^2 + X^2}$, where R is the resistance and X is the reactance. If $R = 300\ \Omega$ and $X = 225\ \Omega$, find dZ when R changes to $310\ \Omega$.

CHAPTER 3 SUMMARY

1. *Algebraic curve-sketching aids:*

    (a) *Intercepts:*

        (i) To find the *x*-intercepts, substitute $y = 0$ into the given equation and solve for x. Each resulting value of x is an *x*-intercept.

        (ii) To find the *y*-intercepts, substitute $x = 0$ into the given equation and solve for y. Each resulting value of y is a *y*-intercept.

    (b) *Location of the curve above and below the x-axis:*

        (i) Solve the given equation for y.

        (ii) Factor the result from Step (i) as much as possible.

        (iii) Set each factor from Step (ii) equal to zero.

        (iv) Find the sign of y in each region by choosing a test point. Substitute this test point value into each factor of the given equation and determine whether each factor is positive or negative in the region. If the sign of y is *positive*, the curve is *above* the *x*-axis in this region. If the sign of y is *negative*, the curve is *below* the *x*-axis in this region.

    (c) *Symmetry:*

        (i) *Symmetry about the y-axis:* The graph of an equation is symmetric about the *y*-axis if replacement of x by $-x$ in the original equation results in an equivalent equation.

(ii) *Symmetry about the x-axis:* The graph of an equation is symmetric about the x-axis if replacement of y by $-y$ in the original equation results in an equivalent equation.

(iii) *Symmetry about the origin:* The graph of an equation is symmetric about the origin if replacement of both x by $-x$ and y by $-y$ in the original equation results in an equivalent equation.

(iv) If any two of the three symmetry tests are satisfied, then the graph contains all three symmetries.

(d) *Asymptotes (for rational functions):*

(i) *Vertical:* Set the denominator equal to zero and solve for x. Each solution a gives the equation of a vertical asymptote, $x = a$.

(ii) *Horizontal:* $y = 0$ if the degree of the numerator is less than the degree of the denominator.

$y = a_n/b_n$ if the degree of the numerator equals the degree of the denominator of the rational function in the form

$$f(x) = \frac{a_n x^n + \cdots + a_0}{b_n x^n + \cdots + b_0}$$

(iii) *Slant:* If the degree of the numerator is one greater than the degree of the denominator, the slant asymptote is found by dividing the numerator by the denominator. (Drop the remainder.) Then $y = $ *the quotient* is the equation of the slant asymptote.

(e) *Restricted domains:* Check for any restrictions in the domain of certain functions, such as factors that make the denominator zero in a rational function, values of the variable that make the radicand negative in an even root function, values that make the logarithm function undefined, and so forth.

2. *Increasing and decreasing functions:*

(a) A function $y = f(x)$ is *increasing* on an interval if $f(x_2) > f(x_1)$ for any two points $x_2 > x_1$ in the interval.

(b) A function $y = f(x)$ is *decreasing* on an interval if $f(x_2) < f(x_1)$ for any two points $x_2 > x_1$ in the interval.

(c) $f(x)$ is increasing when $f'(x) > 0$.

(d) $f(x)$ is decreasing when $f'(x) < 0$.

3. *Critical points:* Critical points are points of continuity $(x, f(x))$ on $y = f(x)$ where

(a) $f'(x) = 0$ or

(b) $f'(x)$ is undefined.

That is, where $f'(x)$ is neither positive nor negative.

4. *First derivative test:* Given $(c, f(c))$ is a critical point of $y = f(x)$:

(a) If $f'(x)$ changes from positive to negative at $x = c$, then $f(x)$ is changing from increasing to decreasing, and the point $(c, f(c))$ is a relative maximum.

(b) If $f'(x)$ changes from negative to positive at $x = c$, then $f(x)$ is changing from decreasing to increasing, and the point $(c, f(c))$ is a relative minimum.

(c) If $f'(x)$ does not change sign at $x = c$, then the point $(c, f(c))$ is neither a relative maximum nor a relative minimum.

5. *Calculus curve-sketching aids:* To sketch $y = f(x)$:

(a) Find all critical points for $y = f(x)$. That is, find all values of x where $f'(x) = 0$ or where $f'(x)$ is undefined.

(b) Knowing the critical points, determine where the function is increasing and where it is decreasing.

$$y = f(x) \quad \text{is increasing where} \quad f'(x) > 0$$
$$y = f(x) \quad \text{is decreasing where} \quad f'(x) < 0$$

(c) Find the relative maximum and minimum values. That is, find all values of x where $f'(x) = 0$ or is undefined. Check the critical points for possible relative maximums and relative minimums using the information obtained in Step (b).

(d) Find the x-coordinate of each possible point of inflection. That is, find all values of x where $f''(x) = 0$ or is undefined.

(e) From the possible points of inflection, determine the concavity of $y = f(x)$.

$$y = f(x) \quad \text{is concave upward where} \quad f''(x) > 0$$
$$y = f(x) \quad \text{is concave downward where} \quad f''(x) < 0$$

(f) Find which points from Step (d) are points of inflection using the information obtained in Step (e). Note that it is possible for the second derivative to be zero at $x = a$ and $f''(a) = 0$, while $f(x)$ does not have a point of inflection at $x = a$. That is, the curve does not necessarily change concavity where $f''(x) = 0$. This must be checked in Step (e).

(g) Sketch the curve.

6. *Second derivative test:*
(a) If $f'(a) = 0$ and $f''(a) < 0$, then $M = f(a)$ is a relative maximum.
(b) If $f'(a) = 0$ and $f''(a) > 0$, then $m = f(a)$ is a relative minimum.

7. *Newton's method:* Given an equation and "*Ans*," the initial estimate of a solution:
(a) Write the equation in the form $f(x) = 0$.
(b) Find the derivative, $f'(x)$.
(c) Evaluate the iteration formula $Ans - \dfrac{f(Ans)}{f'(Ans)}$ and use the value obtained as the new estimate (the new value of *Ans*). Repeat this step of the process until the estimates converge to the desired accuracy. To use your calculator in performing this part of the method, type the estimate and press **ENTER**, then type the iteration formula, $Ans - \dfrac{f(Ans)}{f'(Ans)}$, and press **ENTER** *repeatedly* until the estimates converge to a solution.
(d) To find another solution (or if the estimates did not converge), examine the graph of $y = f(x)$ to get a good initial estimate of the corresponding x-intercept. Repeat Step (c), beginning with this estimate as the value of *Ans*.

8. *Maximum and minimum problems:*
(a) Make a sketch of the conditions given in the problem whenever possible.
(b) Label appropriate quantities and assign symbols for variable quantities.
(c) Determine which variable quantity is to be maximized or minimized.
(d) Write an equation that expresses the quantity identified in Step (c) as a function of one variable. You may need to combine different equations to obtain the desired function in one variable. These equations are obtained either from given conditions or from your understanding of the relationship between quantities involved in the problem.
(e) Differentiate the function obtained from Step (d).
(f) Set the derivative from Step (e) equal to zero. Solve for the values of the variable that make the derivative zero or undefined.
(g) Determine which values of the variable from Step (f) provide the desired maximum or minimum.

9. *Related-rate problems:*
(a) Determine the equation for the variables whose rates are related. This equation may or may not be directly stated in the problem.
(b) Differentiate each side of the resulting equation with respect to time (or other desired variable).

(c) *After* differentiating in Step (b), substitute all given rates and given values of variables into the equation.

(d) Solve for the unknown rate-of-change quantity.

10. *Differential:* $dy = f'(x)\, dx$

11. *Errors:*

(a) Relative error in $x = \dfrac{\text{error in } x}{x} = \dfrac{dx}{x}$

(b) Percentage error in $x = \dfrac{\text{error in } x}{x} \cdot 100\% = \dfrac{dx}{x} \cdot 100\%$

CHAPTER 3 REVIEW

Graph each equation.

1. $y = x^3 - 16x$

2. $y = \sqrt{-2 - 4x}$

3. $y = (x + 2)(25 - x^2)$

4. $y = (x^2 + 4x)(x - 1)^2$

5. $x = y^2 + 4$

6. $y = \dfrac{x - 2}{(x + 4)(x - 1)}$

7. $y = \dfrac{2x^2}{x^2 - 1}$

8. $y = \dfrac{x^2 + x - 12}{x + 3}$

9. $y = \dfrac{2x}{x^2 + 9}$

10. $y^2 = \dfrac{x}{(1 - x)(x + 4)}$

*For each function find **(a)** intervals for which it is increasing and decreasing, **(b)** relative maximums and relative minimums, **(c)** intervals for which it is concave upward and concave downward, and **(d)** points of inflection, and **(e)** sketch the curve.*

11. $y = 6x - x^3$

12. $y = x^2 - 3x - 4$

13. $y = x^3 - 7$

14. $y = 2x^3 - 9x^2 - 24x - 2$

15. $y = \dfrac{1}{(x + 1)^2}$

16. $y = \dfrac{x^2 - 1}{x^2 + 4}$

17. $y = \dfrac{10}{x^2 + 1}$

18. $y = \dfrac{x + 1}{x^2}$

An equation and an initial estimate of one of its solutions is given. Use Newton's method to improve the estimate to at least six significant digits.

19. $x^2 - 95 = 0, x = 10$

20. $x^3 - 120 = 0, x = 5$

Use a graph to find estimates for the real solutions of each equation, then use Newton's method to improve your estimates to at least six significant digits.

21. $x^3 - 4x^2 + 3 = 0$

22. $2x^3 + 5x^2 - x - 7 = 0$

23. The height of a missile fired vertically upward is given by $y = 240t - 16t^2$. Find the maximum height (in feet) that the missile will reach.

24. Find the dimensions of a right triangle with maximum area and hypotenuse 20.

25. The electric power in watts (W) produced by a source is given by $p = 3r - r^3$, where r is the resistance in ohms (Ω) in the circuit. Find the value of r that provides the maximum power.

26. Find the area of the largest rectangle that can be inscribed in the right triangle in Fig. 3.35.

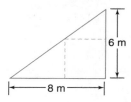

6 m

8 m

Figure 3.35

27. A long rectangular sheet of metal 12 cm wide is bent lengthwise to form a V-shaped trough. Find the depth of the trough that gives the maximum cross-sectional area and hence the greatest volume of flow.

28. Find the point on the curve $y = \sqrt{x}$ nearest the point $(1, 0)$.

29. A hot air balloon (spherical) is being inflated at the rate of 2 ft³/s. Find the rate at which the radius is increasing when the radius is 12 ft.

30. The voltage V produces a current i in a wire of radius r given by $V = 0.06i/r^2$. Find the rate at which the voltage is increasing when the current is increasing at the rate of 0.03 A/s in a wire with radius 0.01 in.

31. The current i through a circuit with resistance R and a battery whose voltage is E and whose internal resistance is r is given by $i = \dfrac{E}{R + r}$. The circuit has a variable resistor changing at the rate of 0.4 Ω/min with a 1.5-V battery whose resistance is 0.3 Ω. Find how fast the current is changing when the resistance of the variable resistor is 8 Ω.

32. A circular plate is being cooled. Find the rate of decrease in the area of the plate as it contracts if the radius is decreasing 0.05 cm/min when the radius is 8 cm.

33. Oil is leaking from an offshore well into a circular slick. If the area of the oil slick is increasing at a rate of 4 km²/day, at what rate is the radius increasing when the radius is 2.5 km?

34. A ground TV camera is 12 km from where a rocket is to be launched vertically. At what rate is the distance from the camera to the rocket increasing when the rocket is at an altitude of 10 km and rising at a rate of 3 km/s?

Find the differential for each expression.

35. $y = 4x^5 - 6x^3 + 2x$
36. $y = (3x - 5)^{-2/3}$
37. $s = \dfrac{3t^2 - 4}{5t + 1}$
38. Find dy: $(x^2 + y^2)^2 = y + 2x$

Using a differential expression, find the change in each expression for the given change in the given independent variable.

39. $s = 3t^2 - 5t + 6$ from $t = 9.50$ to 9.55
40. $y = (8x + 3)^{-3/4}$ from $x = 10.00$ to 10.06

41. Using differentials, find the increase in volume if the radius of a sphere increases from 6.0 in. to 6.1 in.

42. A particle moves along a straight line according to $s = \frac{1}{3}t^3 - 3t + 5$, where s is the distance in metres and t is the time in seconds. Find the approximate distance covered by the particle between 3.00 s and 3.05 s.

43. Using differentials, approximate how much paint is needed to paint a cube 16 ft on a side if the thickness of the paint is to be 0.02 in. (One gallon contains 231 in³.)

44. A metal sphere is 8.00 cm in diameter. How much nickel is needed to plate the sphere with a thickness of 0.4 mm?

45. The attractive force F in newtons (N) between two unlike charged particles is given by $F = k/x^2$, where k is a constant and x is the distance between the particles. If x increases from 0.030 m to 0.031 m, find the approximate decrease in F using differentials.

SPECIAL NASA APPLICATION
The Space Shuttle Landing*

INTRODUCTION

Space Shuttle missions have become a familiar topic on the evening news and undoubtedly the fiery launch from the Kennedy Space Center is a marvel to behold. However, the final and most critical phases of a Space Shuttle mission are deorbit, re-entry into the atmosphere, and landing. This application will focus on the final landing approach of the Shuttle, but first we give a brief description of the events from deorbit until final approach.

The Space Shuttle has no power and essentially acts as a glider, although it is much heavier and has less of an aerodynamic shape than an actual glider (it has been referred to as a "flying brick"). It has only one chance to land since, without engines, it cannot climb and try another approach. The process begins half a world away from the landing runway, when the Shuttle is traveling 200 mi above the ground at a speed of over 17,000 mi/h. It now has 60 min to touchdown. During the deorbit burn, the Space Shuttle travels tail first and loses some speed and altitude. Once the burn is complete, the space shuttle position is reversed, its nose is raised, and the atmosphere entry begins. It is now 31 min to touchdown. During this phase, there is a tremendous heat buildup around the Shuttle and portions of the vehicle's exterior reach 2800°F (you have probably heard about the tiles used on the surface of the vehicle to protect it at this critical time). The heat strips electrons from the air around the Space Shuttle, enveloping it in a sheath of ionized air that blocks all communications from the ground for about 12 min. During this interval the pilot performs several banking maneuvers called roll reversals or S-turns to control descent. When the Space Shuttle comes out of the communications blackout, its speed is about 8275 mi/h and 12 min remain to touchdown. It is now committed to a particular landing site and must begin the final approach with enough altitude and speed to reach the touchdown point. At this point the vehicle travels a circular path around an imaginary cone that will line it up with the center line of the runway.

THE FINAL APPROACH TO THE RUNWAY

Coming out of its turn, the Space Shuttle should be at an altitude of 13,365 ft, have a speed of 424 mi/h, and be 7.5 mi (horizontal distance) from the runway. It is now 86 s to touchdown. The nose is down so that the Space Shuttle can descend steeply to a point 7500 ft from

---

* From NASA—AMATYC—NSF Project Mathematics Explorations II, grant principals John S. Pazdar, Patricia L. Hirschy, and Peter A. Wursthorn; copyright Capital Community College, 2000.

the runway threshold, where its altitude should be 1750 ft. The vehicle then enters a transitional phase. The Shuttle's nose is raised as it heads for a position where its altitude is 131 ft and its distance from the runway threshold is 2650 ft. The Shuttle is now 17 s to touchdown. From here the Space Shuttle enters the final phase, aiming at a point 2200 ft down the runway.

The four data points given in the paragraph describing the final approach are (39600, 13365), (7500, 1750), (2650, 131), and (−2200, 0). This assumes that the origin is the runway threshold. Notice that in this coordinate system, the Shuttle would be coming in from right to left.

The flight path between the first and second points is $y_1 = 0.36184x - 963.78505$.

The flight path between the last two data points is $y_3 = 0.02701x + 59.42268$.

In between these two linear paths, the Shuttle is in a transitional phase in which the orientation changes from nose down to nose up. Since a NASA training pilot had referred to this phase as the "exponential capture" phase, it seemed reasonable to model this phase with an exponential function which contains the points (7500, 1750) and (2650, 131). Its equation is $y_2 = 31.78057(1.000534612)^x$. See Fig. 3.36.

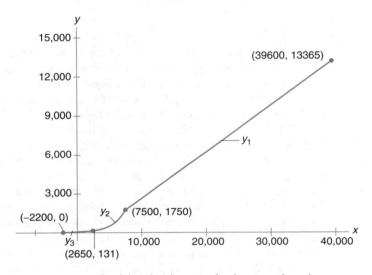

Figure 3.36 Path of the Shuttle on its final approach to the runway.

These three pieces, put together as the following piecewise function, provide a model for the final landing path of the Shuttle:

$$f(x) = \begin{cases} 0.36184x - 963.78505 & \text{for} \quad 7500 \le x \le 39{,}600 \\ 31.78057(1.000534612)^x & \text{for} \quad 2650 < x < 7500 \\ 0.02701x + 59.42268 & \text{for} \quad -2200 \le x \le 2650 \end{cases}$$

Note: We will be working with decimal numbers using many digits. You will need to use a TI-89 or a computer program that solves equations.

The exponential function in the transitional phase is supposed to produce a path with a steep slope on entry and a shallow slope on exit. For a nonlinear graph, the slope of the graph is changing. The slope of the graph is, of course, the derivative function. To find the derivative of the exponential function, recall that for $f(x) = ab^x$, $f'(x) = a(b^x/\log_b e)$. Also recall that $\log_b e = \ln e/\ln b$. Thus,

$$f'(x) = 31.78057(1.000534612)^x[\ln(1.000534612)]$$
$$f'(x) = 0.016985734105(1.000534612)^x$$

Evaluating $f'(x)$ at (7500, 1750), we see that the slope is

$$f'(7500) = 0.016985734105(1.000534612)^{7500}$$
$$f'(7500) = 0.935323459841$$

The slope of the linear piece of the first phase is 0.36184, and it is clear that these slopes are not the same. This means that the piecewise function is not differentiable at $x = 7500$, that is, the curve is not smooth. Evaluating $f'(x)$ at (2650, 131), we see that the slope is

$$f'(2650) = 0.016985734105(1.000534612)^{2650}$$
$$f'(2650) = 0.070015528847$$

The slope of the linear piece of the last phase is 0.02701, and again, these slopes are not the same. This means that the piecewise function is not differentiable at $x = 2650$. So while the exponential function seemed like a good idea, we find that problems exist where it meets each of the two linear functions.

Our goal now is to find a function that satisfies four conditions: the two points (2650, 131) and (7500, 1750) must belong to the function and the function must also satisfy the two derivative (slope) conditions. When these four conditions are present, mathematicians who work with curve fitting use a cubic polynomial called a **cubic spline**. Cubic splines are used in computer graphics programs and in industrial design. We will begin by writing our third-degree polynomial:

$$y = f(x) = ax^3 + bx^2 + cx + d$$

We will use this function and the entry and exit points of the transition phase to write two equations in a, b, c, and d.

$$(7500^3)a + (7500^2)b + (7500)c + d = 1750$$
$$(2650^3)a + (2650^2)b + (2650)c + d = 131$$

The derivative of the third-degree polynomial is $f'(x) = 3ax^2 + 2bx + c$. To satisfy the slope conditions, $f'(7500)$ should be 0.36184, the slope of the linear first phase, and $f'(2650)$ should be 0.02701, the slope of the linear last phase. This yields the equations

$$3(7500^2)a + 2(7500)b + c = 0.36184$$
$$3(2650^2)a + 2(2650)b + c = 0.02701$$

We now have four equations and four unknowns. Solving with a TI-89 or a computer, we get

$$a = -1.18515832066(10^{-8}) \qquad b = 0.000214958911022$$
$$c = -0.862588999214 \qquad d = 1127.86541439$$

The polynomial model is

$$y = -1.18515832066(10^{-8})x^3 + 0.000214958911022x^2$$
$$-0.862588999214x + 1127.86541439$$

The derivative is

$$f'(x) = -3.55547496198(10^{-8})x^2 + 0.000429917822044x$$
$$-0.862588999214$$

We have

$$f'(7500) = 0.361840000002$$

which agrees with the slope of the linear function to five decimal places, and

$$f'(2650) = 0.0270099999975$$

which agrees with the slope of the linear function to four decimal places. See Fig. 3.37 for a graph of the new piecewise function.

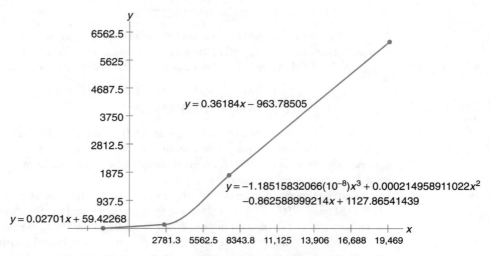

Figure 3.37 New path of the Shuttle on its final approach to the runway.

4

Derivatives of Transcendental Functions

INTRODUCTION

Many problems that deal with maximizing or minimizing a quantity are expressed using trigonometric, logarithmic, or exponential functions. In addition, current in a circuit may be expressed using the derivative of the voltage across a capacitor or the derivative of the charge of a capacitor. For example, the equation $q = e^{-0.2t}(0.04 \cos 2t - 0.5 \sin 3t)$ represents the charge of a capacitor at time t. The current is represented by $i = \dfrac{dq}{dt}$. Thus we need to learn how to differentiate transcendental functions to expand our problem-solving abilities.

Objectives

- Use trigonometric identities to simplify trigonometric expressions or change a trigonometric expression into an equivalent expression.
- Differentiate trigonometric functions.
- Find an algebraic expression for a trigonometric function whose argument is an inverse trigonometric function.
- Find the derivative of an inverse trigonometric function.
- Find the derivative of a logarithmic function.
- Find the derivative of an exponential function.
- Use l'Hospital's rule to evaluate limits involving trigonometric, logarithmic, and exponential functions.
- Use derivatives to solve application problems.

4.1 THE TRIGONOMETRIC FUNCTIONS

Before we begin to develop the calculus of the trigonometric functions, we briefly review some of the basics of trigonometry.

An angle is in **standard position** when its vertex is located at the origin and its initial side is lying on the positive x-axis. An angle resulting from a counterclockwise rotation, as indicated by the direction of the arrow, is a **positive angle.** But if the rotation is clockwise, the angle is **negative** (see Fig. 4.1).

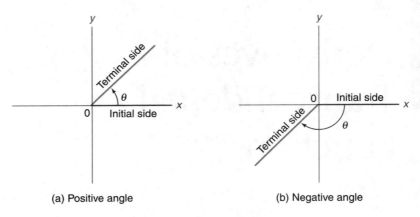

(a) Positive angle   (b) Negative angle

Figure 4.1

There are six trigonometric functions associated with angle θ in standard position. They can be expressed in terms of the coordinates of the point $P(x, y)$ as ratios where the point P is on the terminal side of the angle θ as in Fig. 4.2.

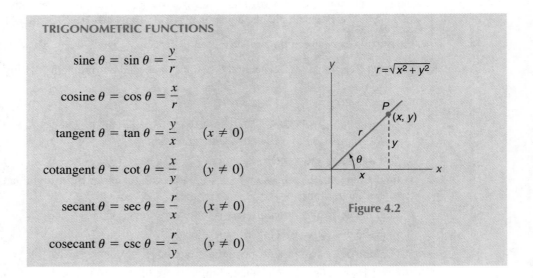

TRIGONOMETRIC FUNCTIONS

$$\text{sine } \theta = \sin \theta = \frac{y}{r}$$

$$\text{cosine } \theta = \cos \theta = \frac{x}{r}$$

$$\text{tangent } \theta = \tan \theta = \frac{y}{x} \qquad (x \neq 0)$$

$$\text{cotangent } \theta = \cot \theta = \frac{x}{y} \qquad (y \neq 0)$$

$$\text{secant } \theta = \sec \theta = \frac{r}{x} \qquad (x \neq 0)$$

$$\text{cosecant } \theta = \csc \theta = \frac{r}{y} \qquad (y \neq 0)$$

$r = \sqrt{x^2 + y^2}$

Figure 4.2

We know from algebra that $\dfrac{y}{r}$ and $\dfrac{r}{y}$ are reciprocals of each other; that is,

$$\sin \theta = \frac{y}{r} = \frac{1}{\dfrac{r}{y}} = \frac{1}{\csc \theta}$$

For this reason, $\sin \theta$ and $\csc \theta$ are called **reciprocal trigonometric functions.** In much the same way, we can complete the following table using the defining ratios:

RECIPROCAL TRIGONOMETRIC FUNCTIONS

$$\sin \theta = \frac{1}{\csc \theta} \qquad \csc \theta = \frac{1}{\sin \theta}$$

$$\cos \theta = \frac{1}{\sec \theta} \qquad \sec \theta = \frac{1}{\cos \theta}$$

$$\tan \theta = \frac{1}{\cot \theta} \qquad \cot \theta = \frac{1}{\tan \theta}$$

We must be careful to watch for angles where the point P on the terminal side has its abscissa x or its ordinate y equal to zero. Since we cannot divide by zero, $\tan \theta$ and $\sec \theta$ do not exist when $x = 0$. Likewise, $\cot \theta$ and $\csc \theta$ do not exist when $y = 0$.

Two or more angles in standard position are *coterminal* if they have the same terminal side. For example, $60°$, $420°$, and $-300°$ are coterminal.

A **quadrantal angle** is one which, when in standard position, has its terminal side coinciding with one of the axes.

EXAMPLE 1

Find the values of $\sin \theta$, $\cos \theta$, and $\tan \theta$ if θ is in standard position and its terminal side passes through the point $(-3, 4)$ (see Fig. 4.3).

$$r = \sqrt{x^2 + y^2} = \sqrt{9 + 16} = 5$$

$$\sin \theta = \frac{y}{r} = \frac{4}{5}$$

$$\cos \theta = \frac{x}{r} = \frac{-3}{5} = -\frac{3}{5}$$

$$\tan \theta = \frac{y}{x} = \frac{4}{-3} = -\frac{4}{3}$$

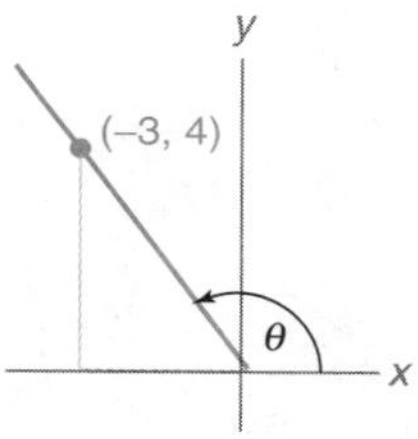

Figure 4.3

The **reference angle** α of any nonquadrantal angle θ in standard position is the *acute* angle between the terminal side of θ and the x-axis. Angle α is always considered to be a positive angle less than $90°$.

EXAMPLE 2

Find the reference angle α for each given angle θ (see Fig. 4.4).

Note that if angle θ is in standard position and

1. $0° < \theta < 90°$, then $\alpha = \theta$.

2. $90° < \theta < 180°$, then $\alpha = 180° - \theta$.

3. $180° < \theta < 270°$, then $\alpha = \theta - 180°$.

4. $270° < \theta < 360°$, then $\alpha = 360° - \theta$.

The reference angle α is often used to determine the angle θ when the value of the trigonometric function is known.

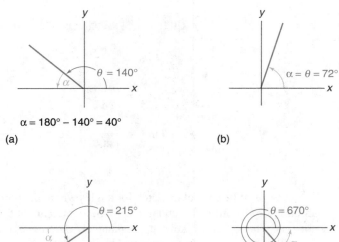

$\alpha = 180° - 140° = 40°$

(a)

(b)

$\alpha = 215° - 180° = 35°$

(c)

$\alpha = 720° - 670° = 50°$

(d)

Figure 4.4

EXAMPLE 3

Given $\cos \theta = -\frac{1}{2}$, find θ for $0° \leq \theta < 360°$.

Using a calculator, we find that $\alpha = 60°$. The cosine function is negative in quadrants II and III. The second-quadrant angle is $180° - 60° = 120°$. The third-quadrant angle is $180° + 60° = 240°$ (see Fig. 4.5).

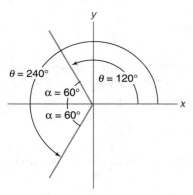

Figure 4.5

Angles are commonly given in degree measure and in radian measure. Since

$$1 \text{ revolution} = 360°$$

and

$$1 \text{ revolution} = 2\pi \text{ rad}$$

the basic relationship between radians and degrees is

$$\pi \text{ rad} = 180°$$

The degree and radian measures of several common angles are given in Table 4.1.

TABLE 4.1 Values of Common Angles

Radians	0	$\dfrac{\pi}{6}$	$\dfrac{\pi}{4}$	$\dfrac{\pi}{3}$	$\dfrac{\pi}{2}$	$\dfrac{2\pi}{3}$	$\dfrac{3\pi}{4}$	$\dfrac{5\pi}{6}$	π	$\dfrac{3\pi}{2}$	2π
Degrees	$0°$	$30°$	$45°$	$60°$	$90°$	$120°$	$135°$	$150°$	$180°$	$270°$	$360°$
$\sin\theta$	0	$\dfrac{1}{2}$	$\dfrac{\sqrt{2}}{2}$	$\dfrac{\sqrt{3}}{2}$	1	$\dfrac{\sqrt{3}}{2}$	$\dfrac{\sqrt{2}}{2}$	$\dfrac{1}{2}$	0	-1	0
$\cos\theta$	1	$\dfrac{\sqrt{3}}{2}$	$\dfrac{\sqrt{2}}{2}$	$\dfrac{1}{2}$	0	$-\dfrac{1}{2}$	$-\dfrac{\sqrt{2}}{2}$	$-\dfrac{\sqrt{3}}{2}$	-1	0	1
$\tan\theta$	0	$\dfrac{\sqrt{3}}{3}$	1	$\sqrt{3}$	Undefined	$-\sqrt{3}$	-1	$-\dfrac{\sqrt{3}}{3}$	0	Undefined	0
$\cot\theta$	Undefined	$\sqrt{3}$	1	$\dfrac{\sqrt{3}}{3}$	0	$-\dfrac{\sqrt{3}}{3}$	-1	$-\sqrt{3}$	Undefined	0	Undefined
$\sec\theta$	1	$\dfrac{2\sqrt{3}}{3}$	$\sqrt{2}$	2	Undefined	-2	$-\sqrt{2}$	$-\dfrac{2\sqrt{3}}{3}$	-1	Undefined	1
$\csc\theta$	Undefined	2	$\sqrt{2}$	$\dfrac{2\sqrt{3}}{3}$	1	$\dfrac{2\sqrt{3}}{3}$	$\sqrt{2}$	2	Undefined	-1	Undefined

Listed inside the back cover are the trigonometric identities commonly used in any trigonometry course, which we assume you have successfully completed. Trigonometric identities will be used to simplify trigonometric expressions, to change a given trigonometric expression into a different but equivalent expression that is easier to differentiate or integrate, and to compare results of integration by different methods to see that they are equivalent.

EXAMPLE 4

Prove $\sin^2\theta + \sin^2\theta \tan^2\theta = \tan^2\theta$.

$$\sin^2\theta + \sin^2\theta \tan^2\theta = \sin^2\theta(1 + \tan^2\theta)$$
$$= \sin^2\theta \sec^2\theta$$
$$= \sin^2\theta\left(\frac{1}{\cos^2\theta}\right)$$
$$= \tan^2\theta$$

Therefore, $\sin^2\theta + \sin^2\theta \tan^2\theta = \tan^2\theta$.

EXAMPLE 5

Prove $\dfrac{\cos x}{1 + \sin x} = \dfrac{1 - \sin x}{\cos x}$.

Multiply the numerator and the denominator of the right-hand side by $1 + \sin x$.

$$\frac{1 - \sin x}{\cos x} \cdot \frac{1 + \sin x}{1 + \sin x} = \frac{1 - \sin^2 x}{\cos x(1 + \sin x)}$$
$$= \frac{\cos^2 x}{\cos x(1 + \sin x)}$$
$$= \frac{\cos x}{1 + \sin x}$$

Therefore, $\dfrac{\cos x}{1 + \sin x} = \dfrac{1 - \sin x}{\cos x}$.

EXAMPLE 6

Prove $\dfrac{1 - \cos 2x}{\sin 2x} = \tan x$.

$$\frac{1 - \cos 2x}{\sin 2x} = \frac{1 - (1 - 2\sin^2 x)}{2\sin x \cos x}$$

$$= \frac{2\sin^2 x}{2\sin x \cos x}$$

$$= \frac{\sin x}{\cos x}$$

$$= \tan x$$

Therefore, $\dfrac{1 - \cos 2x}{\sin 2x} = \tan x$.

EXAMPLE 7

Simplify $2 \sin 3x \cos 3x$.

Using Formula 24 of the Common Trigonometric Identities listed inside the back cover, we obtain

$$2 \sin \theta \cos \theta = \sin 2\theta$$

$$2 \sin 3x \cos 3x = \sin 2(3x) = \sin 6x$$

EXAMPLE 8

Simplify $1 - 2\cos^2 5x$.

Using Formula 25b of the Common Trigonometric Identities listed inside the back cover, we obtain

$$1 - 2\cos^2 5x = -\cos 2(5x) = -\cos 10x$$

EXAMPLE 9

Simplify $\cos 2\theta \cos 3\theta - \sin 2\theta \sin 3\theta$.

By Formula 20 of the Common Trigonometric Identities listed inside the back cover,

$$\cos 2\theta \cos 3\theta - \sin 2\theta \sin 3\theta = \cos (2\theta + 3\theta) = \cos 5\theta$$

Using a calculator, we have

2nd COS 2 **green diamond** θ) **2nd COS** 3 **green diamond** θ)
F2 9 2 -**2nd SIN** 2 **green diamond** θ) **2nd SIN** 3 **green diamond** θ)) **ENTER**

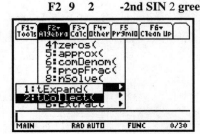
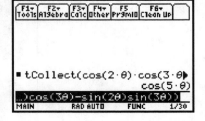

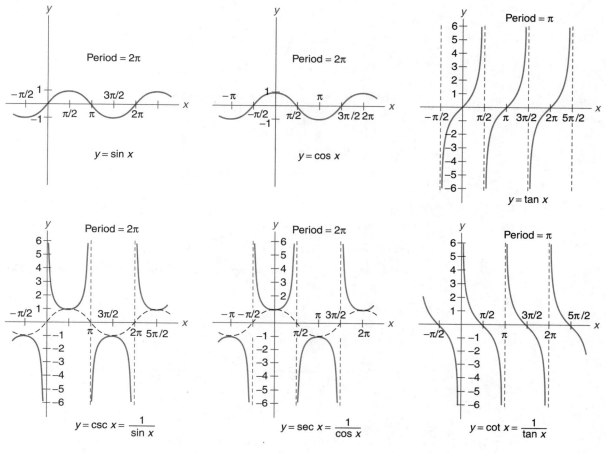

Figure 4.6

Figure 4.6 shows the graphs of each of the six basic trigonometric functions. Recall that each is periodic. The *period* is the length of each cycle, that is, the period is the horizontal distance between any point on the curve and the next corresponding point in the next cycle where the graph begins to repeat itself.

The *amplitude* of the sine and cosine functions is one-half the distance difference between the maximum and minimum values of the function. Recall the following graphing facts and relationships for the six trigonometric functions.

$$\text{period} = \frac{2\pi}{b} \quad \left. \begin{cases} y = a \sin(bx + c) \\ y = a \cos(bx + c) \end{cases} \right\} \text{amplitude} = |a| \quad\quad \text{phase shift} = \frac{c}{b}$$

$$y = a \sec(bx + c)$$
$$y = a \csc(bx + c)$$

$$\text{period} = \frac{\pi}{b} \quad \begin{cases} y = a \tan(bx + c) \\ y = a \cot(bx + c) \end{cases}$$

to the *left* if $\dfrac{c}{b} > 0$ and

to the *right* if $\dfrac{c}{b} < 0$

EXAMPLE 10

Graph $y = 2 \cos 3x$.

The amplitude is 2. The period is $P = \dfrac{2\pi}{b} = \dfrac{2\pi}{3}$ (see Fig. 4.7).

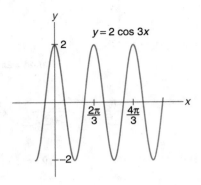

$y = 2 \cos 3x$

Figure 4.7

EXAMPLE 11

Graph $y = -3 \sin \frac{1}{2}x$.

The amplitude is 3. The period is $\dfrac{2\pi}{b} = \dfrac{2\pi}{\frac{1}{2}} = 4\pi$.

The effect of the negative sign is to flip, or invert, the curve $y = 3 \sin \frac{1}{2}x$ (see Fig. 4.8).

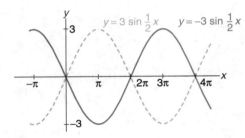

Figure 4.8

EXAMPLE 12

Graph $y = 3 \cos\left(6x + \dfrac{\pi}{4}\right)$.

The amplitude is 3. The period is $\dfrac{2\pi}{b} = \dfrac{2\pi}{6} = \dfrac{\pi}{3}$. The phase shift is $\dfrac{c}{b} = \dfrac{\pi/4}{6} = \dfrac{\pi}{24}$, or $\dfrac{\pi}{24}$ to the left (see Fig. 4.9).

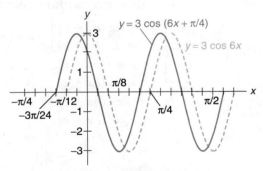

Each division on the x-axis is $\pi/24$.

Figure 4.9

Exercises 4.1

Prove each identity.

1. $\cos x \tan x = \sin x$

2. $(1 - \cos^2 x) \csc^2 x = 1$

3. $(\cot^2 x + 1) \tan^2 x = \sec^2 x$

4. $\cos \theta (\csc \theta - \sec \theta) = \cot \theta - 1$

5. $\tan^2 \theta - \tan^2 \theta \sin^2 \theta = \sin^2 \theta$

6. $\dfrac{\sin^2 x}{1 + \cos x} = 1 - \cos x$

7. $\dfrac{\cos x \tan x + \sin x}{\tan x} = 2 \cos x$

8. $\cos^4 \theta - \sin^4 \theta = 2 \cos^2 \theta - 1$

9. $\dfrac{1 + \sec x}{\csc x} = \sin x + \tan x$

10. $\dfrac{1 + \tan^2 x}{\tan^2 x} = \csc^2 x$

11. $(\sec x - \tan x)(\csc x + 1) = \cot x$

12. $\dfrac{1 - \cos \theta}{\cos \theta \tan \theta} = \dfrac{\sin \theta}{1 + \cos \theta}$

13. $\dfrac{1 - \tan x}{1 + \tan x} = \dfrac{\cot x - 1}{\cot x + 1}$

14. $\dfrac{1 - \sin^2 x}{1 - \cos^2 x} = \cot^2 x$

15. $\sin(x + \pi) = -\sin x$

16. $\cos(x + 180°) = -\cos x$

17. $\sin(x + 2\pi) = \sin x$

18. $\tan(x + \pi) = \tan x$

19. $\tan(\pi - x) = -\tan x$

20. $\sin(90° - \theta) = \cos \theta$

21. $\cos\left(\dfrac{\pi}{2} - \theta\right) = \sin \theta$

22. $\cos\left(\dfrac{\pi}{2} + \theta\right) = -\sin \theta$

23. $\cos(x + y) \cos(x - y) = \cos^2 x - \sin^2 y$

24. $\sin(x + y) \sin(x - y) = \sin^2 x - \sin^2 y$

25. $(\sin x + \cos x)^2 = 1 + \sin 2x$

26. $\sin 2x = \dfrac{2 \tan x}{1 + \tan^2 x}$

27. $\dfrac{1 - \tan^2 x}{1 + \tan^2 x} = \cos 2x$

28. $2 \tan x \csc 2x = \sec^2 x$

29. $\cot 2x = \dfrac{\cot^2 x - 1}{2 \cot x}$

30. $\sec 2x = \dfrac{\sec^2 x}{2 - \sec^2 x}$

31. $\tan x + \cot 2x = \csc 2x$

32. $\sin^2 \dfrac{x}{2} = \dfrac{\sec x - 1}{2 \sec x}$

33. $2 \cos^2 \dfrac{\theta}{2} = \dfrac{1 + \sec \theta}{\sec \theta}$

34. $\sec^2 \dfrac{x}{2} = \dfrac{2}{1 + \cos x}$

35. $\tan \dfrac{x}{2} = \dfrac{\sin x}{1 + \cos x}$

36. $2 \cos \dfrac{x}{2} = (1 + \cos x) \sec \dfrac{x}{2}$

Simplify each expression.

37. $\sin \theta \cos 3\theta + \cos \theta \sin 3\theta$

38. $\cos 2\theta \cos \theta - \sin 2\theta \sin \theta$

39. $\cos 4\theta \cos 3\theta + \sin 4\theta \sin 3\theta$

40. $\sin 2\theta \cos 3\theta - \cos 2\theta \sin 3\theta$

41. $\dfrac{\tan 3\theta + \tan 2\theta}{1 - \tan 3\theta \tan 2\theta}$

42. $\dfrac{\tan \theta - \tan 2\theta}{1 + \tan \theta \tan 2\theta}$

43. $\sin(\theta + \phi) + \sin(\theta - \phi)$

44. $\cos(\theta + \phi) + \cos(\theta - \phi)$

45. $2 \sin \dfrac{x}{4} \cos \dfrac{x}{4}$

46. $20 \sin^2 x \cos^2 x$

47. $1 - 2 \sin^2 3x$

48. $\sqrt{\dfrac{1 - \cos 6\theta}{2}}$

49. $\sqrt{\dfrac{1 + \cos \dfrac{\theta}{4}}{2}}$

50. $\cos 2x + 2 \sin^2 x$

51. $\cos^2 \dfrac{x}{6} - \sin^2 \dfrac{x}{6}$

52. $2 \sin 3x \cos 3x$

53. $20 \sin 4\theta \cos 4\theta$

54. $1 - 2 \sin^2 7t$

55. $4 - 8 \sin^2 \theta$

56. $15 \sin \dfrac{x}{6} \cos \dfrac{x}{6}$

Sketch each curve.

57. $y = 2 \cos x$

58. $y = \cos 3x$

59. $y = 3 \cos 6x$

60. $y = -\dfrac{1}{2} \sin \dfrac{2}{3} x$

61. $y = 2 \sin 3\pi x$

62. $y = 3 \sin \left(x - \dfrac{\pi}{3} \right)$

63. $y = -\sin \left(4x - \dfrac{2\pi}{3} \right)$

64. $y = -\cos (4x + \pi)$

65. $y = 3 \sin \left(\dfrac{1}{2} x - \dfrac{\pi}{4} \right)$

66. $y = 5 \cos \left(\dfrac{2}{3} x + \pi \right)$

67. $y = \tan 3x$

68. $y = 4 \sin \left(\dfrac{\pi x}{6} - \dfrac{\pi}{3} \right)$

4.2 DERIVATIVES OF SINE AND COSINE FUNCTIONS

So far we have differentiated only algebraic functions; that is, functions in the form $y = f(x)$ where $f(x)$ is an algebraic expression. But many important applications involve the use of non-algebraic functions called *transcendental functions*. The trigonometric and logarithmic functions are examples of transcendental functions. We will first find the derivative of $y = \sin u$.

By the definition of the derivative we have

$$\frac{d}{du} (\sin u) = \frac{dy}{du} = \lim_{\Delta u \to 0} \frac{\Delta y}{\Delta u}$$

$$= \lim_{\Delta u \to 0} \frac{\sin (u + \Delta u) - \sin u}{\Delta u}$$

Using the trigonometric identity 33 found inside the back cover, we obtain

$$\sin A - \sin B = 2 \sin \left(\frac{A - B}{2} \right) \cos \left(\frac{A + B}{2} \right)$$

and letting $A = u + \Delta u$ and $B = u$, we have

$$\sin (u + \Delta u) - \sin u = 2 \sin \left(\frac{u + \Delta u - u}{2} \right) \cos \left(\frac{u + \Delta u + u}{2} \right)$$

$$= 2 \sin \left(\frac{\Delta u}{2} \right) \cos \left(u + \frac{\Delta u}{2} \right)$$

So now,

$$\frac{dy}{du} = \lim_{\Delta u \to 0} \frac{2 \sin \left(\dfrac{\Delta u}{2} \right) \cos \left(u + \dfrac{\Delta u}{2} \right)}{\Delta u}$$

Next, divide numerator and denominator by 2:

$$\frac{dy}{du} = \lim_{\Delta u \to 0} \frac{\sin \left(\dfrac{\Delta u}{2} \right) \cos \left(u + \dfrac{\Delta u}{2} \right)}{\dfrac{\Delta u}{2}}$$

$$= \lim_{\Delta u \to 0} \frac{\sin\left(\dfrac{\Delta u}{2}\right)}{\dfrac{\Delta u}{2}} \cdot \lim_{\Delta u \to 0} \cos\left(u + \frac{\Delta u}{2}\right)$$

The right-hand factor, $\lim_{\Delta u \to 0} \cos\left(u + \dfrac{\Delta u}{2}\right)$, is $\cos u$. We need, however, to determine

$$\lim_{\Delta u \to 0} \frac{\sin\left(\dfrac{\Delta u}{2}\right)}{\dfrac{\Delta u}{2}}$$

For this purpose we construct the geometric figure as shown in Fig. 4.10.

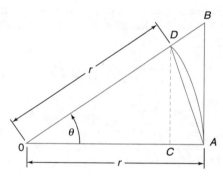

Figure 4.10

Angle θ is the central angle (measured in radians) of a circle of radius $r = OA = OD$. Note that

area of triangle OAD < area of sector OAD < area of right triangle OAB

$(\frac{1}{2}r)(r \sin \theta) <$	$\frac{1}{2}r^2 \theta$	$< (\frac{1}{2}r)(r \tan \theta)$	
$\sin \theta <$	θ	$< \tan \theta$	(Divide each term by $\frac{1}{2}r^2$.)
$\sin \theta <$	θ	$< \dfrac{\sin \theta}{\cos \theta}$	$\left(\tan \theta = \dfrac{\sin \theta}{\cos \theta}\right)$
$1 <$	$\dfrac{\theta}{\sin \theta}$	$< \dfrac{1}{\cos \theta}$	(Divide each term by $\sin \theta$. Note: $\sin \theta > 0$.)
$1 >$	$\dfrac{\sin \theta}{\theta}$	$> \cos \theta$	(Take the reciprocal of each term.)

As θ approaches 0, $\cos \theta$ approaches 1, so we have

$$\lim_{\theta \to 0} 1 = 1 \quad \text{and} \quad \lim_{\theta \to 0} \cos \theta = 1$$

We conclude that $\dfrac{\sin \theta}{\theta}$, which is between 1 and $\cos \theta$, must *also* approach 1 as θ approaches 0, that is,

$$\lim_{\theta \to 0} \frac{\sin \theta}{\theta} = 1$$

So

$$\frac{d}{du}(\sin u) = \lim_{\Delta u \to 0} \frac{\sin\left(\frac{\Delta u}{2}\right)}{\frac{\Delta u}{2}} \cdot \lim_{\Delta u \to 0} \cos\left(u + \frac{\Delta u}{2}\right) = 1 \cdot \cos u = \cos u$$

Thus

$$\frac{d}{du}(\sin u) = \cos u$$

We are still unable, however, to find the derivative of a function such as

$$\frac{d}{dx}\sin(x^2 + 3x)$$

To find the derivative of $\sin u$ with respect to x when u is itself a function of x, we use the chain rule from Section 2.7. Recall that if $y = f(u)$ where $u = g(x)$, then $y = f[g(x)]$ is a function of x. Then,

CHAIN RULE

$$\frac{dy}{dx} = \frac{dy}{du} \cdot \frac{du}{dx}$$

EXAMPLE 1

Find the derivative of $y = \sin(x^2 + 3x)$.

Let $u = x^2 + 3x$ and $y = \sin u$ so that

$$\frac{dy}{du} = \cos u \quad \text{and} \quad \frac{du}{dx} = 2x + 3$$

and

$$\frac{dy}{dx} = \frac{dy}{du} \cdot \frac{du}{dx} = (\cos u)(2x + 3)$$

$$\frac{dy}{dx} = (2x + 3)\cos(x^2 + 3x)$$

EXAMPLE 2

Find $\dfrac{d}{dx}(\sin 2x)$.

Let $u = 2x$ and $y = \sin u$.

$$\frac{dy}{dx} = \frac{dy}{du} \cdot \frac{du}{dx}$$

$$= (\cos u)(2)$$

$$= 2\cos 2x$$

EXAMPLE 3

Find the derivative of $y = \sin(3x - 5)^2$.

Let $u = (3x - 5)^2$ and $y = \sin u$.

$$\frac{dy}{du} = \cos u \quad \text{and} \quad \frac{du}{dx} = 2(3x - 5)(3) = 6(3x - 5)$$

$$\frac{dy}{dx} = \frac{dy}{du} \cdot \frac{du}{dx}$$

$$= (\cos u)[6(3x - 5)]$$

$$= 6(3x - 5)\cos (3x - 5)^2$$

EXAMPLE 4

Find the derivative of $y = \sin^3 (2x - 3)$.

The chain rule is also used to find the derivative of a function which is a chain of more than two functions of functions.

$$\frac{dy}{dx} = \frac{d}{dx}[\sin^3 (2x - 3)]$$

$$= 3\sin^2 (2x - 3)\frac{d}{dx}[\sin (2x - 3)] \qquad \left[\frac{d}{dx}(u^n) = nu^{n-1}\frac{du}{dx}\right]$$

$$= 3\sin^2 (2x - 3)\cos (2x - 3)\frac{d}{dx}(2x - 3) \qquad \left[\frac{d}{dx}(\sin u) = \cos u \frac{du}{dx}\right]$$

$$= 3\sin^2 (2x - 3)\cos (2x - 3)(2)$$

$$= 6\sin^2 (2x - 3)\cos (2x - 3)$$

To find the derivative of $y = \cos u$, first recall that $\cos u = \sin\left(\frac{\pi}{2} - u\right)$ and let $w = \frac{\pi}{2} - u$. Then $y = \cos u = \sin\left(\frac{\pi}{2} - u\right) = \sin w$. Using the chain rule,

$$\frac{dy}{du} = \frac{dy}{dw} \cdot \frac{dw}{du}$$

and noting that

$$\frac{dy}{dw} = \frac{d}{dw}(\sin w) = \cos w \quad \text{and} \quad \frac{dw}{du} = \frac{d}{du}\left(\frac{\pi}{2} - u\right) = -1$$

then we have

$$\frac{dy}{du} = (\cos w)(-1) = -\cos w$$

$$= -\cos\left(\frac{\pi}{2} - u\right)$$

$$= -\sin u \qquad \left[\text{since } \cos\left(\frac{\pi}{2} - u\right) = \sin u\right]$$

Thus

$$\frac{d}{du}(\cos u) = -\sin u$$

EXAMPLE 5

Find the derivative of $y = \cos(5x^2 + x)$.
Let $u = 5x^2 + x$ and $y = \cos u$.

$$\frac{dy}{du} = -\sin u \quad \text{and} \quad \frac{du}{dx} = 10x + 1$$

$$\frac{dy}{dx} = \frac{dy}{du} \cdot \frac{du}{dx}$$

$$= (-\sin u)(10x + 1)$$

$$= -(10x + 1)\sin(5x^2 + x)$$

EXAMPLE 6

Find the derivative of $y = \cos(x^2 - 1)^5$.

$$\frac{dy}{dx} = -\sin(x^2 - 1)^5[5(x^2 - 1)^4](2x)$$

$$= -10x(x^2 - 1)^4 \sin(x^2 - 1)^5$$

EXAMPLE 7

Find the derivative of $y = \sin(7x^2 + 2)\cos 4x$.
Use the product rule for differentiation, followed by the chain rule.

$$\frac{dy}{dx} = \sin(7x^2 + 2)\frac{d}{dx}(\cos 4x) + \cos 4x \frac{d}{dx}[\sin(7x^2 + 2)]$$

$$= \sin(7x^2 + 2)(-\sin 4x)\frac{d}{dx}(4x) + \cos 4x \cos(7x^2 + 2)\frac{d}{dx}(7x^2 + 2)$$

$$= \sin(7x^2 + 2)(-\sin 4x)(4) + \cos 4x \cos(7x^2 + 2)(14x)$$

$$= -4\sin(7x^2 + 2)\sin 4x + 14x \cos 4x \cos(7x^2 + 2)$$

In summary,

$$\frac{d}{dx}(\sin u) = \cos u \frac{du}{dx}$$

$$\frac{d}{dx}(\cos u) = -\sin u \frac{du}{dx}$$

Exercises 4.2

Find the derivative of each function.

1. $y = \sin 7x$ **2.** $y = 5\sin 2x$ **3.** $y = 2\cos 5x$

4. $y = 4\cos 6x$ **5.** $y = 2\sin x^3$ **6.** $y = -3\cos x^4$

7. $y = 3\cos 4x^2$ **8.** $y = 5\sin 8x^3$ **9.** $y = 4\sin(1 - x)$

10. $y = 6\cos(1 - 3x)$ **11.** $y = 3\sin(x^2 + 4)$ **12.** $y = \sin(x^3 + 2x^2 - 4)$

13. $y = 4\cos(5x^2 + x)$ **14.** $y = 2\cos(x - 3)$ **15.** $y = \cos(x^4 - 2x^2 + 3)$

16. $y = 3\cos(x^2 - 4)$ **17.** $y = \cos^2(3x - 1)$ **18.** $y = \sin^2(1 - 2x)$

19. $y = \sin^3(2x + 3)$ **20.** $y = \cos^4(x^2 - 1)$ **21.** $y = \sin(2x - 5)^2$

22. $y = \cos(5x + 4)^3$ **23.** $y = \cos(x^3 - 4)^4$ **24.** $y = 4\sin(x^2 + x - 3)^6$

25. $y = \sin x \cos 3x$ **26.** $y = \sin x^2 \cos 5x$

27. $y = \sin 5x \cos 6x$ **28.** $y = \sin(3x - 1)\cos(4x + 3)$

29. $y = \cos 4x \cos 7x$

30. $y = \sin 3x \sin 5x$

31. $y = \sin(x^2 + 2x) \cos x^3$

32. $y = \sin(x + 2)^3 \cos(x^2 - 3)$

33. $y = (x^2 + 3x) \sin(5x - 2)$

34. $y = \sqrt{4x - 3} \cos(x^2 + 2)$

35. $y = \dfrac{\sin 5x}{x}$

36. $y = \dfrac{\cos 6x}{3x^2}$

37. $y = \dfrac{x^2 - 1}{\cos 3x}$

38. $y = \dfrac{4x - 5}{\sin(2x - 1)}$

39. $y = \sin 5x + \cos 6x$

40. $y = 2 \sin 3x - 5 \sin 6x$

41. $y = \sin(x^2 - 3x) + \cos 4x$

42. $y = x^2 - 3 \sin^3 2x$

43. $y = \dfrac{\sin x}{\cos x}$

44. $y = \dfrac{\cos x}{\sin x}$

45. Find $\dfrac{d^2y}{dx^2}$ for $y = \cos x$.

46. Find $\dfrac{d^2y}{dx^2}$ for $y = \sin x$.

47. Find $\dfrac{d^3y}{dx^3}$ for $y = \sin x$.

48. Find $\dfrac{d^4y}{dx^4}$ for $y = \cos x$.

49. Find $\dfrac{d^2y}{dx^2}$ for Exercise 39.

50. Find $\dfrac{d^2y}{dx^2}$ for Exercise 40.

51. Find the slope of the tangent line to $y = 4 \sin 3x$ at $x = \pi/18$.

52. Find the slope of the tangent line to $y = -4 \cos 2x$ at $x = 5\pi/12$.

53. Find the equation of the tangent line to $y = 2 \cos 5x$ at $x = \pi/10$.

54. Find the equation of the tangent line to $y = 6 \cos 4x$ at $x = 5\pi/24$.

4.3 DERIVATIVES OF OTHER TRIGONOMETRIC FUNCTIONS

Using $\tan u = \dfrac{\sin u}{\cos u}$ and the quotient rule for differentiation, we have

$$\frac{d}{du}(\tan u) = \frac{d}{du}\left(\frac{\sin u}{\cos u}\right)$$

$$= \frac{\cos u \dfrac{d}{du}(\sin u) - \sin u \dfrac{d}{du}(\cos u)}{\cos^2 u}$$

$$= \frac{(\cos u)(\cos u) - (\sin u)(-\sin u)}{\cos^2 u}$$

$$= \frac{\cos^2 u + \sin^2 u}{\cos^2 u}$$

$$= \frac{1}{\cos^2 u} \qquad\qquad (\cos^2 u + \sin^2 u = 1)$$

$$= \sec^2 u \qquad\qquad \left(\frac{1}{\cos u} = \sec u\right)$$

and

$$\frac{d}{dx}(\tan u) = \sec^2 u \frac{du}{dx} \qquad\qquad \text{(using the chain rule)}$$

In a similar manner it can be shown that

$$\frac{d}{du}(\cot u) = -\csc^2 u$$

and

$$\frac{d}{dx}(\cot u) = -\csc^2 u \frac{du}{dx}$$

Since $\sec u = \dfrac{1}{\cos u}$, we have

$$\frac{d}{du}(\sec u) = \frac{d}{du}(\cos u)^{-1}$$

$$= -(\cos u)^{-2} \frac{d}{du}(\cos u)$$

$$= \frac{-1}{\cos^2 u}(-\sin u)$$

$$= \frac{\sin u}{\cos^2 u}$$

$$= \frac{1}{\cos u} \cdot \frac{\sin u}{\cos u}$$

$$= \sec u \tan u$$

and using the chain rule, we obtain

$$\frac{d}{dx}(\sec u) = \sec u \tan u \frac{du}{dx}$$

In a similar manner we can show that

$$\frac{d}{du}(\csc u) = -\csc u \cot u$$

and

$$\frac{d}{dx}(\csc u) = -\csc u \cot u \frac{du}{dx}$$

EXAMPLE 1

Find the derivative of $y = \tan(x^2 + 3)$.

$$\frac{dy}{dx} = \sec^2(x^2 + 3)\frac{d}{dx}(x^2 + 3) \qquad (u = x^2 + 3)$$

$$= \sec^2(x^2 + 3)(2x)$$

$$= 2x \sec^2(x^2 + 3)$$

EXAMPLE 2

Find the derivative of $y = \sec^3 5x$.

First, use the power rule for differentiation.

$$\frac{dy}{dx} = 3 \sec^2 5x \frac{d}{dx}(\sec 5x)$$

$$= (3 \sec^2 5x)(\sec 5x \tan 5x)\frac{d}{dx}(5x) \qquad (u = 5x)$$

$$= 15 \sec^3 5x \tan 5x$$

Using a calculator, we have

F3 1 1/ 2nd COS 5x)^3,x) **ENTER**

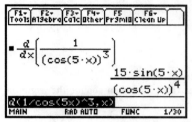

Note that the TI-89 uses $1/\cos(x)$ for sec x and that the derivative is obtained in terms of sine and cosine.

EXAMPLE 3

Find the derivative of $y = \cot \sqrt{3x + 1}$.

$$\frac{dy}{dx} = -\csc^2 \sqrt{3x + 1}\left[\frac{d}{dx}(3x + 1)^{1/2}\right] \qquad (u = \sqrt{3x + 1})$$

$$= (-\csc^2 \sqrt{3x + 1})\left[\frac{1}{2}(3x + 1)^{-1/2}(3)\right]$$

$$= \frac{-3 \csc^2 \sqrt{3x + 1}}{2\sqrt{3x + 1}}$$

EXAMPLE 4

Find the derivative of $y = \sec 3x \tan 4x$.

$$\frac{dy}{dx} = (\sec 3x)(\sec^2 4x)(4) + (\tan 4x)(\sec 3x \tan 3x)(3)$$

$$= 4 \sec 3x \sec^2 4x + 3 \sec 3x \tan 3x \tan 4x$$

EXAMPLE 5

Find the derivative of $y = (x^2 + \cot^3 4x)^6$.

$$\frac{dy}{dx} = 6(x^2 + \cot^3 4x)^5[2x + 3(\cot^2 4x)(-\csc^2 4x)(4)]$$

$$= 6(x^2 + \cot^3 4x)^5[2x - 12 \cot^2 4x \csc^2 4x]$$

$$= 12(x^2 + \cot^3 4x)^5(x - 6 \cot^2 4x \csc^2 4x)$$

EXAMPLE 6

Find the derivative of $y = \csc (\sin 5x)$.

$$\frac{dy}{dx} = [-\csc (\sin 5x) \cot (\sin 5x)]\frac{d}{dx}(\sin 5x) \qquad (u = \sin 5x)$$

$$= -5 \csc (\sin 5x) \cot (\sin 5x) \cos 5x$$

When you prove trigonometric identities, you often have a choice of which identities to use. Similarly, here in finding the derivative of a trigonometric expression, you may use a trigonometric identity to change the form of the original expression before finding the derivative, to simplify the result, or to change the result to another form. When finding the derivative, or later when finding the integral of a trigonometric expression, you will often need to use trigonometric identities to show that your answer is equivalent to the given answer.

EXAMPLE 7

Find the derivative of $y = \dfrac{\sin x}{\cot^2 x}$.

Method 1: First, find the derivative and then change the trigonometric functions to sine and cosine.

$$\frac{dy}{dx} = \frac{(\cot^2 x)(\cos x) - (\sin x)[(2 \cot x)(-\csc^2 x)]}{\cot^4 x}$$

$$= \frac{\cot x (\cot x \cos x + 2 \sin x \csc^2 x)}{\cot^4 x}$$

$$= \frac{\dfrac{\cos x}{\sin x} \cos x + 2 \sin x \dfrac{1}{\sin^2 x}}{\cot^3 x}$$

$$= \frac{\dfrac{\cos^2 x + 2}{\sin x}}{\dfrac{\cos^3 x}{\sin^3 x}}$$

$$= \frac{\sin^2 x(\cos^2 x + 2)}{\cos^3 x}$$

Method 2: Change the expression to sine and cosine first and then find the derivative.

$$y = \frac{\sin x}{\cot^2 x} = \frac{\sin x}{\dfrac{\cos^2 x}{\sin^2 x}} = \frac{\sin^3 x}{\cos^2 x}$$

$$\frac{dy}{dx} = \frac{(\cos^2 x)[(3 \sin^2 x)(\cos x)] - (\sin^3 x)[(2 \cos x)(-\sin x)]}{\cos^4 x}$$

$$= \frac{\cos x \sin^2 x[3 \cos^2 x + 2 \sin^2 x]}{\cos^4 x}$$

$$= \frac{\sin^2 x[\cos^2 x + 2(\cos^2 x + \sin^2 x)]}{\cos^3 x}$$

$$= \frac{\sin^2 x(\cos^2 x + 2)}{\cos^3 x}$$

In summary, the derivatives of the trigonometric functions are as follows:

$$\frac{d}{dx}(\sin u) = \cos u \frac{du}{dx}$$

$$\frac{d}{dx}(\cos u) = -\sin u \frac{du}{dx}$$

$$\frac{d}{dx}(\tan u) = \sec^2 u \frac{du}{dx}$$

$$\frac{d}{dx}(\cot u) = -\csc^2 u \frac{du}{dx}$$

$$\frac{d}{dx}(\sec u) = \sec u \tan u \frac{du}{dx}$$

$$\frac{d}{dx}(\csc u) = -\csc u \cot u \frac{du}{dx}$$

Exercises 4.3

Find the derivative of each function.

1. $y = \tan 3x$ **2.** $y = \cot 2x$ **3.** $y = \sec 7x$

4. $y = \csc 4x$ **5.** $y = \cot(3x^2 - 7)$ **6.** $y = \tan(x^3 + 4)$

7. $y = 3\csc(3x - 4)$ **8.** $y = 4\sec\left(x - \frac{\pi}{3}\right)$ **9.** $y = \tan^2(5x - 2)$

10. $y = \sec^4 7x$ **11.** $y = 4\cot^3 2x$ **12.** $y = \csc^3 x^4$

13. $y = \sec\sqrt{x^2 + x}$ **14.** $y = \sqrt{\tan 5x}$ **15.** $y = \dfrac{\csc x}{3x}$

16. $y = \dfrac{\cot 2x}{x}$ **17.** $y = \tan 3x - \sec(x^2 + 1)$ **18.** $y = \tan 2x + \cot 3x$

19. $y = \sec x \tan x$ **20.** $y = \sin x \sec x$ **21.** $y = \sin^2 x \cot x$

22. $y = \tan^2 x \sin x$ **23.** $y = x \sec x$ **24.** $y = x^2 \tan^2 x$

25. $y = x^2 + x^2 \tan^2 x$ **26.** $y = x^2 \csc^2 x - x^2$ **27.** $y = \csc 3x \cot 3x$

28. $y = \cot 2x \cos 4x$ **29.** $y = \csc^2 3x \sin 3x$ **30.** $y = \cos 2x \csc^2 x$

31. $y = (\sin x - \cos x)^2$ **32.** $y = \sec^2 x - \tan^2 x$ **33.** $y = (x + \sec^2 3x)^4$

34. $y = (\sin x - \tan^2 x)^3$ **35.** $y = (\sec x + \tan x)^3$ **36.** $y = (1 + \cot^3 x)^4$

37. $y = \sin(\tan x)$ **38.** $y = \sec(2\cos x)$ **39.** $y = \tan(\cos x)$

40. $y = \cos(\cot x)$ **41.** $y = \sin^2(\cos x)$ **42.** $y = \tan^2(\sin x)$

43. $y = \dfrac{\tan x}{\cos x}$ **44.** $y = \dfrac{\sec x}{\cot x}$ **45.** $y = \dfrac{\sin^2 x}{\tan^2 x}$

46. $y = \dfrac{\csc^2 x}{\tan x}$ **47.** $y = \dfrac{\sin x}{1 + \tan x}$ **48.** $y = \dfrac{\sin x}{1 + \cos x}$

Find the second derivative of each function.

49. $y = \tan 3x$ **50.** $y = \sec 2x$ **51.** $y = x \cot x$ **52.** $y = \dfrac{\tan x}{x}$

53. Find the slope of the tangent line to the curve $y = \tan x$ at $x = \pi/4$.

54. Find the slope of the tangent line to the curve $y = \sec^2 x$ at $x = \pi/4$.

55. Show that $\dfrac{d}{du}(\cot u) = -\csc^2 u$. **56.** Show that $\dfrac{d}{du}(\csc u) = -\csc u \cot u$.

4.4 INVERSE TRIGONOMETRIC FUNCTIONS

The inverse of a given equation is defined as the resulting equation when the variables x and y are interchanged. Recall that

$$\text{the inverse of } y = b^x \text{ is } x = b^y$$
$$\text{the inverse of } y = \sqrt[3]{x} \text{ is } x = \sqrt[3]{y}$$

Likewise, each basic trigonometric equation has an inverse.

The inverse of	is
$y = \sin x$	$x = \sin y$
$y = \cos x$	$x = \cos y$
$y = \tan x$	$x = \tan y$
$y = \cot x$	$x = \cot y$
$y = \sec x$	$x = \sec y$
$y = \csc x$	$x = \csc y$

Inverse functions are found by solving for y in the inverse equation. As previously mentioned, $y = \sqrt[3]{x}$ has the inverse equation $x = \sqrt[3]{y}$. Solving it for y (by cubing both sides) gives the inverse function $y = x^3$. This inverse function is often written as $f^{-1}(x) = x^3$ when the original function is written as $f(x) = \sqrt[3]{x}$. The symbolism "$f^{-1}(x)$" is pronounced "f inverse of x" and must not be confused with the reciprocal function $\dfrac{1}{f(x)}$. That is, the -1 in "$f^{-1}(x)$" should *not* be interpreted as an exponent.

On your calculator, the inverse trig functions are marked using this raised -1 since it gives a very short, convenient notation that fits comfortably on the calculator's keyboard. For example, the inverse of $f(x) = \sin x$ is shown as $f^{-1}(x) = \sin^{-1} x$. However, this symbolism is awkward for computer programming languages and other software which require commands to be typewritten on a computer keyboard. When working with computers, expect to use the notation "arcsin x" (or an abbreviation based on this idea). Learning to read and write both notations will provide the best preparation for modern technical work. Capitalized versions of these notations, $\text{Sin}^{-1} x$ and Arcsin x, are also commonly used, but are no longer considered standard.

There are two common forms of the inverse trigonometric equations solved for y.

The inverse of	is	Solved for y is[a]	is
$y = \sin x$	$x = \sin y$	$y = \arcsin x$	$y = \sin^{-1} x$
$y = \cos x$	$x = \cos y$	$y = \arccos x$	$y = \cos^{-1} x$
$y = \tan x$	$x = \tan y$	$y = \arctan x$	$y = \tan^{-1} x$
$y = \cot x$	$x = \cot y$	$y = \text{arccot } x$	$y = \cot^{-1} x$
$y = \sec x$	$x = \sec y$	$y = \text{arcsec } x$	$y = \sec^{-1} x$
$y = \csc x$	$x = \csc y$	$y = \text{arccsc } x$	$y = \csc^{-1} x$

[a]Note that $y = \arcsin x$, for example, is read, "y equals the arc sine of x" and means that y is the angle whose sine is x.

EXAMPLE 1

What is the meaning of each equation?

(a) $y = \arctan x$ (a) y is the angle whose tangent is x.

(b) $y = \arccos 3x$ (b) y is the angle whose cosine is $3x$.

(c) $y = 4 \text{ arccsc } 5x$ (c) y is four times the angle whose cosecant is $5x$.

Remember that $x = \sin y$ and $y = \arcsin x$ express the same relationship. The first form expresses the relationship in terms of the function (sine) of the angle; the second form expresses the relationship in terms of the angle itself.

EXAMPLE 2

Solve the equation $y = \cos 2x$ for x.
This equation is equivalent to

$$\arccos y = 2x$$

So

$$x = \frac{1}{2} \arccos y$$

EXAMPLE 3

Solve the equation $2y = \arctan 3x$ for x.
This equation is equivalent to

$$\tan 2y = 3x$$

So

$$x = \frac{1}{3} \tan 2y$$

EXAMPLE 4

Solve the equation $y = \frac{1}{3} \operatorname{arcsec} 2x$ for x.
First, multiply both sides by 3.

$$3y = \operatorname{arcsec} 2x$$

This equation is equivalent to

$$\sec 3y = 2x$$

Thus

$$x = \frac{1}{2} \sec 3y$$

To understand an inverse trigonometric function like

$$y = \arcsin x$$

first graph the corresponding inverse trigonometric equation solved for x, that is,

$$x = \sin y$$

as shown in Fig. 4.11(a). The graphs of all six inverse trigonometric equations are shown in Fig. 4.12. To easily produce these graphs yourself, use a transparency (or a thin piece of paper with markers that will bleed through enough to be visible on the back side) and draw the graph of the original trigonometric function, like $y = \sin x$, carefully labeling the (positive) x- and y-axes. Rotate the transparency (or paper) 90° counterclockwise and notice that the positive x-axis is where the positive y-axis used to be; unfortunately, the positive y-axis is where the *negative* x-axis was. Now turn the transparency over (looking at it from the back) and you will finally see the perfect reversal of the roles of x and y, and thus you will be viewing a graph of $x = \sin y$ instead of your drawing of $y = \sin x$. This transformation can also be performed with a graphing calculator and a mirror. Graph $y = \sin x$ (using **ZoomTrig**), then tilt the calculator sideways so that the keyboard is on your right as you are viewing the screen. Now look at the back of the calculator, viewing the image in the mirror in Fig. 4.11(b). This will show you the graph with the positive x-axis replacing the positive y-axis and vice versa, so you will be viewing $x = \sin y$ instead of $y = \sin x$. To go directly to this correct mirror image position, you should be looking at the back of the calculator in a sideways orientation, with its tapered (battery chamber) end on the left-hand side.

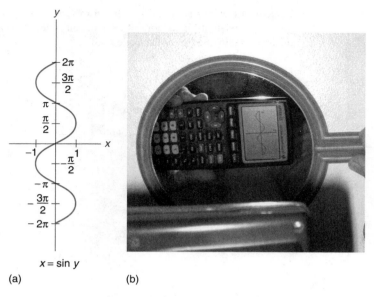

$x = \sin y$

(a)   (b)

Figure 4.11

As you can see from the graphs in Fig. 4.12, each x-value in each domain corresponds to (infinitely) many values of y. Thus, none of the inverse trigonometric equations describes a function unless we restrict the y-values in an appropriate way. The customary restrictions are as follows:

INVERSE TRIGONOMETRIC FUNCTIONS

$y = \arcsin x, \qquad -\dfrac{\pi}{2} \leq y \leq \dfrac{\pi}{2}$

$y = \arccos x, \qquad 0 \leq y \leq \pi$

$y = \arctan x, \qquad -\dfrac{\pi}{2} < y < \dfrac{\pi}{2}$

$y = \operatorname{arccot} x, \qquad 0 < y < \pi$

$y = \operatorname{arcsec} x, \qquad 0 \leq y \leq \pi, y \neq \dfrac{\pi}{2}$

$y = \operatorname{arccsc} x, \qquad -\dfrac{\pi}{2} \leq y \leq \dfrac{\pi}{2}, y \neq 0$

Look at the graphs of the inverse trigonometric equations in Fig. 4.12. The colored lines indicate the portions of the graphs that correspond to the inverse trigonometric *functions.*

Note: The three inverse trigonometric functions on calculators are programmed to these same restricted ranges. When using a calculator to find the value of arccot x, arcsec x, or arccsc x, use the following:

1. $\operatorname{arccot} x = \begin{cases} \arctan \dfrac{1}{x} & \text{if } x > 0 \\[2mm] \pi + \arctan \dfrac{1}{x} & \text{if } x < 0 \end{cases}$

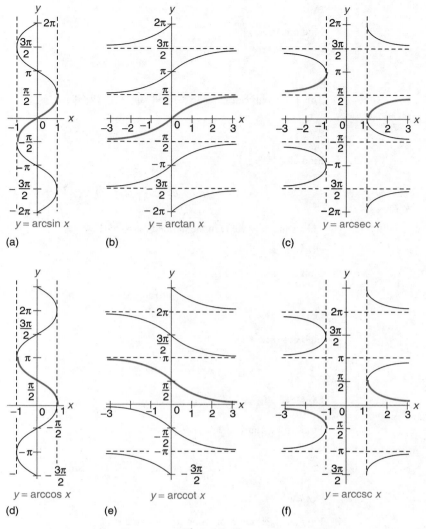

(a) $y = \arcsin x$

(b) $y = \arctan x$

(c) $y = \text{arcsec } x$

(d) $y = \arccos x$

(e) $y = \text{arccot } x$

(f) $y = \text{arccsc } x$

Figure 4.12

2. $\text{arcsec } x = \arccos \dfrac{1}{x}$ where $x \geq 1$ or $x \leq -1$

3. $\text{arccsc } x = \arcsin \dfrac{1}{x}$ where $x \geq 1$ or $x \leq -1$

EXAMPLE 5

Find $\arcsin\left(\dfrac{1}{2}\right)$.

$$\arcsin\left(\frac{1}{2}\right) = \frac{\pi}{6}$$

This is the only value in the defined range of $-\dfrac{\pi}{2} \leq y \leq \dfrac{\pi}{2}$.

EXAMPLE 6

Find arctan (-1).

$$\arctan(-1) = -\frac{\pi}{4}$$

This is the only value in the defined range of $-\frac{\pi}{2} < y < \frac{\pi}{2}$.

EXAMPLE 7

Find $\cos^{-1}\left(-\frac{1}{2}\right)$.

$$\cos^{-1}\left(-\frac{1}{2}\right) = \frac{2\pi}{3}$$

This is the only value in the defined range of $0 \le y \le \pi$.

EXAMPLE 8

Find $\tan[\arccos(-1)]$.

$$\tan[\arccos(-1)] = \tan\pi = 0$$

EXAMPLE 9

Find $\cos(\sec^{-1} 2)$.

$$\cos(\sec^{-1} 2) = \cos\frac{\pi}{3} = \frac{1}{2}$$

EXAMPLE 10

Find $\sin\left[\arctan\left(-\frac{1}{\sqrt{3}}\right)\right]$.

$$\sin\left[\arctan\left(-\frac{1}{\sqrt{3}}\right)\right] = \sin\left(-\frac{\pi}{6}\right) = -\frac{1}{2}$$

EXAMPLE 11

Find an algebraic expression for $\sin(\arccos x)$.

Let $\theta = \arccos x$. Then

$$\cos\theta = x = \frac{x}{1}$$

Draw a right triangle with θ as an acute angle, x as the adjacent side, and 1 as the hypotenuse as in Fig. 4.13(a). Using the Pythagorean theorem, we obtain

$$c^2 = a^2 + b^2$$
$$1^2 = x^2 + (\text{side opposite } \theta)^2$$
$$\text{side opposite } \theta = \sqrt{1 - x^2} \qquad \text{(Fig. 4.13b)}$$

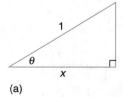

(a)

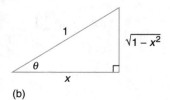

(b)

Figure 4.13

Now we see that

$$\sin(\arccos x) = \sin\theta$$
$$= \frac{\text{side opposite }\theta}{\text{hypotenuse}}$$
$$= \frac{\sqrt{1 - x^2}}{1}$$
$$= \sqrt{1 - x^2}$$

Using a calculator, we have

2nd SIN green diamond COS⁻¹ x)) ENTER

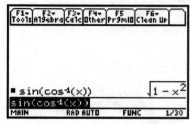

EXAMPLE 12

Find an algebraic expression for sec (arctan x).
    Let $\theta = \arctan x$. Then

$$\tan\theta = x = \frac{x}{1}$$

Draw a right triangle with θ as an acute angle, x as the opposite side, and 1 as the adjacent side as in Fig. 4.14. Using the Pythagorean theorem, we find the hypotenuse is $\sqrt{x^2 + 1}$.

$$\sec(\arctan x) = \sec\theta$$
$$= \frac{\text{hypotenuse}}{\text{side adjacent to }\theta}$$
$$= \frac{\sqrt{x^2 + 1}}{1}$$
$$= \sqrt{x^2 + 1}$$

Figure 4.14

To use a calculator, you must write secant in terms of cosine.

1/ 2nd COS green diamond TAN⁻¹ x)) ENTER

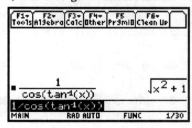

EXAMPLE 13

Find an algebraic expression for cos ($2\sin^{-1} x$).
    Let $\theta = \sin^{-1} x$. Then

$$\sin\theta = \frac{x}{1}$$

Draw a right triangle with θ as an acute angle, x as the opposite side, and 1 as the hypotenuse as in Fig. 4.15. Using the Pythagorean theorem, we find the side adjacent to θ is $\sqrt{1 - x^2}$.

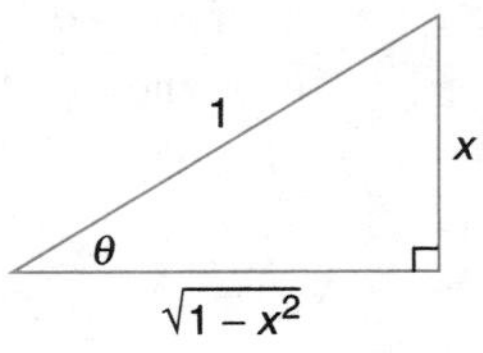

Figure 4.15

$$\cos\left(2\sin^{-1}x\right) = \cos 2\theta$$
$$= 1 - 2\sin^2\theta$$
$$= 1 - 2x^2$$

(Formula 25c of the Common Trigonometric Identities listed inside the back cover.)

Exercises 4.4

Solve each equation for x.

1. $y = \sin 3x$

2. $y = \tan 4x$

3. $y = 4\cos x$

4. $y = 3\sec x$

5. $y = 5\tan\dfrac{x}{2}$

6. $y = \dfrac{1}{2}\cos 3x$

7. $y = \dfrac{3}{2}\cot\dfrac{x}{4}$

8. $y = \dfrac{5}{2}\sin\dfrac{2x}{3}$

9. $y = 3\sin(x - 1)$

10. $y = 4\tan(2x + 1)$

11. $y = \dfrac{1}{2}\cos(3x + 1)$

12. $y = \dfrac{1}{3}\sec(1 - 4x)$

Find the value of each expression in radians.

13. $\arcsin\left(\dfrac{\sqrt{3}}{2}\right)$

14. $\arccos\left(\dfrac{1}{2}\right)$

15. $\tan^{-1}\left(-\dfrac{1}{\sqrt{3}}\right)$

16. $\sin^{-1}\left(-\dfrac{1}{2}\right)$

17. $\arccos\left(-\dfrac{\sqrt{3}}{2}\right)$

18. $\arctan\left(\dfrac{1}{\sqrt{3}}\right)$

19. $\operatorname{arccsc}\sqrt{2}$

20. $\arcsin(-1)$

21. $\arctan\sqrt{3}$

22. $\arccos 0$

23. $\cos^{-1}\left(\dfrac{1}{\sqrt{2}}\right)$

24. $\sin^{-1}1$

25. $\sin^{-1}\left(-\dfrac{\sqrt{3}}{2}\right)$

26. $\tan^{-1}(-\sqrt{3})$

Find the value of each expression.

27. $\cos(\arctan\sqrt{3})$

28. $\tan\left[\arcsin\left(\dfrac{1}{\sqrt{2}}\right)\right]$

29. $\sin\left[\arccos\left(-\dfrac{1}{\sqrt{2}}\right)\right]$

30. $\sin[\arctan(-1)]$

31. $\tan[\cos^{-1}(-1)]$

32. $\sec\left[\cos^{-1}\left(-\dfrac{1}{2}\right)\right]$

33. $\sin\left[\arcsin\left(\dfrac{\sqrt{3}}{2}\right)\right]$

34. $\tan[\arctan(-\sqrt{3})]$

35. $\cos\left[\sin^{-1}\left(\dfrac{3}{5}\right)\right]$

36. $\tan\left[\sin^{-1}\left(\dfrac{12}{13}\right)\right]$

37. $\tan[\arcsin(-0.1560)]$

38. $\sin[\operatorname{arccot}(1.635)]$

Find an algebraic expression for each.

39. $\cos(\arcsin x)$

40. $\tan(\arccos x)$

41. $\sin(\operatorname{arcsec} x)$

42. $\cot(\operatorname{arcsec} x)$

43. $\sec(\cos^{-1}x)$

44. $\sin(\tan^{-1}x)$

45. $\tan(\arctan x)$

46. $\sin(\arcsin x)$

47. $\cos(\arcsin 2x)$

48. $\tan(\cos^{-1}3x)$

49. $\sin(2\sin^{-1}x)$

50. $\cos(2\arctan x)$

4.5 DERIVATIVES OF INVERSE TRIGONOMETRIC FUNCTIONS

To differentiate $y = \arcsin u$, first differentiate its inverse, the function $u = \sin y$ for $-\dfrac{\pi}{2} \le y \le \dfrac{\pi}{2}$. Then

$$\frac{du}{dx} = \frac{d}{dx}(\sin y) = \cos y \,\frac{dy}{dx}$$

Solving for $\dfrac{dy}{dx}$, we obtain

$$\frac{dy}{dx} = \frac{1}{\cos y} \cdot \frac{du}{dx}$$

Now, express $\cos y$ in terms of $\sin y$ using the identity $\sin^2 y + \cos^2 y = 1$, that is,

$$\cos y = \sqrt{1 - \sin^2 y}$$

Note that $\cos y = +\sqrt{1 - \sin^2 y}$ because $-\dfrac{\pi}{2} \le \arcsin u \le \dfrac{\pi}{2}$ and $\cos y > 0$ in quadrants I and IV. So

$$\frac{dy}{dx} = \frac{1}{\sqrt{1 - \sin^2 y}}\,\frac{du}{dx}$$

$$= \frac{1}{\sqrt{1 - u^2}}\,\frac{du}{dx} \qquad (\text{since } u = \sin y)$$

EXAMPLE 1

Find the derivative of $y = \arcsin 2x$.

Let $u = 2x$, then

$$\frac{dy}{dx} = \frac{1}{\sqrt{1 - (2x)^2}}(2) = \frac{2}{\sqrt{1 - 4x^2}}$$

To differentiate $y = \arctan u$, begin with its inverse:

$$u = \tan y$$

$$\frac{du}{dx} = \frac{d}{dx}(\tan y) = \sec^2 y \,\frac{dy}{dx}$$

Solving for $\dfrac{dy}{dx}$, we obtain

$$\frac{dy}{dx} = \frac{1}{\sec^2 y}\,\frac{du}{dx}$$

$$= \frac{1}{1 + \tan^2 y}\,\frac{du}{dx} \qquad (\sec^2 y = 1 + \tan^2 y)$$

$$= \frac{1}{1 + u^2}\,\frac{du}{dx} \qquad (u = \tan y)$$

EXAMPLE 2

Find the derivative of $y = \arctan 3x^2$.

Let $u = 3x^2$, then

$$\frac{dy}{dx} = \frac{1}{1 + (3x^2)^2}(6x) = \frac{6x}{1 + 9x^4}$$

Formulas for the derivatives of the other trigonometric functions are found in a similar manner and are left as exercises. The formulas for the derivatives of the six inverse trigonometric functions follow:

DERIVATIVES OF THE INVERSE TRIGONOMETRIC FUNCTIONS

$$\frac{d}{dx}(\arcsin u) = \frac{1}{\sqrt{1 - u^2}}\frac{du}{dx}$$

$$\frac{d}{dx}(\arccos u) = -\frac{1}{\sqrt{1 - u^2}}\frac{du}{dx}$$

$$\frac{d}{dx}(\arctan u) = \frac{1}{1 + u^2}\frac{du}{dx}$$

$$\frac{d}{dx}(\text{arccot } u) = -\frac{1}{1 + u^2}\frac{du}{dx}$$

$$\frac{d}{dx}(\text{arcsec } u) = \frac{1}{|u|\sqrt{u^2 - 1}}\frac{du}{dx}$$

$$\frac{d}{dx}(\text{arccsc } u) = -\frac{1}{|u|\sqrt{u^2 - 1}}\frac{du}{dx}$$

EXAMPLE 3

Find the derivative of $y = \arccos^3 6x$.

Find the derivative of a power u^3, where $u = \arccos 6x$.

$$\frac{dy}{dx} = (3\arccos^2 6x)\left(-\frac{1}{\sqrt{1 - (6x)^2}}\right)(6)$$

$$= \frac{-18\arccos^2 6x}{\sqrt{1 - 36x^2}}$$

EXAMPLE 4

Find the derivative of $y = x^2\text{ arcsec}(1 - 3x)$.

$$\frac{dy}{dx} = x^2\left(\frac{1}{|1 - 3x|\sqrt{(1 - 3x)^2 - 1}}\right)(-3) + 2x\text{ arcsec}(1 - 3x)$$

$$= \frac{-3x^2}{|1 - 3x|\sqrt{9x^2 - 6x}} + 2x\text{ arcsec}(1 - 3x)$$

Exercises 4.5

Find the derivative of each.

1. $y = \arcsin 5x$

2. $y = \arccos 6x$

3. $y = \arctan 3x$

4. $y = \text{arcsec } 4x$

5. $y = \text{arccsc } (1 - x)$

6. $y = \text{arccot } \sqrt{x}$

7. $y = 3 \arccos (x - 1)$

8. $y = 4 \arcsin(1/x)$

9. $y = 2 \text{ arccot } 3x^2$

10. $y = 3 \arctan (x^2 - 1)$

11. $y = 5 \text{ arcsec } x^3$

12. $y = 6 \text{ arccsc } (x/2)$

13. $y = \arcsin^3 x$

14. $y = \arctan^2 5x$

15. $y = 2 \arccos^2 3x$

16. $y = 4 \text{ arcsec}^3 2x$

17. $y = 3 \arctan^4 \sqrt{x}$

18. $y = 6 \arcsin^2 (1 - x)$

19. $y = \arcsin x + \arccos x$

20. $y = x - \arctan x$

21. $y = \sqrt{1 - x^2} + \arcsin x$

22. $y = \sqrt{1 - x^2} + \arccos x$

23. $y = x \arcsin 3x$

24. $y = x^2 \arccos x$

25. $y = x \arctan x$

26. $y = x \arcsin x^2$

27. $y = x \arcsin x + \sqrt{1 - x^2}$

28. $y = \dfrac{x}{\sqrt{1 - x^2}} - \arcsin x$

29. $y = \dfrac{x}{\arcsin x}$

30. $y = \dfrac{\arctan x}{x}$

Find the slope of the tangent line to each curve at the given value.

31. $y = x \arcsin x$ at $x = \frac{1}{2}$

32. $y = \arctan x$ at $x = 1$

33. $y = x \arctan x$ at $x = -1$

34. $y = \arccos^2 x$ at $x = \dfrac{\sqrt{3}}{2}$

35. Show that $\dfrac{d}{dx} \arccos u = -\dfrac{1}{\sqrt{1 - u^2}} \dfrac{du}{dx}$.

36. Show that $\dfrac{d}{dx} \text{arccot } u = -\dfrac{1}{1 + u^2} \dfrac{du}{dx}$.

37. Show that $\dfrac{d}{dx} \text{arcsec } u = \dfrac{1}{|u| \sqrt{(u^2 - 1)}} \dfrac{du}{dx}$.

38. Show that $\dfrac{d}{dx} \text{arccsc } u = -\dfrac{1}{|u| \sqrt{(u^2 - 1)}} \dfrac{du}{dx}$.

4.6 EXPONENTIAL AND LOGARITHMIC FUNCTIONS

We have considered equations with a *constant* exponent in the form

$$y = x^n$$

These are called **power functions.** Two examples are $y = x^2$ and $y = x^{4/3}$.

> **EXPONENTIAL FUNCTION**
>
> Equations with a variable exponent in the form
>
> $$y = b^x$$
>
> where $b > 0$ and $b \neq 1$, are called **exponential functions.**

Two examples are $y = 2^x$ and $y = \left(\frac{3}{4}\right)^x$.

EXAMPLE 1

Graph $y = 2^x$ by plotting points (see Fig. 4.16).

x	y	$y = 2^x$
0	1	$y = 2^0 = 1$
1	2	$y = 2^1 = 2$
2	4	$y = 2^2 = 4$
3	8	$y = 2^3 = 8$
-1	$\dfrac{1}{2}$	$y = 2^{-1} = \dfrac{1}{2}$
-2	$\dfrac{1}{4}$	$y = 2^{-2} = \dfrac{1}{4}$
-3	$\dfrac{1}{8}$	$y = 2^{-3} = \dfrac{1}{8}$

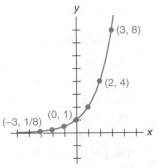

Figure 4.16

In general, for $b > 1$, $y = b^x$ is an **increasing** function. That is, as x increases, y increases.

EXAMPLE 2

Graph $y = \left(\frac{1}{2}\right)^x$ by plotting points (see Fig. 4.17).

x	y	$y = \left(\dfrac{1}{2}\right)^x$
0	1	$y = \left(\dfrac{1}{2}\right)^0 = 1$
1	$\dfrac{1}{2}$	$y = \left(\dfrac{1}{2}\right)^1 = \dfrac{1}{2}$
2	$\dfrac{1}{4}$	$y = \left(\dfrac{1}{2}\right)^2 = \dfrac{1}{4}$
3	$\dfrac{1}{8}$	$y = \left(\dfrac{1}{2}\right)^3 = \dfrac{1}{8}$
-1	2	$y = \left(\dfrac{1}{2}\right)^{-1} = 2$
-2	4	$y = \left(\dfrac{1}{2}\right)^{-2} = 4$
-3	8	$y = \left(\dfrac{1}{2}\right)^{-3} = 8$

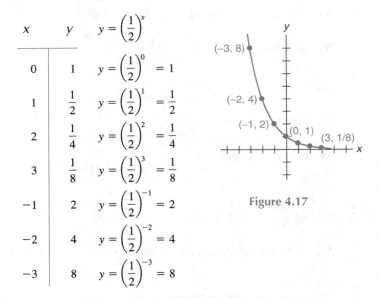

Figure 4.17

In general, for $0 < b < 1$, $y = b^x$ is a **decreasing** function. That is, as x increases, y decreases.

Some basic laws of exponents are given below for $a \neq 0$, $b \neq 0$.

LAWS OF EXPONENTS

1. $a^m \cdot a^n = a^{m+n}$

2. $\dfrac{a^m}{a^n} = a^{m-n}$

3. $(a^m)^n = a^{mn}$

$$4.\ (ab)^n = a^n b^n$$

$$5.\ \left(\frac{a}{b}\right)^n = \frac{a^n}{b^n}$$

$$6.\ a^0 = 1$$

When the values of x and y are interchanged in an equation, the resulting equation is called the **inverse** of the given equation. The inverse of the exponential equation $y = b^x$ is the exponential equation $x = b^y$. We define this inverse equation to be the **logarithmic** equation. The middle and right equations below show how to express this logarithmic equation in either exponential form or logarithmic form:

Exponential equation	Logarithmic equation in exponential form	Logarithmic equation in logarithmic form
$y = b^x$	$x = b^y$	$y = \log_b x$

That is, $x = b^y$ and $y = \log_b x$ are equivalent equations for $b > 0$ but $b \neq 1$.

The logarithm of a number is the *exponent* indicating the power to which the base must be raised to equal that number. The expression $\log_b x$ is read "the logarithm of x to the base b" or "the log, base b, of x."

Remember: A logarithm is an exponent.

EXAMPLE 3

Write each equation in logarithmic form.

	Exponential form	Logarithmic form
(a)	$2^3 = 8$	$\log_2 8 = 3$
(b)	$5^2 = 25$	$\log_5 25 = 2$
(c)	$4^{-2} = \dfrac{1}{16}$	$\log_4\left(\tfrac{1}{16}\right) = -2$
(d)	$36^{1/2} = 6$	$\log_{36} 6 = \tfrac{1}{2}$
(e)	$p^q = r$	$\log_p r = q$

EXAMPLE 4

Write each equation in exponential form.

	Logarithmic form	Exponential form
(a)	$\log_7 49 = 2$	$7^2 = 49$
(b)	$\log_4 64 = 3$	$4^3 = 64$
(c)	$\log_{10} 0.01 = -2$	$10^{-2} = 0.01$
(d)	$\log_{27} 3 = \tfrac{1}{3}$	$27^{1/3} = 3$
(e)	$\log_m p = n$	$m^n = p$

EXAMPLE 5

Graph $y = \log_2 x$ by plotting points.

First, change the equation from logarithmic form to exponential form. That is, $y = \log_2 x$ is equivalent to $x = 2^y$. Then choose values for y and compute values for x (see Fig. 4.18).

x	y	$x = 2^y$	
1	0	$x = 2^0$	$= 1$
2	1	$x = 2^1$	$= 2$
4	2	$x = 2^2$	$= 4$
8	3	$x = 2^3$	$= 8$
$\dfrac{1}{2}$	-1	$x = 2^{-1}$	$= \dfrac{1}{2}$
$\dfrac{1}{4}$	-2	$x = 2^{-2}$	$= \dfrac{1}{4}$
$\dfrac{1}{8}$	-3	$x = 2^{-3}$	$= \dfrac{1}{8}$

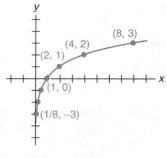

Figure 4.18

EXAMPLE 6

If $\log_3 81 = x$, find x.

The exponential form of $\log_3 81 = x$ is

$$3^x = 81$$

We know that

$$3^4 = 81$$

Therefore,

$$x = 4$$

EXAMPLE 7

If $\log_3 x = -2$, find x.

$$\log_3 x = -2 \quad \text{or} \quad 3^{-2} = x$$

Therefore,

$$x = \frac{1}{9}$$

EXAMPLE 8

If $\log_x 32 = \dfrac{5}{3}$, find x.

$$\log_x 32 = \frac{5}{3} \quad \text{or} \quad x^{5/3} = 32$$

$$x^{1/3} = 2 \qquad \text{(Take the fifth root of each side.)}$$
$$x = 8 \qquad \text{(Cube each side.)}$$

Or begin with

$$x^{5/3} = 32$$
$$(x^{5/3})^{3/5} = 32^{3/5} \qquad \text{(Raise each side to the } \tfrac{3}{5} \text{ power.)}$$
$$x = 8$$

The following are three basic logarithmic properties.

1. *Multiplication:* If M and N are positive real numbers,

$$\log_a(M \cdot N) = \log_a M + \log_a N$$
$$\text{where } a > 0 \text{ and } a \neq 1.$$

That is, the logarithm of a product equals the sum of the logarithms of its factors.

2. *Division:* If M and N are positive real numbers,

$$\log_a\left(\frac{M}{N}\right) = \log_a M - \log_a N$$

where $a > 0$ and $a \neq 1$.

That is, the logarithm of a quotient equals the difference of the logarithms of its numerator and denominator.

3. *Powers:* If M is a positive real number and n is any real number,

$$\log_a M^n = n \log_a M$$

where $a > 0$ and $a \neq 1$.

That is, the logarithm of a power of a number equals the product of the exponent times the logarithm of the number.

There are three special cases of the power property that are helpful.

(a) *Roots:* If M is any positive real number and n is any positive integer,

$$\log_a \sqrt[n]{M} = \frac{1}{n} \cdot \log_a M$$

Note that this is a special case of Property 3, since $\sqrt[n]{M} = M^{1/n}$. That is, the logarithm of the root of a number equals the logarithm of the number divided by the index of the root.

(b) For $n = 0$,

$$\begin{aligned}\log_a M^0 &= \log_a 1 \qquad\quad (M^0 = 1)\\ \log_a M^0 &= 0 \cdot \log_a M \qquad \text{(Property 3)}\\ &= 0\end{aligned}$$

Therefore,

$$\log_a 1 = 0$$

That is, the logarithm of one is zero, regardless of the base.

(c) For $n = -1$,

$$\begin{aligned}\log_a M^{-1} &= \log_a \frac{1}{M} \qquad\quad \left(M^{-1} = \frac{1}{M}\right)\\ \log_a M^{-1} &= (-1)\log_a M \qquad \text{(Property 3)}\end{aligned}$$

Therefore,

$$\log_a \frac{1}{M} = -\log_a M$$

That is, the logarithm of the reciprocal of a number is the negative of the logarithm of the number.

EXAMPLE 9

Write $\log_4 2x^5 y^2$ as a sum and multiple of logarithms of a single variable.

$$\log_4 2x^5 y^2 = \log_4 2 + \log_4 x^5 + \log_4 y^2 \qquad \text{(Property 1)}$$
$$= \log_4 2 + 5\log_4 x + 2\log_4 y \qquad \text{(Property 3)}$$

EXAMPLE 10

Write $\log_3 \dfrac{\sqrt{x(x-2)}}{(x+3)^2}$ as a sum, difference, or multiple of the logarithms of x, $x-2$, and $x+3$.

$$\log_3 \frac{\sqrt{x(x-2)}}{(x+3)^2} = \log_3 \frac{[x(x-2)]^{1/2}}{(x+3)^2}$$
$$= \log_3 [x(x-2)]^{1/2} - \log_3 (x+3)^2 \qquad \text{(Property 2)}$$
$$= \frac{1}{2}\log_3 [x(x-2)] - 2\log_3 (x+3) \qquad \text{(Property 3)}$$
$$= \frac{1}{2}\left[\log_3 x + \log_3 (x-2)\right] - 2\log_3 (x+3) \qquad \text{(Property 1)}$$
$$= \frac{1}{2}\log_3 x + \frac{1}{2}\log_3 (x-2) - 2\log_3 (x+3)$$

EXAMPLE 11

Write $3\log_2 x + 4\log_2 y - 2\log_2 z$ as a single logarithmic expression.

$$3\log_2 x + 4\log_2 y - 2\log_2 z = \log_2 x^3 + \log_2 y^4 - \log_2 z^2 \qquad \text{(Property 3)}$$
$$= \log_2 (x^3 y^4) - \log_2 z^2 \qquad \text{(Property 1)}$$
$$= \log_2 \frac{x^3 y^4}{z^2} \qquad \text{(Property 2)}$$

EXAMPLE 12

Write $3\log_{10} (x-1) - \dfrac{1}{3}\log_{10} x - \log_{10} (2x+3)$ as a single logarithmic expression.

$$3\log_{10} (x-1) - \frac{1}{3}\log_{10} x - \log_{10} (2x+3)$$
$$= \log_{10} (x-1)^3 - \log_{10} x^{1/3} - \log_{10} (2x+3) \qquad \text{(Property 3)}$$
$$= \log_{10} (x-1)^3 - [\log_{10} x^{1/3} + \log_{10} (2x+3)]$$
$$= \log_{10} (x-1)^3 - [\log_{10} (x^{1/3})(2x+3)] \qquad \text{(Property 1)}$$
$$= \log_{10} \frac{(x-1)^3}{x^{1/3}(2x+3)} \qquad \text{(Property 2)}$$
$$= \log_{10} \frac{(x-1)^3}{\sqrt[3]{x}(2x+3)}$$

Two other logarithmic properties that are useful in simplifying expressions are

$$\log_a a^x = x \quad \text{and} \quad a^{\log_a x} = x$$

To show the first one, we begin with the identity

$$(a^x) = a^x$$

Then, writing this exponential equation in logarithmic form, we have

$$\log_a (a^x) = x$$

To show the second one, we begin with the identity

$$\log_a x = (\log_a x)$$

Then, writing this logarithmic equation in exponential form, we have

$$a^{(\log_a x)} = x$$

EXAMPLE 13

Find the value of $\log_2 16$.

$$\log_2 16 = \log_2 2^4 \qquad \text{(Note that this simplification is}$$
$$= 4 \qquad\qquad \text{possible because 16 is a power of 2.)}$$

EXAMPLE 14

Find the value of $\log_{10} 0.01$.

$$\log_{10} 0.01 = \log_{10} 10^{-2} \qquad \text{(Note that } 0.01 = \tfrac{1}{100} = 10^{-2}.)$$
$$= -2$$

EXAMPLE 15

Find the value of $5^{\log_5 8}$.

$$5^{\log_5 8} = 8$$

Another useful law is for change of base:

$$\log_b x = \frac{\log_a x}{\log_a b}$$

Although all the laws of exponents and logarithms hold for any base b ($b > 0$ and $b \neq 1$), there are two standard bases for logarithms:

1. *Common logarithms:* Base 10

   Usual notation: $\log_{10} x = \log x$

2. *Natural logarithms:* Base e

   Usual notation: $\log_e x = \ln x$

As we shall see, the most convenient base for use in calculus is base e, which is defined as

$$e = \lim_{x \to 0} (1 + x)^{1/x} \approx 2.7182818$$

Exercises 4.6

Graph each equation.

1. $y = 4^x$ 2. $y = 3^x$ 3. $y = (\tfrac{1}{3})^x$ 4. $y = (\tfrac{1}{4})^x$

5. $y = 4^{-x}$ 6. $y = (\tfrac{2}{3})^x$ 7. $y = (\tfrac{4}{3})^{-x}$ 8. $y = 4^{2x}$

Write each equation in logarithmic form.

9. $3^2 = 9$ **10.** $7^2 = 49$ **11.** $5^3 = 125$ **12.** $10^3 = 1000$

13. $9^{1/2} = 3$ **14.** $4^0 = 1$ **15.** $10^{-5} = 0.00001$ **16.** $d^e = f$

Write each equation in exponential form.

17. $\log_5 25 = 2$ **18.** $\log_8 64 = 2$ **19.** $\log_{25} 5 = \frac{1}{2}$ **20.** $\log_{27} 3 = \frac{1}{3}$

21. $\log_2 \left(\frac{1}{4}\right) = -2$ **22.** $\log_2 \left(\frac{1}{8}\right) = -3$ **23.** $\log_{10} 0.01 = -2$ **24.** $\log_g h = k$

Graph each equation.

25. $y = \log_4 x$ **26.** $y = \log_3 x$ **27.** $y = \log_{10} x$

28. $y = \log_5 x$ **29.** $y = \log_{1/4} x$ **30.** $y = \log_{1/3} x$

Solve for x.

31. $\log_4 x = 3$ **32.** $\log_2 x = -1$ **33.** $\log_9 3 = x$ **34.** $\log_6 36 = x$

35. $\log_2 8 = x$ **36.** $\log_3 27 = x$ **37.** $\log_{25} 5 = x$ **38.** $\log_{27} 3 = x$

39. $\log_x 25 = 2$ **40.** $\log_x \left(\frac{1}{27}\right) = -3$ **41.** $\log_{1/2} \left(\frac{1}{8}\right) = x$ **42.** $\log_x 3 = \frac{1}{2}$

43. $\log_{12} x = 2$ **44.** $\log_8 \left(\frac{1}{64}\right) = x$ **45.** $\log_x 9 = \frac{2}{3}$ **46.** $\log_x 64 = \frac{3}{2}$

47. $\log_x \left(\frac{1}{8}\right) = -\frac{3}{2}$ **48.** $\log_x \left(\frac{1}{27}\right) = -\frac{3}{4}$

Write each expression as a sum, difference, or multiple of single logarithms.

49. $\log_2 5x^3 y$ **50.** $\log_3 \dfrac{8x^2 y^3}{z^4}$ **51.** $\log_b \dfrac{y^3 \sqrt{x}}{z^2}$

52. $\log_b \dfrac{7xy}{\sqrt[3]{z}}$ **53.** $\log_b \sqrt[3]{\dfrac{x^2}{y}}$ **54.** $\log_5 \sqrt[4]{xy^2 z}$

55. $\log_2 \dfrac{1}{x}\sqrt{\dfrac{y}{z}}$ **56.** $\log_b \dfrac{1}{z^2}\sqrt[3]{\dfrac{x^2}{y}}$ **57.** $\log_b \dfrac{z^3 \sqrt{x}}{\sqrt[3]{y}}$

58. $\log_b \dfrac{\sqrt{y}\sqrt{x}}{z^2}$ **59.** $\log_b \dfrac{x^2(x+1)}{\sqrt{x+2}}$ **60.** $\log_b \dfrac{\sqrt{x}(x+4)}{x^2}$

Write each as a single logarithmic expression.

61. $\log_b x + 2 \log_b y$

62. $2 \log_b z - 3 \log_b x$

63. $\log_b x + 2 \log_b y - 3 \log_b z$

64. $3 \log_7 x - 4 \log_7 y - 5 \log_7 z$

65. $\log_3 x + \frac{1}{3} \log_3 y - \frac{1}{2} \log_3 z$

66. $\frac{1}{2} \log_2 x - \frac{1}{3} \log_2 y - \log_2 z$

67. $2 \log_{10} x - \frac{1}{2} \log_{10} (x - 3) - \log_{10} (x + 1)$

68. $\log_3 (x + 1) + \frac{1}{2} \log_3 (x + 2) - 3 \log_3 (x - 1)$

69. $5 \log_b x + \frac{1}{3} \log_b (x - 1) - \log_b (x + 2)$

70. $\log_b (x + 1) + \frac{1}{3} \log_b (x - 7) - 2 \log_b x$

71. $\log_{10} x + 2 \log_{10} (x - 1) - \frac{1}{3}[\log_{10} (x + 2) + \log_{10} (x - 5)]$

72. $\frac{1}{2} \log_b (x + 1) - 3[\log_b x + \log_b (x - 1) + \log_b (2x - 1)]$

Find the value of each expression.

73. $\log_b b^3$ **74.** $\log_2 2^5$ **75.** $\log_3 9$ **76.** $\log_2 16$

77. $\log_5 125$ **78.** $\log_4 64$ **79.** $\log_2 \frac{1}{4}$ **80.** $\log_3 \frac{1}{27}$

81. $\log_{10} 0.001$ **82.** $\log_{10} 0.1$ **83.** $\log_3 1$ **84.** $\log_{10} 1$

85. $6^{\log_6 5}$ **86.** $3^{\log_3 9}$ **87.** $25^{\log_5 6}$ **88.** $27^{\log_3 2}$

89. $4^{\log_2 (1/5)}$ **90.** $8^{\log_2 (1/3)}$

We now find the derivative of a logarithmic function in the form $y = \log_b u$.

$$\frac{dy}{du} = \lim_{\Delta u \to 0} \frac{\Delta y}{\Delta u}$$

where

$$\frac{\Delta y}{\Delta u} = \frac{\log_b (u + \Delta u) - \log_b u}{\Delta u}$$

Recall that the difference of two logarithms is the logarithm of their quotient, so

$$\frac{\Delta y}{\Delta u} = \frac{\log_b \left(\dfrac{u + \Delta u}{u}\right)}{\Delta u}$$

$$= \frac{1}{u} \cdot \frac{u}{\Delta u} \log_b \left(\frac{u + \Delta u}{u}\right) \qquad \text{(Multiply numerator and denominator by } u\text{.)}$$

Also recall that $n \log_b a = \log_b a^n$. We then have

$$\frac{\Delta y}{\Delta u} = \frac{1}{u} \log_b \left(\frac{u + \Delta u}{u}\right)^{u/\Delta u}$$

$$= \frac{1}{u} \log_b \left(1 + \frac{\Delta u}{u}\right)^{u/\Delta u}$$

and then

$$\frac{dy}{du} = \lim_{\Delta u \to 0} \frac{1}{u} \cdot \lim_{\Delta u \to 0} \log_b \left(1 + \frac{\Delta u}{u}\right)^{u/\Delta u}$$

The limit of the left-hand factor is

$$\lim_{\Delta u \to 0} \frac{1}{u} = \frac{1}{u} \qquad \text{(As } \Delta u \to 0, u \text{ itself is not affected.)}$$

Next, to determine the limit of the right-hand factor, one can show that the function $(1 + h)^{1/h}$ approaches a limiting number as h approaches 0. We denote this number by e, that is,

$$\lim_{h \to 0} (1 + h)^{1/h} = e$$

This is an irrational number whose decimal value can only be approximated. An approximation of e to seven decimal places is 2.7182818.

Note that if we let $h = \dfrac{\Delta u}{u}$, then h approaches 0 as Δu approaches 0. Then

$$\frac{dy}{du} = \frac{1}{u} \cdot \lim_{\Delta u \to 0} \log_b \left(1 + \frac{\Delta u}{u}\right)^{1/(\Delta u/u)} \qquad \left(\frac{u}{\Delta u} = \frac{1}{\dfrac{\Delta u}{u}}\right)$$

$$= \frac{1}{u} \log_b e$$

Using the chain rule, we also have

$$\frac{dy}{dx} = \frac{1}{u} \log_b e \frac{du}{dx}$$

Thus,

$$\frac{d}{du}(\log_b u) = \frac{1}{u}\log_b e$$

$$\frac{d}{dx}(\log_b u) = \frac{1}{u}\log_b e\,\frac{du}{dx}$$

Since $\log_e e = 1$ and since we denote $\log_e u$ by $\ln u$ (called the natural logarithm of u), we have

$$\frac{d}{du}(\ln u) = \frac{1}{u}$$

$$\frac{d}{dx}(\ln u) = \frac{1}{u}\frac{du}{dx}$$

Note: u must always be positive since $\log_b u$ or $\ln u$ is defined only for positive values of u.

EXAMPLE 1

Find the derivative of $y = \ln 5x$.

$$\frac{dy}{dx} = \frac{1}{5x}\frac{d}{dx}(5x) = \frac{5}{5x} = \frac{1}{x} \qquad (u = 5x)$$

Alternate method: Use the property of logarithms from Section 4.6: The logarithm of a product equals the sum of the logarithms of its factors.

$$y = \ln 5x = \ln 5 + \ln x$$

$$\frac{dy}{dx} = 0 + \frac{1}{x} = \frac{1}{x}$$

EXAMPLE 2

Find the derivative of $y = \log(3x + 1)$.

$$\frac{dy}{dx} = \left(\frac{1}{3x + 1}\right)(\log e)\left[\frac{d}{dx}(3x + 1)\right] \qquad (u = 3x + 1)$$

$$= \frac{3\log e}{3x + 1} \quad \text{or} \quad \frac{3(0.4343)}{3x + 1} = \frac{1.3029}{3x + 1}$$

EXAMPLE 3

Find the derivative of $y = \ln(\sin 3x)$.

$$\frac{dy}{dx} = \frac{1}{\sin 3x}\frac{d}{dx}(\sin 3x) \qquad (u = \sin 3x)$$

$$= \frac{3\cos 3x}{\sin 3x}$$

$$= 3\cot 3x$$

You will need to make simplifications using the properties of logarithms.

EXAMPLE 4

Find the derivative of $y = \ln\left(\dfrac{x^3}{2x-5}\right)$

$$y = \ln\left(\frac{x^3}{2x-5}\right) = \ln x^3 - \ln(2x-5)$$

$$= 3\ln x - \ln(2x-5)$$

Then,

$$\frac{dy}{dx} = 3\left(\frac{1}{x}\right) - \frac{1}{2x-5}\frac{d}{dx}(2x-5)$$

$$= \frac{3}{x} - \frac{2}{2x-5}$$

$$= \frac{4x-15}{x(2x-5)}$$

EXAMPLE 5

Find the derivative of $y = \ln(x\sqrt{4+x})$.

Rewriting, we have

$$y = \ln x + \tfrac{1}{2}\ln(4+x)$$

$$\frac{dy}{dx} = \frac{1}{x} + \frac{1}{2}\left(\frac{1}{4+x}\right)(1)$$

$$= \frac{8+3x}{2x(4+x)}$$

For more complicated algebraic expressions, consider the following method, called *logarithmic differentiation.*

EXAMPLE 6

Find the derivative of $y = \sqrt[3]{\dfrac{x^2(3x+4)}{1-2x^2}}$.

First, take the natural logarithm of both sides.

$$\ln y = \ln\left(\frac{x^2(3x+4)}{1-2x^2}\right)^{1/3}$$

$$\ln y = \frac{1}{3}\ln\left(\frac{x^2(3x+4)}{1-2x^2}\right)$$

$$\ln y = \frac{1}{3}[2\ln x + \ln(3x+4) - \ln(1-2x^2)]$$

Next, find the derivative of both sides.

$$\frac{1}{y}\frac{dy}{dx} = \frac{1}{3}\left[\frac{2}{x} + \frac{3}{3x+4} - \frac{-4x}{1-2x^2}\right]$$

$$\frac{dy}{dx} = \frac{y}{3}\left[\frac{2}{x} + \frac{3}{3x+4} + \frac{4x}{1-2x^2}\right] \qquad \left(\text{Solve for } \frac{dy}{dx}.\right)$$

$$= \frac{1}{3}\sqrt[3]{\frac{x^2(3x+4)}{1-2x^2}}\left[\frac{2}{x} + \frac{3}{3x+4} + \frac{4x}{1-2x^2}\right]$$

Logarithmic differentiation is especially helpful for functions having both a variable base and a variable exponent.

EXAMPLE 7

Find the derivative of $y = x^{4x}$.

First, take the natural logarithm of both sides.

$$\ln y = \ln x^{4x}$$

$$\ln y = 4x \ln x$$

Then, find the derivative of both sides.

$$\frac{1}{y}\frac{dy}{dx} = 4x\frac{1}{x} + 4\ln x$$

$$\frac{dy}{dx} = 4y(1 + \ln x)$$

$$= 4x^{4x}(1 + \ln x)$$

Exercises 4.7

Find the derivative of each function.

1. $y = \log(4x - 3)$ **2.** $y = \log(x^2 - 1)$ **3.** $y = \log_2 3x$

4. $y = \log_7(5x + 2)$ **5.** $y = \ln(2x^3 - 3)$ **6.** $y = \ln(x^2 - 4)$

7. $y = \ln(\tan 3x)$ **8.** $y = \ln(\sec x^2)$ **9.** $y = \ln(x \sin x)$

10. $y = \ln(x^3 \cos 2x)$ **11.** $y = \ln\sqrt{3x - 2}$ **12.** $y = \ln(x^2 - 1)^{1/3}$

13. $y = \ln\dfrac{x^3}{x^2 + 1}$ **14.** $y = \ln\dfrac{5x}{1 - x^2}$ **15.** $y = \tan(\ln x)$

16. $y = (\ln x)(\sin x)$ **17.** $y = \ln(\ln x)$ **18.** $y = x^2 + \ln(3x - 2)$

19. $y = \arctan(\ln x^2)$ **20.** $y = \arcsin(\ln x)$ **21.** $y = \ln(\arccos^2 x)$

22. $y = \ln(\arctan^3 x)$

Find $\dfrac{dy}{dx}$ using logarithmic differentiation.

23. $y = (3x + 2)(6x - 1)^2(x - 4)$ **24.** $y = \sqrt{x(2x + 1)(1 - 5x)}$

25. $y = \dfrac{(x + 1)(2x + 1)}{(3x - 4)(1 - 8x)}$ **26.** $y = \dfrac{x(2x - 1)^{3/2}}{\sqrt[3]{x + 1}}$

27. $y = x^x$ **28.** $y = x^{x+1}$ **29.** $y = x^{2/x}$ **30.** $y = (1 + x)^{1/x}$

31. $y = (\sin x)^x$ **32.** $y = (\tan x)^x$ **33.** $y = (1 + x)^{x^2}$ **34.** $y = x^{\sin x}$

Find the equation of the tangent line at the given value.

35. $y = \ln x$ at $x = 1$ **36.** $y = \ln x^2$ at $x = 1$

37. $y = \ln(\sin x)$ at $x = \pi/6$ **38.** $y = \tan(\ln x)$ at $x = 1$

4.8   DERIVATIVES OF EXPONENTIAL FUNCTIONS

An *exponential function* is a function in the form $y = b^u$ where b is a positive constant, $b \neq 1$, and u is a variable. If $y = b^u$, then $u = \log_b y$ in logarithmic form. Then from the preceding section,

$$\frac{du}{dx} = \frac{1}{y} \cdot \log_b e \frac{dy}{dx}$$

Solving for $\frac{dy}{dx}$, we have

$$\frac{dy}{dx} = \frac{y}{\log_b e} \frac{du}{dx}$$

$$= \frac{b^u}{\log_b e} \frac{du}{dx} \qquad (y = b^u)$$

That is,

$$\frac{d}{dx}(b^u) = \frac{b^u}{\log_b e} \frac{du}{dx}$$

When the base $b = e$, the previous expression simplifies to

$$\frac{d}{dx}(e^u) = e^u \frac{du}{dx} \qquad (\log_e e = 1)$$

EXAMPLE 1

Find the derivative of $y = e^{3x}$.

$$\frac{dy}{dx} = e^{3x}\frac{d}{dx}(3x) = 3e^{3x} \qquad (u = 3x)$$

EXAMPLE 2

Find the derivative of $y = 10^{2x}$.

$$\frac{dy}{dx} = \frac{10^{2x}}{\log e} \cdot \frac{d}{dx}(2x) \qquad (u = 2x)$$

$$= \frac{(2)10^{2x}}{\log e}$$

EXAMPLE 3

Find the derivative of $y = e^{x^2+3}$.

$$\frac{dy}{dx} = e^{x^2+3}(2x) \qquad (u = x^2 + 3)$$

$$= 2xe^{x^2+3}$$

EXAMPLE 4

Find the derivative of $y = e^{\tan x}$.

$$\frac{dy}{dx} = e^{\tan x}(\sec^2 x) \qquad (u = \tan x)$$

EXAMPLE 5

Find the derivative of $y = x^2 e^{-5x}$.
First, apply the product rule for differentiation.

$$\frac{dy}{dx} = x^2 \frac{d}{dx}(e^{-5x}) + e^{-5x}\frac{d}{dx}(x^2)$$

$$= x^2 e^{-5x}(-5) + e^{-5x}(2x)$$

$$= xe^{-5x}(2 - 5x)$$

EXAMPLE 6

Find the derivative of $y = \arcsin e^{3x}$.

Let $u = e^{3x}$; then

$$\frac{dy}{dx} = \frac{1}{\sqrt{1 - (e^{3x})^2}}(3e^{3x}) = \frac{3e^{3x}}{\sqrt{1 - e^{6x}}}$$

Using a calculator, we have

F3 1 green diamond SIN^{-1} green diamond e^x 3x)),x) ENTER

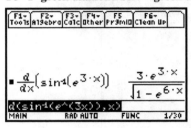

Exercises 4.8

Find the derivative of each function.

1. $y = e^{5x}$ **2.** $y = 2e^{3x+1}$ **3.** $y = 4e^{x^3}$

4. $y = e^{x^2 + 3x}$ **5.** $y = 10^{3x}$ **6.** $y = 4^{x^2}$

7. $y = \dfrac{1}{e^{6x}}$ **8.** $y = e^{-x^3}$ **9.** $y = e^{\sqrt{x}}$

10. $y = e^{\sqrt{3x-2}}$ **11.** $y = e^{\sin x}$ **12.** $y = 5e^{\cos x^2}$

13. $y = 6xe^{x^2 - 1}$ **14.** $y = xe^{x^3}$ **15.** $y = (\cos x)e^{3x^2}$

16. $y = 3e^{\tan x^2}$ **17.** $y = \ln(\cos e^{5x})$ **18.** $y = \tan e^{4x}$

19. $y = e^x - e^{-x}$ **20.** $y = \dfrac{e^x}{x}$ **21.** $y = \dfrac{2x^2}{3e^x - x}$

22. $y = \dfrac{e^{x^2}}{x - 2}$ **23.** $y = 2 \arctan e^{3x}$ **24.** $y = \arcsin e^{4x}$

25. $y = \arccos^3 e^{-2x}$ **26.** $y = \arctan e^{x^2}$ **27.** $y = xe^x - e^x$

28. $y = (e^x + e^{-x})^3$ **29.** $y = \ln e^{x^2}$ **30.** $y = \ln(x - e^x)$

4.9 L'HOSPITAL'S RULE

Limits of quotients involving trigonometric, exponential, and logarithmic functions are often difficult to evaluate by elementary methods, especially in the cases where the numerator and the denominator are both headed toward zero or both headed toward an infinite expression ($\pm\infty$). In these cases, l'Hospital's rule offers a sophisticated way to find the limit of such a quotient of functions by instead evaluating the limit of the quotient of their *derivatives*. The proof of l'Hospital's rule can be found in books on advanced calculus.

Note carefully that l'Hospital's rule speaks only of the equality of *limits*. It does not say that $\dfrac{f(x)}{g(x)}$ and $\dfrac{f'(x)}{g'(x)}$ are the same *functions*. By contrast, algebraic steps for evaluating limits have always yielded equal limit values simply because the function remains the same (just written in a different form). The power of l'Hospital's rule is that it uses differentiation in the numerator and the denominator to drastically alter the function without changing the value of the limit.

EXAMPLE 1

Find $\lim\limits_{x \to 1} \dfrac{\ln x}{x^4 - 1}$.

Note that $\lim\limits_{x \to 1} \ln x = 0$ and $\lim\limits_{x \to 1} (x^4 - 1) = 0$, so l'Hospital's rule applies:

$$\lim_{x \to 1} \frac{\ln x}{x^4 - 1} = \lim_{x \to 1} \frac{\dfrac{1}{x}}{4x^3} \qquad \left[\text{Note: } \frac{d}{dx}(\ln x) = \frac{1}{x} \text{ and } \frac{d}{dx}(x^4 - 1) = 4x^3. \right]$$

$$= \frac{\dfrac{1}{1}}{4(1)^3}$$

$$= \frac{1}{4}$$

EXAMPLE 2

Evaluate $\lim\limits_{x \to 0} \dfrac{x^2}{1 - \cos x}$ using l'Hospital's rule, then verify the reasonableness of your answer with your calculator's **TABLE** feature.

Since $\lim\limits_{x \to 0} x^2 = 0$ and $\lim\limits_{x \to 0}(1 - \cos x) = 1 - 1 = 0$, l'Hospital's rule applies.

$$\lim_{x \to 0} \frac{x^2}{1 - \cos x} = \lim_{x \to 0} \frac{2x}{\sin x} \qquad (\text{Use l'Hospital's rule; note: } \lim_{x \to 0} 2x = 0 \text{ and } \lim_{x \to 0} \sin x = 0.)$$

$$= \lim_{x \to 0} \frac{2}{\cos x} \qquad (\text{L'Hospital's rule applies again.})$$

$$= \frac{2}{1}$$

$$= 2$$

Using a calculator's **TABLE** feature, we have

green diamond Y = green diamond TblSet -.002 down arrow .001 **ENTER ENTER green diamond TABLE**

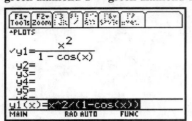 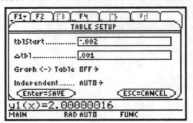 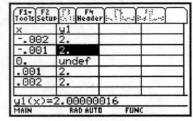

Y =   **2nd TBLSET** -.003 **ENTER** .001 **2nd TABLE**   right arrow down arrows

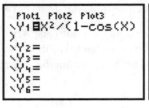  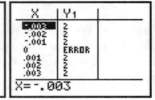 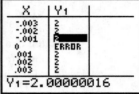

Note that the highlighted function value in the table is not exactly 2, but is 2.00000016 (as shown at the bottom of the screen image). Feel free to highlight other values in this table to see that the function does seem to be approaching 2 as $x \to 0$.

EXAMPLE 3

Find $\lim\limits_{x \to \infty} x \sin \dfrac{1}{x}$.

    L'Hospital's rule only applies to the limit of a *quotient* of functions. To write a product of two functions as a quotient, simply show it as division by one of their reciprocals.

$$\lim_{x \to \infty} x \sin \frac{1}{x} = \lim_{x \to \infty} \frac{\sin \dfrac{1}{x}}{\dfrac{1}{x}} \qquad \left(\text{Note: } \lim_{x \to \infty} \sin \frac{1}{x} = \sin 0 = 0 \text{ and } \lim_{x \to \infty} \frac{1}{x} = 0. \right)$$

$$= \lim_{x \to \infty} \frac{\cos \dfrac{1}{x} \cdot \left(-\dfrac{1}{x^2} \right)}{-\dfrac{1}{x^2}} \qquad \left(\text{Use l'Hospital's rule;} \atop \text{recall that } \dfrac{d}{dx}\left(\dfrac{1}{x} \right) = \dfrac{d}{dx}(x^{-1}) = -1x^{-2} = -\dfrac{1}{x^2}. \right)$$

$$= \lim_{x \to \infty} \cos \frac{1}{x}$$

$$= \cos 0$$

$$= 1$$

The preceding examples showed cases in which the numerator and the denominator were both approaching *zero*. The next three examples illustrate l'Hospital's rule when the numerator and denominator are both approaching *infinite* expressions ($\pm \infty$).

EXAMPLE 4

Find the horizontal asymptote of the graph of $f(x) = \dfrac{7x^2 - 5x + 2}{3x^2 - 8x + 4}$, contrasting algebraic methods with l'Hospital's rule.

To name the horizontal asymptote, we need to evaluate $\displaystyle\lim_{x\to\infty}\frac{7x^2-5x+2}{3x^2-8x+4}$. Previously, we evaluated limits of this type *algebraically,* by multiplying the numerator and the denominator by $\dfrac{1}{x^2}$ (the reciprocal of the highest power of x).

$$\lim_{x\to\infty}\frac{7x^2-5x+2}{3x^2-8x+4}=\lim_{x\to\infty}\frac{7x^2-5x+2}{3x^2-8x+4}\cdot\frac{\dfrac{1}{x^2}}{\dfrac{1}{x^2}}$$

$$=\lim_{x\to\infty}\frac{7-\dfrac{5}{x}+\dfrac{2}{x^2}}{3-\dfrac{8}{x}+\dfrac{4}{x^2}}$$

$$=\frac{7-0+0}{3-0+0}$$

$$=\frac{7}{3}$$

Using l'Hospital's rule twice will give the same result in a very different way. Note that $\displaystyle\lim_{x\to\infty}(7x^2-5x+2)=\infty$ and $\displaystyle\lim_{x\to\infty}(3x^2-8x+4)=\infty$, so

$$\lim_{x\to\infty}\frac{7x^2-5x+2}{3x^2-8x+4}=\lim_{x\to\infty}\frac{14x-5}{6x-8}\qquad\begin{array}{l}[\text{Use l'Hospital's rule; note:}\\[4pt]\lim_{x\to\infty}(14x-5)=\infty\text{ and }\lim_{x\to\infty}(6x-8)=\infty.]\end{array}$$

$$=\lim_{x\to\infty}\frac{14}{6}\qquad\text{(l'Hospital's rule)}$$

$$=\frac{7}{3}$$

Using either style of work, we can conclude the horizontal asymptote is $y=\dfrac{7}{3}$.

EXAMPLE 5

Find $\displaystyle\lim_{x\to0}x^2\ln x$.

First, write this limit of the *product* of two functions as the limit of a *quotient:*

$$\lim_{x\to0}x^2\ln x=\lim_{x\to0}\frac{\ln x}{\dfrac{1}{x^2}}\qquad\left(\text{Note: }\lim_{x\to0}\ln x=-\infty\text{ and }\lim_{x\to0}\frac{1}{x^2}=\infty.\right)$$

$$=\lim_{x\to0}\frac{\dfrac{1}{x}}{-\dfrac{2}{x^3}}\qquad\left[\text{l'Hospital's rule }\left(\frac{-\infty}{\infty}\right)\right]$$

$$=\lim_{x\to0}\frac{1}{x}\cdot\left(-\frac{x^3}{2}\right)\qquad\text{(algebra)}$$

$$=\lim_{x\to0}-\frac{x^2}{2}\qquad\text{(algebra)}$$

$$=0$$

EXAMPLE 6

Find $\lim\limits_{x \to \infty} \dfrac{e^{x^2}}{x^3}$.

$$\lim_{x \to \infty} \frac{e^{x^2}}{x^3} = \lim_{x \to \infty} \frac{2xe^{x^2}}{3x^2} \qquad \left[\text{l'Hospital's rule } \left(\frac{\infty}{\infty}\right)\right]$$

$$= \lim_{x \to \infty} \frac{2e^{x^2}}{3x} \qquad \text{(algebra)}$$

$$= \lim_{x \to \infty} \frac{4xe^{x^2}}{3} \qquad \left[\text{l'Hospital's rule } \left(\frac{\infty}{\infty}\right)\right]$$

$$= \infty$$

This limit *does not exist*.

In cases where the limit involves a *difference* of two quantities which are both approaching infinite expressions ($\infty - \infty$), l'Hospital's rule often applies after establishing a common denominator and combining the expressions into a single fraction ($\frac{0}{0}$ or $\frac{\infty}{\infty}$).

EXAMPLE 7

Find $\lim\limits_{x \to 0}\left(\dfrac{1}{x} - \dfrac{1}{\tan x}\right)$.

$$\lim_{x \to 0}\left(\frac{1}{x} - \frac{1}{\tan x}\right) = \lim_{x \to 0} \frac{\tan x - x}{x \tan x} \qquad \text{(algebra)}$$

$$= \lim_{x \to 0} \frac{\sec^2 x - 1}{x \cdot (\sec^2 x) + \tan x \cdot (1)} \qquad \left[\text{l'Hospital's rule } \left(\frac{0}{0}\right)\right]$$

$$= \lim_{x \to 0} \frac{2 \sec x \cdot \sec x \tan x}{x \cdot (2 \sec x \cdot \sec x \tan x) + \sec^2 x \cdot (1) + \sec^2 x} \qquad \left[\text{l'Hospital's rule } \left(\frac{0}{0}\right)\right]$$

$$= \lim_{x \to 0} \frac{2 \sec^2 x \tan x}{2x \sec^2 x \tan x + 2 \sec^2 x} \qquad \text{(algebra)}$$

$$= \frac{2(1)^2(0)}{2(0)(1)^2(0) + 2(1)^2}$$

$$= \frac{0}{2}$$

$$= 0$$

Using a calculator, we have

F3   3

1/x-1/ 2nd TAN x),x,0) ENTER

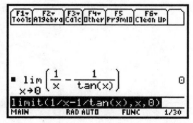

Before concluding this section, two warnings need to be made. First, always be sure that your limit is of the form $\dfrac{0}{0}$ or $\dfrac{\pm\infty}{\pm\infty}$ before you consider applying l'Hospital's rule. Misapplications of this rule often look like convincing work, but they generally give very wrong answers. For example, compare the correct limit evaluation steps $\lim\limits_{x \to 0} \dfrac{3x}{e^{2x}} = \dfrac{3(0)}{e^0} = \dfrac{0}{1} = 0$

to a thoughtless misapplication of l'Hospital's rule: $\lim\limits_{x \to 0} \dfrac{3x}{e^{2x}} \neq \lim\limits_{x \to 0} \dfrac{3}{2e^{2x}} = \dfrac{3}{2e^0} = \dfrac{3}{2}$.

The second warning is that when l'Hospital's rule *does* apply, it can sometimes yield an infinite sequence of perfectly true statements that are *not helpful*. In Example 5, if we had kept x^2 in the numerator instead of $\ln x$, we would have seen the following sequence of useless steps that generate successive negative powers of $\ln x$ in the denominator without reducing the degree of the numerator:

$$\lim_{x \to 0} x^2 \ln x = \lim_{x \to 0} \frac{x^2}{(\ln x)^{-1}} \qquad \text{(algebra)}$$

$$= \lim_{x \to 0} \frac{2x}{-1(\ln x)^{-2} \cdot \dfrac{1}{x}} \qquad \left[\text{l'Hospital's rule} \left(\dfrac{0}{0}\right)\right]$$

$$= \lim_{x \to 0} \frac{2x^2}{-1(\ln x)^{-2}} \qquad \text{(algebra)}$$

$$= \lim_{x \to 0} \frac{4x}{2(\ln x)^{-3} \cdot \dfrac{1}{x}} \qquad \left[\text{l'Hospital's rule} \left(\dfrac{0}{0}\right)\right]$$

$$= \lim_{x \to 0} \frac{2x^2}{(\ln x)^{-3}} \qquad \text{(algebra)}$$

etc.

It is also possible for l'Hospital's rule to turn a quotient of functions into its reciprocal, so that, with a second application of the rule, we arrive back where we started!

EXAMPLE 8

Show why l'Hospital's rule is initially ineffective in evaluating $\lim\limits_{x \to \infty} \dfrac{x}{\sqrt{x^2 - 1}}$, then use some preliminary algebra, followed by l'Hospital's rule, to evaluate this limit.

If we start by using l'Hospital's rule, we soon arrive back at the original question!

$$\lim_{x \to \infty} \frac{x}{\sqrt{x^2 - 1}} = \lim_{x \to \infty} \frac{1}{\frac{1}{2}(x^2 - 1)^{-1/2} \cdot 2x} \qquad \left[\text{l'Hospital's rule} \left(\dfrac{\infty}{\infty}\right)\right]$$

$$= \lim_{x \to \infty} \frac{\sqrt{x^2 - 1}}{x} \qquad \text{(algebra)}$$

$$= \lim_{x \to \infty} \frac{\frac{1}{2}(x^2 - 1)^{-1/2} \cdot 2x}{1} \qquad \left[\text{l'Hospital's rule} \left(\dfrac{\infty}{\infty}\right)\right]$$

$$= \lim_{x \to \infty} \frac{x}{\sqrt{x^2 - 1}} \qquad \text{(algebra)}$$

Instead, start by using the property of radicals $\dfrac{\sqrt{a}}{\sqrt{b}} = \sqrt{\dfrac{a}{b}}$. L'Hospital's rule will apply in a helpful way once the limit is taken under the combined radical.

$$\lim_{x \to \infty} \frac{x}{\sqrt{x^2 - 1}} = \lim_{x \to \infty} \frac{\sqrt{x^2}}{\sqrt{x^2 - 1}} \qquad \text{(algebra)}$$

$$= \lim_{x \to \infty} \sqrt{\frac{x^2}{x^2 - 1}} \qquad \text{(algebra)}$$

$$= \sqrt{\lim_{x \to \infty} \frac{x^2}{x^2 - 1}} \qquad \text{(limit formula)}$$

$$= \sqrt{\lim_{x \to \infty} \frac{2x}{2x}} \qquad \left[\text{l'Hospital's rule } \left(\frac{\infty}{\infty} \right) \right]$$

$$= \sqrt{\lim_{x \to \infty} 1} \qquad \text{(algebra)}$$

$$= \sqrt{1}$$

$$= 1$$

Thus, an important lesson is that l'Hospital's rule is not a replacement for algebra skills or the limit formulas you learned earlier. Instead, it should be viewed as a powerful *addition* to our previous methods for evaluating limits.

Exercises 4.9

Find the indicated limits, if they exist.

1. $\lim\limits_{x \to 0} \dfrac{\sin x}{5x}$

2. $\lim\limits_{x \to 0} \dfrac{\tan x}{x}$

3. $\lim\limits_{x \to 1} \dfrac{\ln x}{x^2 - 5x + 4}$

4. $\lim\limits_{x \to 1} \dfrac{x^3 - 1}{\ln x}$

5. $\lim\limits_{x \to 0} \dfrac{\ln(\cos x)}{x^2}$

6. $\lim\limits_{x \to 0} \dfrac{\sin^2 x}{4x^2}$

7. $\lim\limits_{x \to 0} \dfrac{x - \sin x}{x^3}$

8. $\lim\limits_{x \to 0} \dfrac{\sin x - x \cos x}{x^3}$

9. $\lim\limits_{x \to 0} x \cot x$

10. $\lim\limits_{x \to 0} x \ln x$

11. $\lim\limits_{x \to \infty} \dfrac{5x^2 + 7x - 1}{2x^2 - x + 9}$

12. $\lim\limits_{x \to \infty} \dfrac{6x^2 + 2x + 11}{2x^2 + 8x - 7}$

13. $\lim\limits_{x \to \infty} \dfrac{\ln x}{\sqrt{x}}$

14. $\lim\limits_{x \to \infty} \dfrac{e^{4x}}{x^2}$

15. $\lim\limits_{t \to \infty} t^2 e^{-5t}$

16. $\lim\limits_{t \to \infty} e^{-2t} \sqrt{t}$

17. $\lim\limits_{x \to \infty} 5x^{-2} e^{x^2}$

18. $\lim\limits_{x \to \infty} x \tan \dfrac{1}{x}$

19. $\lim\limits_{x \to 0} (\csc x - \cot x)$

20. $\lim\limits_{x \to 1} \left(\dfrac{1}{\ln x} - \dfrac{1}{x - 1} \right)$

21. Explain why, even though it applies, l'Hospital's rule is not helpful in evaluating $\lim\limits_{x \to \pi/2} \dfrac{\sec x}{\tan x}$. Use trigonometric identities and algebra to evaluate this limit.

22. Interpret the result of Exercise 12 to name the horizontal asymptote of the graph of the function
$$f(x) = \frac{6x^2 + 2x + 11}{2x^2 + 8x - 7}.$$

4.10 APPLICATIONS

The previous calculus techniques for curve sketching, finding maximums and minimums, solving problems of motion, and so on apply also to the transcendental functions. Some of these applications are given in this section.

EXAMPLE 1

Sketch the curve $y = xe^x$.

The x- and y-intercepts are both $(0, 0)$. To find where the curve is above and below the x-axis:

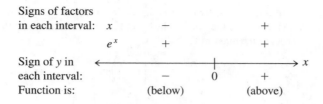

Signs of factors
in each interval: x $-$ $+$

  e^x $+$ $+$

Sign of y in
each interval: $-$ 0 $+$

Function is: (below)   (above)

Note: $e^x > 0$. This factor, being always positive, does not affect the sign in any interval. So we will not list it after this.

$$f'(x) = xe^x + e^x = e^x(x + 1)$$

To find where the curve is increasing and decreasing:

Sign of factor
in each interval: $(x + 1)$ $-$ $+$

Sign of $f'(x)$: $-$ -1 $+$

Function is: (decreasing)   (increasing)

Since $f(x)$ changes from decreasing to increasing at $x = -1$, $(-1, -1/e)$ is a relative minimum.

$$f''(x) = xe^x + 2e^x = e^x(x + 2)$$

To find where the curve is concave upward and concave downward:

Sign of $f''(x)$ in
each interval: $(x + 2)$ $-$ $+$

Function is: concave -2 concave
                      down   up

So, $(-2, -2/e^2)$ is a point of inflection.
With this information we now sketch the curve in Fig. 4.19.

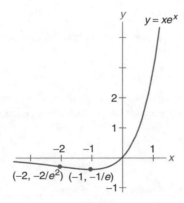

Figure 4.19

EXAMPLE 2

The insulation resistance of a shielded cable is given by

$$R = \frac{\rho}{2\pi} \ln\left(\frac{r_2}{r_1}\right) \Omega$$

where ρ is the resistivity of the insulation material, r_1 is the inner radius (in mm) of the insulation, and r_2 is the outer radius. Find the rate of change of the insulation resistance R with respect to the outer radius r_2.

$$\frac{dR}{dr_2} = \frac{d}{dr_2}\left[\left(\frac{\rho}{2\pi}\right)\ln\left(\frac{r_2}{r_1}\right)\right] \qquad (r_1 \text{ is a constant.})$$

$$= \left(\frac{\rho}{2\pi}\right)\frac{d}{dr_2}\left[\ln\left(\frac{r_2}{r_1}\right)\right]$$

$$= \left(\frac{\rho}{2\pi}\right)\left(\frac{1}{r_2/r_1}\right)\frac{d}{dr_2}\left(\frac{r_2}{r_1}\right)$$

$$= \left(\frac{\rho}{2\pi}\right)\left(\frac{r_1}{r_2}\right)\left(\frac{1}{r_1}\right)$$

$$= \frac{\rho}{2\pi r_2} \; \Omega/\text{mm}$$

EXAMPLE 3

The current in an electric circuit is given by $i = 10(1 - e^{-20t})$. Find the maximum value of the current.

$$\frac{di}{dt} = \frac{d}{dt}[10(1 - e^{-20t})]$$

$$= 10\frac{d}{dt}(1 - e^{-20t})$$

$$= 10(0 + 20e^{-20t})$$

$$= 200e^{-20t}$$

Since $\dfrac{di}{dt}$ is never zero and always positive, there is no maximum value. The current increases with time.

EXAMPLE 4

Find the equation of the line tangent to the curve $y = \ln x^2$ at the point $(1, 0)$.

$$\frac{dy}{dx} = \frac{d}{dx}(\ln x^2) = \frac{1}{x^2}(2x) = \frac{2}{x}$$

Alternate method: Use the property of logarithms from Section 4.6: The logarithm of a power of a number equals the product of the exponent and the logarithm of the number.

$$y = \ln x^2 = 2 \ln x$$

$$\frac{dy}{dx} = 2 \cdot \frac{1}{x} = \frac{2}{x}$$

The slope of the tangent line is

$$m = \frac{dy}{dx}\bigg|_{x=1} = \frac{2}{1} = 2$$

Using the point-slope formula, we have

$$y - y_1 = m(x - x_1)$$
$$y - 0 = 2(x - 1)$$
$$y = 2x - 2$$

Exercises 4.10

Sketch each curve. Find any maximum, minimum, and inflection points.

1. $y = \sin x + \cos x$ 2. $y = x \ln x, x > 0$

3. $y = \dfrac{\ln x}{x}, x > 0$ 4. $y = \ln (\sin x), 0 < x < \pi$

5. $y = e^x + e^{-x}$ 6. $y = \ln x - x, x > 0$ 7. $y = x^2 e^{-x}$

8. $y = \ln \left(\dfrac{1}{x^2 - 1} \right)$ 9. $y = \dfrac{1}{1 - e^x}$ 10. $y = \dfrac{x}{\ln x}, x > 0$

Find any relative maximums or minimums of each function.

11. $y = xe^{-2x}$ 12. $y = x^2 e^{2x}$ 13. $y = \dfrac{x^2}{e^{2x}}$

14. $y = \dfrac{e^x}{x}$ 15. $y = \dfrac{\ln x}{x^2}$ 16. $y = \dfrac{x}{\ln^2 x}$

17. Find the equation of the tangent line to $y = \sin 2x$ at the point $(\pi/2, 0)$.

18. Find the equation of the tangent line to $y = xe^x$ at the point $(1, \ e)$.

19. Find the equation of the tangent line to $y = x^2 + x \ln x$ at $x = 1$.

20. Find the equation of the tangent line to $y = e^{\cos x}$ at $x = \pi/2$.

Find $\dfrac{d^4 y}{dx^4}$ for each function:

21. $y = e^x \sin x$ 22. $y = e^{-x} \cos x$

23. The current in a circuit is given by $i = 50 \cos 2t$. Find the equation of the voltage V_L across a 3-henry (H) inductor $\left(V_L = L \dfrac{di}{dt}, \text{ where } L \text{ is the inductance} \right)$.

24. The current in a circuit is given by $i = 40(1 - 2e^{-20t})$. Find the equation of the voltage V_L across a 5-H inductor.

25. The voltage in a circuit is given by $V = 25e^{0.4t}$. Find $\dfrac{dV}{dt}$ at $t = 3$.

26. The current in a circuit is given by $i = 4t^2 e^{8/t}$. Find the value of t when $\dfrac{di}{dt} = 0$.

27. The apparent power p_a of a circuit is given by $p_a = p \sec \theta$, where p is the power and θ is the impedance phase angle. Find $\dfrac{dp_a}{dt}$ at $t = 1$ s if $\dfrac{d\theta}{dt} = 0.1$ rad/s and $\theta = \dfrac{\pi}{4}$. The power p of the circuit is 15 watts (W).

28. If work in a circuit is given by $W = 25 \sin^2 t$, find the equation for the power $p \left(p = \dfrac{dW}{dt} \right)$.

29. The charge q at any time t on a capacitor is given by $q = e^{-0.02t}(0.05 \cos 2t)$. Find the current in the circuit $\left(i = \dfrac{dq}{dt} \right)$.

30. The voltage across a capacitor at any time t is given by $V = e^{-0.001t}$. If the capacitance C is 2×10^{-5} farad (F), find the current in the circuit $\left(i = C \dfrac{dV}{dt} \right)$.

31. A particle moves along a straight line according to $s = 2e^{3t} + 5e^{-3t}$. Find expressions for its velocity and acceleration.

32. A particle moves along a straight line according to $s = \ln (t^2 + 1)$. Find expressions for its velocity and acceleration.

33. A particle moves along a straight line according to $s = e^{-t/2} \tan \dfrac{\pi t}{2}$. Find its velocity and acceleration at $t = 4$.

34. An object moves along a straight line according to $s = \sin 2t + e^t$. Find its velocity and acceleration at $t = 2$.

35. The charge of a capacitor at time t is given by $q = e^{-0.2t}(0.04 \cos 2t - 0.5 \sin 3t)$. Find the current $\left(i = \dfrac{dq}{dt} \right)$ at $t = \pi/2$.

CHAPTER 4 SUMMARY

1. *Trigonometric functions* (see Fig. 4.20):

$$\sin \theta = \frac{y}{r} \qquad \cot \theta = \frac{x}{y}$$

$$\cos \theta = \frac{x}{r} \qquad \sec \theta = \frac{r}{x}$$

$$\tan \theta = \frac{y}{x} \qquad \csc \theta = \frac{r}{y}$$

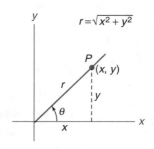

Figure 4.20

2. *Graphing the six trigonometric functions:*

$$\text{period} = \frac{2\pi}{b} \begin{cases} y = a \sin(bx + c) \\ y = a \cos(bx + c) \end{cases} \text{amplitude} = |a| \qquad \text{phase shift} = \frac{c}{b}$$

$$\begin{cases} y = a \sec(bx + c) \\ y = a \csc(bx + c) \end{cases}$$

$$\text{period} = \frac{\pi}{b} \begin{cases} y = a \tan(bx + c) \\ y = a \cot(bx + c) \end{cases}$$

to the *left* if $\dfrac{c}{b} > 0$

and

to the *right* if $\dfrac{c}{b} < 0$

3. A list of *trigonometric identities* is given inside the back cover.

4. *Derivatives of trigonometric functions:*

(a) $\dfrac{d}{dx}(\sin u) = \cos u \dfrac{du}{dx}$

(b) $\dfrac{d}{dx}(\cos u) = -\sin u \dfrac{du}{dx}$

(c) $\dfrac{d}{dx}(\tan u) = \sec^2 u \dfrac{du}{dx}$

(d) $\dfrac{d}{dx}(\cot u) = -\csc^2 u \dfrac{du}{dx}$

(e) $\dfrac{d}{dx}(\sec u) = \sec u \tan u \dfrac{du}{dx}$

(f) $\dfrac{d}{dx}(\csc u) = -\csc u \cot u \dfrac{du}{dx}$

5. *Inverse trigonometric functions:*

(a) $y = \arcsin x, \; -\dfrac{\pi}{2} \le y \le \dfrac{\pi}{2}$

(b) $y = \arccos x, \; 0 \le y \le \pi$

(c) $y = \arctan x, \; -\dfrac{\pi}{2} < y < \dfrac{\pi}{2}$

(d) $y = \text{arccot } x, 0 < y < \pi$

(e) $y = \text{arcsec } x, 0 \leq y \leq \pi, y \neq \dfrac{\pi}{2}$

(f) $y = \text{arccsc } x, -\dfrac{\pi}{2} \leq y \leq \dfrac{\pi}{2}, y \neq 0$

6. *Derivatives of inverse trigonometric functions:*

(a) $\dfrac{d}{dx}(\arcsin u) = \dfrac{1}{\sqrt{1 - u^2}} \dfrac{du}{dx}$

(b) $\dfrac{d}{dx}(\arccos u) = -\dfrac{1}{\sqrt{1 - u^2}} \dfrac{du}{dx}$

(c) $\dfrac{d}{dx}(\arctan u) = \dfrac{1}{1 + u^2} \dfrac{du}{dx}$

(d) $\dfrac{d}{dx}(\text{arccot } u) = -\dfrac{1}{1 + u^2} \dfrac{du}{dx}$

(e) $\dfrac{d}{dx}(\text{arcsec } u) = \dfrac{1}{|u|\sqrt{u^2 - 1}} \dfrac{du}{dx}$

(f) $\dfrac{d}{dx}(\text{arccsc } u) = -\dfrac{1}{|u|\sqrt{u^2 - 1}} \dfrac{du}{dx}$

7. *Exponential function:*

$$y = b^x \quad \text{where} \quad b > 0 \quad \text{and} \quad b \neq 1$$

8. *Laws of exponents:*

$$a^m \cdot a^n = a^{m+n}$$

$$\dfrac{a^m}{a^n} = a^{m-n}$$

$$(a^m)^n = a^{mn}$$

$$(ab)^n = a^n b^n$$

$$\left(\dfrac{a}{b}\right)^n = \dfrac{a^n}{b^n}$$

$$a^0 = 1$$

9. *Logarithmic function:*

In exponential form	In logarithmic form	Is inverse of
$x = b^y$	$y = \log_b x$	$y = b^x$

Note: $b > 0$ and $b \neq 1$.

10. *Logarithmic properties* (for $a > 0$ and $a \neq 1$):

$$\log_a (M \cdot N) = \log_a M + \log_a N$$

$$\log_a \left(\dfrac{M}{N}\right) = \log_a M - \log_a N$$

$$\log_a M^n = n \log_a M$$

$$\log_a \sqrt[n]{M} = \dfrac{1}{n} \cdot \log_a M$$

$$\log_a 1 = 0$$

$$\log_a \frac{1}{M} = -\log_a M$$

$$\log_a (a^x) = x$$

$$a^{\log_a x} = x$$

$$\log_b x = \frac{\log_a x}{\log_a b}$$

11. *Derivatives of logarithmic functions:*

$$\frac{d}{dx}(\ln u) = \frac{1}{u} \frac{du}{dx}$$

$$\frac{d}{dx}(\log_b u) = \frac{1}{u} \log_b e \frac{du}{dx}$$

12. *Derivatives of exponential functions:*

$$\frac{d}{dx}(b^u) = \frac{b^u}{\log_b e} \frac{du}{dx}$$

$$\frac{d}{dx}(e^u) = e^u \frac{du}{dx}$$

13. *L'Hospital's rule:*

Let $f(x)$ and $g(x)$ be differentiable functions, such that $g'(x) \neq 0$.

If $\lim_{x \to c} f(x) = 0$ and $\lim_{x \to c} g(x) = 0$, then $\lim_{x \to c} \frac{f(x)}{g(x)} = \lim_{x \to c} \frac{f'(x)}{g'(x)}$.

Also, if $\lim_{x \to c} f(x) = \pm\infty$ and $\lim_{x \to c} g(x) = \pm\infty$, then $\lim_{x \to c} \frac{f(x)}{g(x)} = \lim_{x \to c} \frac{f'(x)}{g'(x)}$.

CHAPTER 4 REVIEW

Prove each identity.

1. $\sec x \cot x = \csc x$

2. $\sec^2 \theta + \tan^2 \theta + 1 = \dfrac{2}{\cos^2 \theta}$

3. $\dfrac{\cos \theta}{\cos \theta + \sin \theta} = \dfrac{\cot \theta}{1 + \cot \theta}$

4. $\cos\left(\theta - \dfrac{3\pi}{2}\right) = -\sin \theta$

5. $\left(\sin \dfrac{1}{2}x + \cos \dfrac{1}{2}x\right)^2 = 1 + \sin x$

6. $2\cos^2 \dfrac{\theta}{2} = \dfrac{1 + \sec \theta}{\sec \theta}$

7. $\dfrac{2 \cot \theta}{1 + \cot^2 \theta} = \sin 2\theta$

8. $\csc x - \cot x = \tan \dfrac{1}{2}x$

9. $\tan 2x = \dfrac{2 \cos x}{\csc x - 2 \sin x}$

10. $\tan^2 \dfrac{x}{2} + 1 = 2 \tan \dfrac{x}{2} \csc x$

Simplify each expression.

11. $\sin \theta \cos \theta$

12. $\cos^2 3\theta - \sin^2 3\theta$

13. $\dfrac{1 + \cos 4\theta}{2}$

14. $1 - 2\sin^2 \dfrac{\theta}{3}$

15. $\cos 2x \cos 3x - \sin 2x \sin 3x$

16. $\sin 2x \cos x - \cos 2x \sin x$

Sketch each curve.

17. $y = 4 \cos 6x$ **18.** $y = -2 \sin \frac{1}{3}x$ **19.** $y = 3 \sin \left(x - \frac{\pi}{4} \right)$

20. $y = \cos \left(2x + \frac{2\pi}{3} \right)$ **21.** $y = 4 \sin \left(\pi x + \frac{\pi}{2} \right)$ **22.** $y = \tan 5x$

23. $y = -\cot 3x$ **24.** $y = 2 \sec 4x$

Find the derivative of each function.

25. $y = \sin (x^2 + 3)$ **26.** $y = \cos 8x$ **27.** $y = \cos^3 (5x - 1)$

28. $y = \sin 3x \cos 2x$ **29.** $y = \tan (3x - 2)$ **30.** $y = \sec (4x + 3)$

31. $y = \cot 6x^2$ **32.** $y = \csc^2 (8x^2 + x)$ **33.** $y = \sec^2 x \sin x$

34. $y = x^2 - \csc^2 x$ **35.** $y = \tan (\sec x)$ **36.** $y = \dfrac{\cos x}{1 + \sin x}$

37. $y = (1 - \sin x)^3$ **38.** $y = (1 + \sec 4x)^2$

Solve each equation for x.

39. $y = \dfrac{1}{2} \sin \dfrac{3x}{4}$ **40.** $y = 5 \tan (1 - 2x)$

Find the value of each expression in radians.

41. $\arcsin \left(\dfrac{1}{\sqrt{2}} \right)$ **42.** $\arctan \left(-\dfrac{1}{\sqrt{3}} \right)$

43. $\text{arcsec} (-1)$ **44.** $\arccos \left(-\dfrac{1}{2} \right)$

Find the value of each expression.

45. $\sin \left[\arccos \left(-\dfrac{1}{2} \right) \right]$ **46.** $\tan (\arctan \sqrt{3})$

47. Find an algebraic expression for $\sin (\text{arccot } x)$.

Find the derivative of each function.

48. $y = \arcsin x^3$ **49.** $y = \arctan 3x$ **50.** $y = 3 \arccos \dfrac{1}{2x}$

51. $y = 2 \text{ arcsec } 4x$ **52.** $y = \arcsin^2 3\sqrt{x}$ **53.** $y = x \arcsin x$

Graph each equation.

54. $y = 3^x$ **55.** $y = \log_3 x$

Solve for x.

56. $\log_9 x = 2$ **57.** $\log_x 8 = 3$ **58.** $\log_2 32 = x$

Write each expression as a sum, difference, or multiple of single logarithms.

59. $\log_4 6x^2 y$ **60.** $\log_3 \dfrac{5x\sqrt{y}}{z^3}$

61. $\log_{10} \dfrac{x^2(x + 1)^3}{\sqrt{x - 4}}$ **62.** $\ln \dfrac{[x(x - 1)]^3}{\sqrt{x + 1}}$

Write each expression as a single logarithmic expression.

63. $\log_2 x + 3 \log_2 y - 2 \log_2 z$

64. $\frac{1}{2} \log_{10} (x + 1) - 3 \log_{10} (x - 2)$

65. $4 \ln x - 5 \ln (x + 1) - \ln (x + 2)$

66. $\frac{1}{2} [\ln x + \ln (x + 2)] - 2 \ln (x - 5)$

Simplify.

67. $\log_{10} 1000$

68. $\log_{10} 10^{x^2}$

69. $\ln e^2$

70. $\ln e^x$

Find the derivative of each function.

71. $y = \ln (2x^3 - 4)$

72. $y = \log_3 (4x + 1)$

73. $y = \ln \left(\dfrac{x^2}{x^2 + 3} \right)$

74. $y = \cos (\ln x)$

75. $y = \dfrac{\sqrt{x + 1} \, (3x - 4)}{x^2(x + 2)}$

76. $y = x^{1-x}$

77. $y = e^{x^2 + 5}$

78. $y = 8^{3x}$

79. $y = \cot e^{2x}$

80. $y = e^{\sin x^2}$

81. $y = \arcsin e^{-4x}$

82. $y = x^3 e^{-4x}$

Sketch the graph of each equation.

83. $y = xe^{-x}$

84. $y = e^{-x^2}$

Use l'Hospital's rule in evaluating each limit.

85. $\displaystyle \lim_{x \to 2} \frac{\ln(x - 1)}{\sqrt{x - 2}}$

86. $\displaystyle \lim_{x \to \infty} xe^{-3x}$

87. $\displaystyle \lim_{x \to 0} \frac{x \sin x}{1 - \cos x}$

88. $\displaystyle \lim_{x \to \pi/2} \frac{\cos^2 x}{\sin x - 1}$

89. The current in a circuit is given by $i = 100 \cos 5t$. Find the equation of the voltage V_L across a 2-H inductor $\left(V_L = L \dfrac{di}{dt}, \text{ where } L \text{ is the inductance} \right)$.

90. The work done in a circuit is given by $W = 60 \cos^2 3t$. Find the equation for the power p $\left(p = \dfrac{dW}{dt} \right)$.

91. Find the equation of the tangent line to $y = \ln x^2$ at the point $(1, 0)$.

92. Find the velocity of an object moving along a straight line according to $s = e^{\sin t}$.

93. A particle moves along a straight line according to $s = 1 - 4e^{-t}$. Find its acceleration at $t = \frac{1}{2}$.

5

The Integral

INTRODUCTION

A large class of extremely important problems in science, engineering, and technology involves the notion of finding the "sum" of an "infinite number" of "infinitesimal" quantities. The integral calculus develops the mathematics needed to solve such problems.

Objectives

- Integrate polynomials.
- Find the constant of integration.
- Find the area under a curve.
- Evaluate definite integrals.

5.1   THE INDEFINITE INTEGRAL

As we have seen, many applications involve finding the derivative of a function. Following are some examples:

Function	Derivative
Position or displacement	Velocity
Velocity	Acceleration
Function	Slope of tangent line
Amount or quantity	Rate of increase or decrease
Work	Power

Often we have the derivative function and need to find the original function, which requires that we perform the inverse operation of differentiation. Now consider finding the derivative in reverse, that is, given the derivative of a function, find the function. This is called *antidifferentiation* or *integration*. That is, we look for an unknown function whose derivative is known.

> **ANTIDERIVATIVE**
>
> If $f(x)$ is a function, then $F(x)$ is an *antiderivative* of $f(x)$ if $F'(x) = f(x)$.

EXAMPLE 1

Find a function whose derivative is $10x^4$.

We need a function $y = f(x)$ where $\dfrac{dy}{dx} = 10x^4$. Recall that when differentiating a polynomial in x, the exponent of x is reduced by one. This means that the original function $y = f(x)$ must have a power of x with exponent 5, x^5. However, when we differentiate x^5, we obtain $5x^4$. If we rewrite $\dfrac{dy}{dx} = 10x^4 = 2(5x^4)$, observe that the given derivative is a multiple of two times the derivative of x^5.

Since $\dfrac{d}{dx}(2x^5) = 2\dfrac{d}{dx}(x^5) = 2(5x^4)$, we conclude that $y = 2x^5$ is a solution.

Example 1 immediately leads us into an important observation. While $y = 2x^5$ is a solution, so is $y = 2x^5 + 9$ since

$$\frac{d}{dx}(2x^5 + 9) = 10x^4 + 0 = 10x^4$$

In fact, any function of the form $y = 2x^5 + C$, where C is a constant, is a solution.

The process of antidifferentiation, unlike differentiation, does not lead to unique solutions. There are, in fact, infinitely many solutions. Each solution depends on the choice of the value for C.

EXAMPLE 2

Find a function whose derivative is $\dfrac{dy}{dx} = x^2 + 3x$.

The term x^2 requires that the desired function have a term involving x^3, since differentiation decreases the power of x by one. Since $\dfrac{d}{dx}(x^3) = 3x^2$, the coefficient of x^3 must be changed to $\dfrac{1}{3}$. Then

$$\frac{d}{dx}\left(\frac{x^3}{3}\right) = \frac{1}{3}(3x^2) = x^2$$

Similarly, the term $3x$ indicates that the desired function must also have a term involving x^2. Observe that the coefficient of x^2 must be $\dfrac{3}{2}$, so that $\dfrac{d}{dx}\left(\dfrac{3}{2}x^2\right) = \left(\dfrac{3}{2}\right)(2x) = 3x$. The desired function is

$$y = \frac{x^3}{3} + \frac{3x^2}{2}$$

Note:

$$y = \frac{x^3}{3} + \frac{3x^2}{2} + 11$$

is also a solution for Example 2. The general solution is

$$y = \frac{x^3}{3} + \frac{3x^2}{2} + C$$

where C is a constant.

The process of antidifferentiation can be easily checked. Differentiate the solution obtained and compare the result with the original given function. They should be equal. In Example 2,

$$\frac{d}{dx}\left(\frac{x^3}{3} + \frac{3x^2}{2}\right) = x^2 + 3x$$

Any solution $y = F(x)$ resulting from performing the integration process is called an *antiderivative*. In Example 1, $y = 2x^5 + 9$ was found to be an antiderivative of $10x^4$. That is, $F(x)$ is an antiderivative for a given function $f(x)$ if $\dfrac{d}{dx}[F(x)] = f(x)$.

Using any antiderivative $F(x)$ for a given function $f(x)$, $F(x) + C$ is a general solution; that is, $\dfrac{d}{dx}[F(x) + C] = f(x)$. This general solution is called the *indefinite integral* of $f(x)$, where $f(x)$ is called the *integrand*. The symbolism for the indefinite integral is

$$\int f(x)\, dx = F(x) + C$$

where $\int$ is called the *integral sign* and C is called the *constant of integration*. $F(x) + C$ can be considered to be the family of all curves whose derivatives for any given x are all equal to each other. This means that for any given x, the slopes of any two of these curves are equal.

EXAMPLE 3

Find the indefinite integral for $f(x) = 2x$.

Since $\dfrac{d}{dx}(x^2) = 2x$, we have

$$\int f(x)\, dx = \int 2x\, dx = x^2 + C$$

This is a family of parabolas $y = x^2 + C$ (see Fig. 5.1). At $x = 1$, each curve has slope

$$\frac{d}{dx}(x^2 + C)\bigg|_{x=1} = 2x\bigg|_{x=1} = 2(1) = 2$$

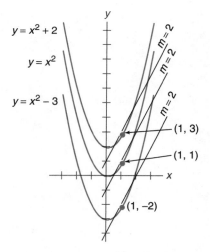

Figure 5.1   Family of parabolas $y = x^2 + C$.

Just as there are basic differentiation formulas, there are basic integration formulas that can be developed. These make the integration process easier.

First,

$$\int x^n\, dx = \frac{x^{n+1}}{n+1} + C \qquad (n \neq -1)$$

This is verified as follows:

$$\frac{d}{dx}\left(\frac{x^{n+1}}{n+1} + C\right) = \frac{(n+1)x^{(n+1)-1}}{n+1} + 0$$

$$= x^n$$

The case for $n = -1$ is discussed in Section 7.2.

EXAMPLE 4

Integrate $y = x^{16}$.

$$\int x^{16}\, dx = \frac{x^{16+1}}{16+1} + C = \frac{x^{17}}{17} + C$$

EXAMPLE 5

Find $\int dx$.

$$\int dx = \int x^0\, dx \qquad \text{(since } x^0 = 1\text{)}$$

$$= \frac{x^{0+1}}{0+1} + C = x + C$$

EXAMPLE 6

Find $\int \frac{dx}{x^3}$.

$$\int \frac{dx}{x^3} = \int x^{-3}\, dx$$

$$= \frac{x^{-3+1}}{-3+1} + C$$

$$= \frac{x^{-2}}{-2} + C$$

$$= -\frac{1}{2x^2} + C$$

EXAMPLE 7

Find $\int \sqrt{x}\, dx$.

$$\int \sqrt{x}\, dx = \int x^{1/2}\, dx$$

$$= \frac{x^{(1/2)+1}}{\frac{1}{2}+1} + C$$

$$= \frac{x^{3/2}}{\frac{3}{2}} + C$$

$$= \frac{2}{3}x^{3/2} + C$$

Next,

$$\int [f(x) + g(x)]\, dx = \int f(x)\, dx + \int g(x)\, dx$$

This follows from the fact that the derivative of the sum of two functions equals the sum of their derivatives.

EXAMPLE 8

Find $\int (x^3 + x^2)\, dx$.

$$\int (x^3 + x^2)\, dx = \int x^3\, dx + \int x^2\, dx$$

$$= \frac{x^{3+1}}{3+1} + \frac{x^{2+1}}{2+1} + C$$

$$= \frac{x^4}{4} + \frac{x^3}{3} + C$$

Finally,

$$\int k f(x)\, dx = k \int f(x)\, dx, \qquad \text{where } k \text{ is a constant}$$

This follows from the fact that the derivative of a constant times a function equals that constant times the derivative of the function.

EXAMPLE 9

Find $\int 12x^3\, dx$.

$$\int 12x^3\, dx = 12 \int x^3\, dx$$

$$= 12\,\frac{x^{3+1}}{3+1} + C$$

$$= 12\,\frac{x^4}{4} + C$$

$$= 3x^4 + C$$

EXAMPLE 10

Find $\int \left(3x^4 + 2x + \frac{1}{x^2} \right) dx$.

$$\int \left(3x^4 + 2x + \frac{1}{x^2} \right) dx = \int 3x^4\, dx + \int 2x\, dx + \int \frac{1}{x^2}\, dx$$

$$= 3\int x^4\, dx + 2\int x\, dx + \int x^{-2}\, dx$$

$$= 3\,\frac{x^{4+1}}{4+1} + 2\,\frac{x^{1+1}}{1+1} + \frac{x^{-2+1}}{-2+1} + C$$

$$= \frac{3x^5}{5} + x^2 - \frac{1}{x} + C$$

EXAMPLE 11

Find $\int 5(x^3 + 4)^4 (3x^2)\, dx$.

This does not seem to fit any of the formulas developed so far. While we could perform the indicated multiplication $5(x^3 + 4)^4(3x^2)$ and integrate the resulting sum of terms, there is an easier method.

Observe that $3x^2$ is the derivative of $x^3 + 4$. Also recall that when differentiating the power formula u^{n+1}, we obtain $(n + 1)u^n \dfrac{du}{dx}$. Then $5(x^3 + 4)^4(3x^2)$ is seen to be the derivative of $(x^3 + 4)^5$. That is,

$$\int 5(x^3 + 4)^4(3x^2)\,dx = (x^3 + 4)^5 + C$$

In Example 11, if we let $u = x^3 + 4$, then $du = 3x^2\,dx$. Then

$$\int 5(x^3 + 4)^4(3x^2)\,dx = \int 5u^4\,du$$

We must see the function to be integrated as a product of two factors. One factor is a power of u, that is, u^n. The other factor is the differential of u, that is, du. Then use the formula

$$\int u^n\,du = \frac{u^{n+1}}{n + 1} + C$$

EXAMPLE 12

Find $\displaystyle\int 6x^2\sqrt{2x^3 + 1}\,dx$.

Observe that $6x^2$ is the *derivative* of $2x^3 + 1$ (or $6x^2\,dx$ is the *differential* of $2x^3 + 1$). Setting $u = 2x^3 + 1$, then $du = 6x^2\,dx$, we have

$$\int 6x^2\sqrt{2x^3 + 1}\,dx = \int \sqrt{u}\,du = \int u^{1/2}\,du$$

$$= \frac{2}{3}u^{3/2} + C$$

$$= \frac{2}{3}(2x^3 + 1)^{3/2} + C$$

Using a calculator, we have

   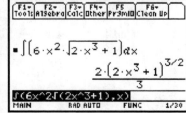

EXAMPLE 13

Find $\displaystyle\int x^3\sqrt{3x^4 + 2}\,dx$.

If we let $u = 3x^4 + 2$, then $du = 12x^3\,dx$.

Then

$$\sqrt{u}\,du = 12x^3\sqrt{3x^4 + 2}\,dx$$

Note that the only difference between the integrand $x^3\sqrt{3x^4 + 2}$ and $\sqrt{u}\,du$ is the factor 12.

So write

$$x^3 \sqrt{3x^4 + 2} \, dx = \sqrt{3x^4 + 2} \left(\frac{12x^3 \, dx}{12} \right) = \sqrt{u} \left(\frac{du}{12} \right)$$

and

$$\int x^3 \sqrt{3x^4 + 2} \, dx = \int \frac{\sqrt{u} \, du}{12}$$

$$= \frac{1}{12} \int (u)^{1/2} \, du$$

$$= \frac{1}{12} \frac{u^{3/2}}{\frac{3}{2}} + C$$

$$= \frac{1}{18} (3x^4 + 2)^{3/2} + C$$

$$\boxed{\begin{array}{l} u = 3x^4 + 2 \\ du = 12x^3 \, dx \end{array}}$$

Note: We will continue to use a box to show the appropriate substitutions for u and du whenever the formula $\int u^n \, du$ is applied. The box will appear at the right of the integral in which the substitutions have been made.

In summary, we have the following formulas:

1. $\int du = u + C$

2. $\int u^n \, du = \dfrac{u^{n+1}}{n + 1} + C \qquad (n \neq -1)$

3. $\int k f(x) \, dx = k \int f(x) \, dx, \qquad$ where k is a constant

4. $\int [f(x) + g(x)] \, dx = \int f(x) \, dx + \int g(x) \, dx$

Exercises 5.1

Integrate.

1. $\int x^7 \, dx$

2. $\int x^{24} \, dx$

3. $\int 3x^8 \, dx$

4. $\int 200x^9 \, dx$

5. $\int 4 \, dx$

6. $\int 8\sqrt{x^3} \, dx$

7. $\int 9\sqrt[6]{x^5} \, dx$

8. $\int \frac{3 \, dx}{x^2}$

9. $\int \frac{6 \, dx}{x^3}$

10. $\int \frac{dx}{\sqrt[6]{x^5}}$

11. $\int (5x^2 - 12x + 8) \, dx$

12. $\int (7x^{10} + 8x^4 - 11x^3) \, dx$

13. $\int \left(3x^2 - x + \frac{5}{x^3} \right) dx$

14. $\int \left(2x^3 + 3x - \frac{5}{x^4} \right) dx$

15. $\int (2x^2 - 3)^2 \, dx$

16. $\int (x^2 - 5)^2 \, dx$

17. $\int \sqrt{6x + 2} \, dx$

18. $\int \sqrt[3]{8x - 1} \, dx$

19. $\int 8x(x^2 + 3)^3 \, dx$

20. $\int 18x^2(x^3 + 2)^5 \, dx$

21. $\int x\sqrt[3]{5x^2 - 1} \, dx$

22. $\int 3x\sqrt{6x^2 + 5} \, dx$

23. $\int x(x^2 - 1)^4 \, dx$

24. $\int x^4(x^5 + 3)^7 \, dx$

25. $\displaystyle\int \frac{2x\,dx}{\sqrt{x^2+1}}$ **26.** $\displaystyle\int \frac{24x\,dx}{\sqrt{8x^2-1}}$ **27.** $\displaystyle\int (3x^2+2)(x^3+2x)^3\,dx$

28. $\displaystyle\int (4x^3-6x)(x^4-3x^2)^4\,dx$ **29.** $\displaystyle\int \frac{x^2\,dx}{(x^3-4)^2}$ **30.** $\displaystyle\int \frac{(6x+1)\,dx}{(3x^2+x-2)^3}$

31. $\displaystyle\int (10x-1)\sqrt{5x^2-x}\,dx$ **32.** $\displaystyle\int (3x^2-2x)\sqrt{x^3-x^2+2}\,dx$

33. $\displaystyle\int \frac{(2x+1)\,dx}{\sqrt{x^2+x}}$ **34.** $\displaystyle\int \frac{(x-4)\,dx}{\sqrt{x^2-8x+3}}$ **35.** $\displaystyle\int (2x+3)^2\,dx$

36. $\displaystyle\int (4x-5)^2\,dx$ **37.** $\displaystyle\int (2x-1)^4\,dx$ **38.** $\displaystyle\int (5x+3)^6\,dx$

39. $\displaystyle\int (x^2+1)^3\,dx$ **40.** $\displaystyle\int (x^2-4)^2\,dx$ **41.** $\displaystyle\int 4x(x^2+1)^3\,dx$

42. $\displaystyle\int 6x(x^2-4)^2\,dx$ **43.** $\displaystyle\int 30x^2(5x^3+1)^4\,dx$ **44.** $\displaystyle\int 12x^3(6x^4-1)^5\,dx$

45. $\displaystyle\int \frac{6x^2\,dx}{\sqrt{x^3+1}}$ **46.** $\displaystyle\int \frac{24x^3\,dx}{\sqrt{2x^4-1}}$ **47.** $\displaystyle\int \frac{(6x^2+6)\,dx}{\sqrt[3]{x^3+3x}}$

48. $\displaystyle\int \frac{(60x^3+36x)\,dx}{\sqrt[4]{5x^4+6x^2}}$ **49.** $\displaystyle\int \frac{(x-1)\,dx}{x^3}$ **50.** $\displaystyle\int \frac{(4-3x^2)\,dx}{6x^4}$

5.2 THE CONSTANT OF INTEGRATION

When additional information about the antiderivative is known, we can determine the constant of integration C.

Note: This section is actually a brief introduction to the study of differential equations, which are more extensively developed in Chapters 11 and 12.

EXAMPLE 1

Find the antiderivative of $\dfrac{dy}{dx} = 3x^2$ where $y = 14$ when $x = 2$.

$$\int 3x^2\,dx = F(x) + C$$
$$= x^3 + C$$

We need the function $y = x^3 + C$ where $y = 14$ when $x = 2$. So,

$$y = x^3 + C$$
$$(14) = (2)^3 + C$$
$$6 = C$$

The antiderivative is then $y = x^3 + 6$.

EXAMPLE 2

Find the equation of the curve that passes through $(4, -1)$ and whose slope is given by $m = \dfrac{dy}{dx} = 2x - 3$.

$$y = \int (2x - 3)\,dx$$
$$y = x^2 - 3x + C$$

$$(-1) = (4)^2 - 3(4) + C$$
$$-5 = C$$

So the equation is $y = x^2 - 3x - 5$.

EXAMPLE 3

Find the equation describing the motion of an object moving along a straight line with constant acceleration 2 m/s² when the velocity at time $t = 3$ s is 10 m/s and when the object has traveled 70 m from the origin at $t = 5$ s.

Since $\dfrac{dv}{dt} = a$, we have

$$v = \int a\, dt = \int 2\, dt = 2t + C_1$$

since

$$v = 2t + C_1 \quad \text{and} \quad v = 10 \quad \text{when} \quad t = 3$$
$$(10) = 2(3) + C_1$$
$$4 = C_1$$

so

$$v = 2t + 4$$

Also, since $\dfrac{ds}{dt} = v$,

$$s = \int v\, dt = \int (2t + 4)\, dt$$

we have

$$s = t^2 + 4t + C_2 \quad \text{and} \quad s = 70 \quad \text{when} \quad t = 5$$
$$(70) = (5)^2 + 4(5) + C_2$$
$$25 = C_2$$

The equation is $s = t^2 + 4t + 25$.

EXAMPLE 4

A bullet is fired vertically from a gun with an initial velocity of 250 m/s. (a) Find the equation that describes its motion. (b) How long does it take to reach its maximum height? (c) How high does the bullet go?

In a problem involving a freely falling body, the acceleration is

$$a = g = -32 \text{ ft/s}^2 = -9.80 \text{ m/s}^2$$

An upward direction is positive and a downward direction is negative.

(a) Since $\dfrac{dv}{dt} = a$, we have

$$v = \int a\, dt = \int -9.80\, dt = -9.80t + C_1$$

At $t = 0$, $v = 250$. Substituting, we have

$$250 = -9.80(0) + C_1$$
$$250 = C_1$$

So,

$$v = -9.80t + 250$$

and since $\dfrac{ds}{dt} = v$,

$$s = \int v \, dt = \int (-9.80t + 250) \, dt = -4.90t^2 + 250t + C_2$$

At $t = 0$, $s = 0$. Substituting, we have

$$0 = -4.90(0)^2 + 250(0) + C_2$$
$$0 = C_2$$

So,

$$s = -4.90t^2 + 250t$$

(b) At the bullet's maximum height, $v = 0$. So,

$$v = -9.80t + 250 = 0$$

$$t = \frac{250}{9.80} = 25.5 \text{ s}$$

(c) At $t = 25.5$ s,

$$s = -4.90t^2 + 250t$$
$$s = -4.90(25.5)^2 + (250)(25.5) = 3190 \text{ m}$$

In general, the position of an object moving freely (no air resistance) along a straight line with constant acceleration a, initial velocity v_0, and initial position s_0 may be written

$$s = \frac{1}{2}at^2 + v_0 t + s_0$$

This equation is derived in Exercise 23.

The voltage V_C across a capacitor at any time t is given by

$$V_C = \frac{1}{C} \int i \, dt$$

where C is the capacitance in farads and i is the current in amperes.

EXAMPLE 5

A 1-microfarad capacitor (1 microfarad $= 1 \ \mu\text{F} = 10^{-6}$ farad) has a voltage of 86 volts (V) across it. At a given instant ($t = 0$), we connect this capacitor to a source that sends a current $i = 3t^2$ amperes (A) through the circuit. Find the voltage across the capacitor when $t = 0.1$ s.

$$V_C = \frac{1}{C} \int i \, dt = \frac{1}{10^{-6}} \int 3t^2 \, dt$$

$$V_C = \frac{1}{10^{-6}} \cdot \frac{3t^3}{3} + C = 10^6 \cdot t^3 + C$$

When $t = 0$, $V_C = 86$ V, so

$$(86) = 10^6 \cdot (0)^3 + C$$
$$86 = C$$

We then have

$$V_C = 10^6 \cdot t^3 + 86$$
$$V_C = 10^6 \cdot (0.1)^3 + 86$$
$$= 10^6 \cdot 10^{-3} + 86$$
$$= 1086 \text{ V}$$

The current i in a circuit at any instant is given by

$$i = \frac{dq}{dt}$$

where q is the charge. That is,

$$q = \int i\, dt$$

EXAMPLE 6

The current in a circuit is given by $i = t^3 + 3t^2 - 4$ amperes (A). Find the charge in coulombs (C) that passes a given point in the circuit after 2 s.

$$q = \int i\, dt = \int (t^3 + 3t^2 - 4)\, dt$$

$$q = \frac{t^4}{4} + t^3 - 4t + C$$

If we assume that $q = 0$ when $t = 0$, then

$$0 = 0 + 0 - 0 + C$$
$$0 = C$$

and

$$q = \frac{t^4}{4} + t^3 - 4t$$

At $t = 2$ s,

$$q = \frac{(2)^4}{4} + (2)^3 - 4(2)$$

$$= 4 + 8 - 8 = 4\,\text{C}$$

Exercises 5.2

Find the equation of the curve $y = f(x)$ satisfying the given conditions.

1. $\dfrac{dy}{dx} = 3x$, passing through $(0, 1)$

2. $\dfrac{dy}{dx} = 5x^2$, passing through $\left(1, -\dfrac{1}{3}\right)$

3. $\dfrac{dy}{dx} = 3x^2 + 3$, passing through $(-1, 2)$

4. $\dfrac{dy}{dx} = 4x^3 - 2x + 2$, passing through $(1, -2)$

5. $\dfrac{dy}{dx} = x(x^2 - 3)^2$, passing through $\left(2, \dfrac{7}{6}\right)$

6. $\dfrac{dy}{dx} = \dfrac{x}{\sqrt{x^2 - 1}}$, passing through $(-3, 2\sqrt{2})$

7. Find the equation describing the motion of an object moving along a straight line when the acceleration is $a = 3t$, when the velocity at $t = 4$ s is 40 m/s, and when the object has traveled 86 m from the origin at $t = 2$ s.

8. Find the equation describing the motion of an object moving along a straight line when the acceleration is $a = 4t - 2$, when the velocity at $t = 5$ s is 25 m/s, and when the object has traveled 238 m from the origin at $t = 12$ s.

9. A stone is dropped from a height of 100 ft. For a free-falling object, the acceleration is $a = -32$ ft/s^2 (the effect of gravity). Find the distance the stone has traveled after 2 s. Note that the initial velocity is 0 because the stone was dropped, not thrown down. Also find the velocity of the stone when it hits the ground.

10. An object is dropped from a stationary balloon at 500 m. (a) Express the object's height above the ground as a function of time. (b) How long does it take to hit the ground? ($a = -9.80$ m/s^2.)

11. An airplane starts from rest and travels 3600 ft down a runway with constant acceleration before lifting off in 30 s. Find its velocity at the moment of lift-off. *Hint:* $s = \frac{1}{2} at^2$.

12. A ball rolls from a rest position down a 200-cm inclined plane in 4 s. Find its acceleration in cm/s^2.

13. A stone is launched straight up from the ground at a velocity of 25 m/s. (a) Find the maximum height that the stone reaches. (b) How long does it take for the stone to hit the ground? (c) Find the speed at which the stone hits the ground.

14. A ball is thrown vertically upward with an initial velocity of 40 ft/s. (a) Find the maximum height of the ball. (b) How long does it take for the ball to hit the ground? (c) Find the speed at which the ball hits the ground.

15. A stone is thrown vertically upward from the edge of a roof of a 200-ft-tall building with an initial velocity of 30 ft/s. (a) Find the equation describing the altitude of the stone from the ground. (b) How long does it take for the stone to hit the ground?

16. A stone is thrown straight down from an 80-m-tall building with an initial velocity of 10 m/s. (a) Find the equation describing the height of the stone from the ground. (b) How long does it take for the stone to hit the ground?

17. A flywheel is turning at a rate given by $\omega = 80 - 12t + 3t^2$, where ω is the angular speed in revolutions per minute (rpm). Find the number of revolutions that the flywheel makes in the first 3 s. $\omega = \dfrac{d\theta}{dt}$. (Assume that $\theta = 0$ when $t = 0$.)

18. The power in a system equals the rate at which energy (work) is expended. That is, $p = \dfrac{dW}{dt}$. At $t = 0$, the energy in an electrical system is 4 joules (J). Find the energy after 4 s if $p = 2\sqrt{t}$ watts (W).

19. A capacitor with capacitance 10^{-4} F has a voltage of 100 V across it. At a given instant ($t = 0$) the capacitor is connected to a source that sends a current $i = \frac{1}{2}\sqrt{t} + 0.2$ amperes through the circuit. Find the voltage across the capacitor when $t = 0.16$ s.

20. A 0.1-F capacitor measures 150 V across it. At $t = 0$ the capacitor is connected to a source that sends current $i = \dfrac{16t}{\sqrt{4t^2 + 9}}$ amperes through the circuit. Find the voltage across the capacitor when $t = 2$ s.

21. The current in a circuit is given by $i = t\sqrt{t^2 + 1}$ amperes. Find the charge (in coulombs) that passes a given point in the circuit after 1 s. (Assume that $q = 0$ when $t = 0$.)

22. The current in a circuit is given by $i = t^{3/2} + 4t$ amperes. Find the charge in coulombs that passes a given point in the circuit after 4 s. (Assume that $q = 0$ when $t = 0$.)

23. In general, the position of an object moving freely (no air resistance) along a straight line with constant acceleration a, initial velocity v_0, and initial position s_0 may be written

$$s = \tfrac{1}{2} at^2 + v_0 t + s_0$$

For freely falling bodies ($a = g = -32$ ft/s^2 = -9.80 m/s^2), this equation becomes

$$s = -16t^2 + v_0 t + s_0 = -4.90t^2 + v_0 t + s_0$$

Derive this equation.

5.3 AREA UNDER A CURVE

Another application of integration is finding the area under a curve, which is actually the geometric interpretation of the integral. We can find the area of regions which would be impossible to determine if we had to rely only on regular geometric methods. The area under a curve $y = f(x)$ refers to the area of the region bounded by the curves $y = f(x)$, $x = a$, $x = b$, and the x-axis ($y = 0$) (see Fig. 5.2). We could approximate this area by forming the rectangles in Fig. 5.3. The sum of the areas of the rectangles could then be used as an approximation of the desired area.

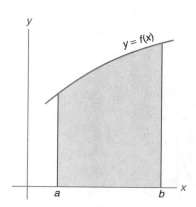

Figure 5.2   Area under a curve.

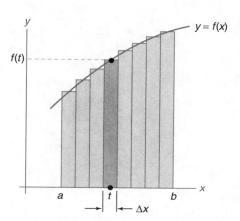

Figure 5.3   Approximating the area under a curve using rectangles.

The height of each rectangle is the value of the function $f(x)$ for some point t along the base of the rectangle. We have chosen Δx to be the base, or the width of each rectangle. The described area is then approximately equal to the sum

$$S_n = f(t_1)\,\Delta x + f(t_2)\,\Delta x + f(t_3)\,\Delta x + \cdots + f(t_k)\,\Delta x + \cdots + f(t_n)\,\Delta x$$

when using n rectangles with base Δx and t_k as a point along the base of the kth rectangle. The smaller we choose the width Δx, the better is the approximation for the area under the curve. Observe that as $\Delta x \rightarrow 0$, the number of terms n in the approximating sum S_n will increase. In fact, as $\Delta x \rightarrow 0$, $n \rightarrow \infty$ and the sums S_n appear to approach the exact area A under the curve.

This summation process is symbolized as follows:

$$\lim_{n \to \infty} S_n = A$$

Although this method can be used to find area as illustrated in Example 1, the method is generally difficult to use. In practice, the approach shown after Example 1 for finding area is easier.

EXAMPLE 1

Find the area under the curve $y = 3x$ from $x = 0$ to $x = 2$.

Form the approximating sum S_n by letting the width of each rectangle be

$$\Delta x = \frac{b - a}{n} = \frac{2 - 0}{n} = \frac{2}{n}$$

In Fig. 5.4, $n = 4$, so $\Delta x = \frac{2}{4} = \frac{1}{2}$ and $t_1 = a = 0$, $t_2 = \frac{1}{2}$, $t_3 = 1$, and $t_4 = \frac{3}{2}$. Then

$$S_4 = f(0)\,\Delta x + f\!\left(\frac{1}{2}\right)\Delta x + f(1)\,\Delta x + f\!\left(\frac{3}{2}\right)\Delta x$$

$$= (0)\!\left(\frac{1}{2}\right) + \left(\frac{3}{2}\right)\!\left(\frac{1}{2}\right) + (3)\!\left(\frac{1}{2}\right) + \left(\frac{9}{2}\right)\!\left(\frac{1}{2}\right)$$

$$= \frac{18}{4} = \frac{9}{2}$$

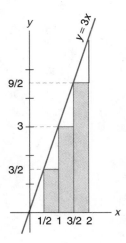

Figure 5.4

In general, since $f(x) = 3x$,

$$S_n = f(0)\,\Delta x + f\!\left(\frac{2}{n}\right)\Delta x + f\!\left(\frac{4}{n}\right)\Delta x + f\!\left(\frac{6}{n}\right)\Delta x + \cdots + f\!\left(\frac{2(n-1)}{n}\right)\Delta x$$

$$= 3(0)\!\left(\frac{2}{n}\right) + 3\!\left(\frac{2}{n}\right)\!\left(\frac{2}{n}\right) + 3\!\left(\frac{4}{n}\right)\!\left(\frac{2}{n}\right) + 3\!\left(\frac{6}{n}\right)\!\left(\frac{2}{n}\right) + \cdots + 3\!\left(\frac{2(n-1)}{n}\right)\!\left(\frac{2}{n}\right)$$

$$= \frac{12}{n^2}\,[1 + 2 + 3 + \cdots + (n-1)]$$

Since $1 + 2 + 3 + \cdots + (n-1)$ is the sum of an arithmetic progression whose last term is $n - 1$, we have

$$1 + 2 + 3 + \cdots + (n-1) = \frac{n-1}{2}[1 + (n-1)]$$

$$= \frac{(n-1)n}{2} \qquad \text{(See Section 9.1.)}$$

Then,

$$S_n = \frac{12}{n^2}\!\left(\frac{(n-1)n}{2}\right)$$

$$= \frac{6(n-1)}{n}$$

$$= 6\!\left(1 - \frac{1}{n}\right)$$

So,

$$A = \lim_{n \to \infty} S_n = \lim_{n \to \infty} 6\left(1 - \frac{1}{n}\right)$$

$$= 6(1 - 0) = 6$$

Note that this is the same area as obtained by using the formula for the area of a triangle with height $h = 6$ and base $b = 2$:

$$A = \frac{1}{2}bh$$

$$= \frac{1}{2}(2)(6) = 6$$

To avoid the complicated summation process, let us now consider only the area under the curve $y = f(x)$ from a to x in Fig. 5.5. Note that the area increases as x increases. Consider the area determined by x as a function of x, which we will denote by $A(x)$. The difference ΔA between $A(x + \Delta x)$ and $A(x)$ is the incremental change in the area for an incremental change Δx.

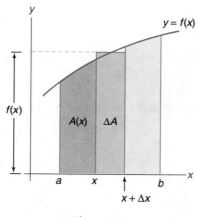

Figure 5.5

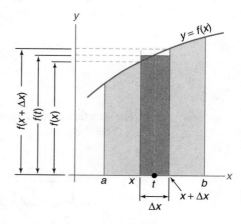

Figure 5.6

From Fig. 5.6 we see that

$$f(x)\,\Delta x \leq \Delta A \leq f(x + \Delta x)\,\Delta x$$

Dividing by Δx, we obtain

$$f(x) \leq \frac{\Delta A}{\Delta x} \leq f(x + \Delta x)$$

We can interpret $\dfrac{\Delta A}{\Delta x}$ as the average rate of change of the area as the area increases from x to $x + \Delta x$. As $\Delta x \to 0, f(x + \Delta x) \to f(x)$. Since $\dfrac{\Delta A}{\Delta x}$ is squeezed between $f(x)$ and $f(x + \Delta x)$, we have $\dfrac{\Delta A}{\Delta x} \to f(x)$ as $\Delta x \to 0$. That is,

$$\lim_{\Delta x \to 0} \frac{\Delta A}{\Delta x} = f(x)$$

Formally, this limit $\lim\limits_{\Delta x \to 0} \dfrac{\Delta A}{\Delta x}$ represents the instantaneous rate of change of the area $A(x)$ at x. Since $\lim\limits_{\Delta x \to 0} \dfrac{\Delta A}{\Delta x} = f(x)$, we have

$$\frac{dA}{dx} = f(x)$$

To find $A(x)$ we integrate $\dfrac{dA}{dx} = f(x)$:

$$A(x) = \int f(x)\,dx = F(x) + C$$

where $F(x)$ is an antiderivative of $f(x)$. To determine the appropriate value for the constant of integration C, note that $A(a) = 0$. (When $x = a$, there is no area under the curve.) Then

$$0 = F(a) + C \quad \text{or} \quad C = -F(a)$$

The desired expression for $A(x)$ is then $A(x) = F(x) - F(a)$.

Finally, the area A under the curve $y = f(x)$ from $x = a$ to $x = b$ is the value $A = F(b) - F(a)$. That is,

$$A = F(b) - F(a), \qquad \text{where} \quad F(x) = \int f(x)\,dx$$

The constant of integration is not involved in the formula for A. Any antiderivative $F(x)$ for $f(x)$ can be used.

EXAMPLE 2

Find the area under the curve $y = x^2$ from $x = 1$ to $x = 2$.

$$\int x^2\,dx = \frac{x^3}{3} + C$$

Using the antiderivative $F(x) = x^3/3$, we have the desired area in Fig. 5.7.

$$A = F(2) - F(1) = \frac{(2)^3}{3} - \frac{(1)^3}{3} = \frac{8}{3} - \frac{1}{3} = \frac{7}{3}$$

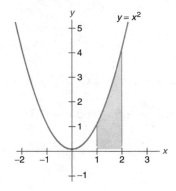

Figure 5.7

EXAMPLE 3

Revisiting the problem of Example 1, we can see geometrically how an antiderivative function is related to the area under the curve. Using Fig. 5.8, find a formula for the area under $y = 3x$ from $x = 0$ to an arbitrary value of x. Just think of the straight line $y = 3x$ as all points of the form $(x, 3x)$. The formula for the area of this triangle is

$$A = \frac{1}{2}bh = \frac{1}{2}(x)(3x) = \frac{3x^2}{2}$$

By comparison,

$$3x \, dx = \frac{3x^2}{2} + C$$

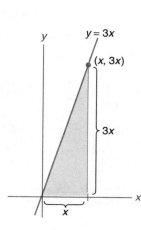

Figure 5.8

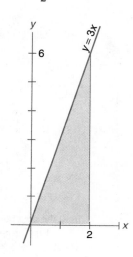

Figure 5.9

EXAMPLE 4

Find the area under the curve $y = 3x$ from $x = 0$ to $x = 2$ as in Fig. 5.9.

Note: We have already computed this area by the summation method in Example 1.

$$\int 3x \, dx = \frac{3x^2}{2} + C$$

Using the antiderivative $F(x) = \frac{3x^2}{2}$, we have

$$A = F(2) - F(0) = \frac{3(2)^2}{2} - \frac{3(0)^2}{2} = 6 - 0 = 6$$

EXAMPLE 5

Find the area bounded by $y = 2 + x - x^2$ and the x-axis.

First, graph the equation by finding the x-intercepts (see Fig. 5.10):

$$y = 2 + x - x^2 = 0$$
$$(2 - x)(1 + x) = 0$$
$$x = 2, -1$$

Then,

$$\int (2 + x - x^2) \, dx = 2x + \frac{x^2}{2} - \frac{x^3}{3} + C$$

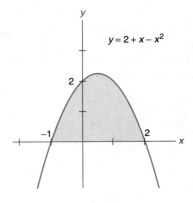

Figure 5.10

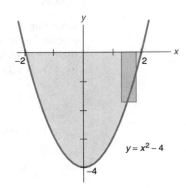

Figure 5.11

and

$$A = F(2) - F(-1) = \left[2(2) + \frac{2^2}{2} - \frac{2^3}{3}\right] - \left[2(-1) + \frac{(-1)^2}{2} - \frac{(-1)^3}{3}\right]$$

$$= \left(4 + 2 - \frac{8}{3}\right) - \left(-2 + \frac{1}{2} + \frac{1}{3}\right) = \frac{9}{2}$$

EXAMPLE 6

Find the area bounded by $y = x^2 - 4$ and the x-axis.

First, graph the equation (see Fig. 5.11).

Then,

$$\int (x^2 - 4)\, dx = \frac{x^3}{3} - 4x + C$$

and

$$A = F(2) - F(-2) = \left[\frac{(2)^3}{3} - 4(2)\right] - \left[\frac{(-2)^3}{3} - 4(-2)\right]$$

$$= \left[\frac{8}{3} - 8\right] - \left[-\frac{8}{3} + 8\right]$$

$$= -\frac{32}{3}$$

Note: An area below the x-axis consists of approximating rectangles whose heights, $f(x) < 0$, and whose widths, $\Delta x > 0$, yield negative products. In such cases, the area is found by finding the absolute value of this result. The area in Example 6 is thus $\left|-\frac{32}{3}\right|$ or $\frac{32}{3}$. As we shall see in Section 6.1, complications occur when finding the area between the x-axis and a curve that crosses the x-axis.

Exercises 5.3

Find the area under each curve.

1. $y = x$ from $x = 0$ to $x = 2$
2. $y = 5x$ from $x = 1$ to $x = 4$
3. $y = 2x^2$ from $x = 1$ to $x = 3$
4. $y = x^2 + 3$ from $x = 0$ to $x = 2$
5. $y = 3x^2 - 2x$ from $x = 1$ to $x = 2$
6. $y = 4 - 3x^2$ from $x = 0$ to $x = 1$

7. $y = \dfrac{3}{x^2}$ from $x = 1$ to $x = 2$

8. $y = \dfrac{1}{x^3}$ from $x = 2$ to $x = 3$

9. $y = \sqrt{3x - 2}$ from $x = 1$ to $x = 2$

10. $y = \sqrt{2x + 3}$ from $x = 0$ to $x = 3$

11. $y = 4x - x^3$ from $x = 0$ to $x = 2$

12. $y = x^3 - 16x$ from $x = -4$ to $x = 0$

13. $y = 1 - x^4$ from $x = -1$ to $x = 1$

14. $y = 16 - x^4$ from $x = -2$ to $x = 2$

15. $y = \sqrt{2x + 1},\ x = 4$ to $x = 12$

16. $y = \sqrt{4 - 3x}$ bounded by the coordinate axes

17. $y = \sqrt[3]{x - 1}$ bounded by the coordinate axes

18. $y = \sqrt[3]{8x + 27}$ bounded by the coordinate axes

19. $y = 1/x^2$ from $x = 1$ to $x = 5$

20. $y = x^4$ from $x = 1$ to $x = 3$

21. $y = \dfrac{1}{(2x - 1)^2}$ from $x = -3$ to y-axis

22. $y = \dfrac{1}{(2x + 3)^3}$ from $x = 3$ to y-axis

Find the area bounded by each curve and the x-axis.

23. $y = 9 - x^2$ **24.** $y = 12 - 3x^2$ **25.** $y = 2x - x^2$ **26.** $y = 5x - 2x^2$

27. $y = x^2 - x^3$ **28.** $y = 4x^2 - x^3$ **29.** $y = x^2 - x^4$ **30.** $y = 9x^2 - x^4$

5.4   THE DEFINITE INTEGRAL

In Section 5.3, we first found the area A under the curve $y = f(x)$ from $x = a$ to $x = b$ by the summation method, that is,

$$A = \lim_{n \to \infty} S_n$$

where $S_n = f(t_1)\,\Delta x + f(t_2)\,\Delta x + \cdots + f(t_k)\,\Delta x + \cdots + f(t_n)\,\Delta x$, where Δx is the width of each rectangle used to approximate the area under the curve and $f(t_k)$ is the height of the kth rectangle with t_k some point along its base.

We then found that we could determine this same area A using integration, that is,

$$A = F(b) - F(a)$$

where

$$\int f(x)\,dx = F(x) \qquad [F'(x) = f(x)]$$

so that

$$A = \lim_{n \to \infty} S_n = F(b) - F(a)$$

The symbol $\int$ indicates a type of summation. The summation process can be applied to situations not involving areas. With few restrictions on the function $y = f(x)$, we can ask whether $\lim_{n \to \infty} S_n$ exists when we consider values of x between a and b. If the limit does exist (unlike our examples in Section 5.3, it need not exist), then we make the following definition: The *definite integral* of a function $y = f(x)$ from $x = a$ to $x = b$ is the number $\lim_{n \to \infty} S_n$. We symbolize this number by

$$\int_a^b f(x)\,dx$$

That is,

$$\int_a^b f(x)\,dx = \lim_{n\to\infty} S_n$$

Note: The definite integral $\int_a^b f(x)\,dx$ is a number and is not to be confused with the indefinite integral $\int f(x)\,dx$, which is a family of functions. The number a is called the *lower limit* of the integral, and b is called the *upper limit.*

The method of evaluating a definite integral is known as the Fundamental Theorem of Calculus.

THE FUNDAMENTAL THEOREM OF CALCULUS

If $f(x)$ is continuous on the internal $a \le x \le b$, then

$$\int_a^b f(x)\,dx = F(b) - F(a), \qquad \text{where} \quad F'(x) = f(x)$$

Thus the technique for evaluating a definite integral is the same as for finding the area under a curve (see Section 5.3).

EXAMPLE 1

Evaluate the integral $\int_1^3 x^3\,dx$.

Since $\int x^3\,dx = \dfrac{x^4}{4} + C$, then $F(x) = \dfrac{x^4}{4}$, and

$$\int_1^3 x^3\,dx = F(3) - F(1)$$

$$= \frac{(3)^4}{4} - \frac{(1)^4}{4}$$

$$= \frac{81}{4} - \frac{1}{4}$$

$$= 20$$

We now introduce a shorthand notation for evaluating $F(b) - F(a)$:

$$F(x)\Big|_a^b = F(b) - F(a)$$

Remember that $F(x)$ can be any antiderivative of a given function $f(x)$ since $[F(b) + C] - [F(a) + C] = F(b) - F(a)$.

EXAMPLE 2

Evaluate $\int_1^2 (x^2 + 3x)\,dx$.

Since

$$\int (x^2 + 3x)\,dx = \frac{x^3}{3} + \frac{3x^2}{2} + C$$

we have

$$\int_1^2 (x^2 + 3x)\,dx = \left(\frac{x^3}{3} + \frac{3x^2}{2} \right)\Big|_1^2$$

$$= \left[\frac{(2)^3}{3} + \frac{3(2)^2}{2} \right] - \left[\frac{(1)^3}{3} + \frac{3(1)^2}{2} \right]$$

$$= \left(\frac{8}{3} + \frac{12}{2}\right) - \left(\frac{1}{3} + \frac{3}{2}\right)$$

$$= \frac{41}{6}$$

EXAMPLE 3

Evaluate $\int_1^3 \frac{dx}{x^3}$.

$$\int_1^3 \frac{dx}{x^3} = \int_1^3 x^{-3}\, dx$$

$$= \frac{x^{-3+1}}{-3+1}\bigg|_1^3 = -\frac{1}{2x^2}\bigg|_1^3$$

$$= \left[-\frac{1}{2(3)^2}\right] - \left[-\frac{1}{2(1)^2}\right]$$

$$= -\frac{1}{18} + \frac{1}{2} = \frac{8}{18} = \frac{4}{9}$$

EXAMPLE 4

Evaluate $\int_{-2}^1 x^2\, dx$.

$$\int_{-2}^1 x^2\, dx = \frac{x^3}{3}\bigg|_{-2}^1 = \frac{(1)^3}{3} - \frac{(-2)^3}{3} = \frac{1}{3} + \frac{8}{3} = 3$$

EXAMPLE 5

Evaluate $\int_1^0 x(x^2 + 1)^2\, dx$.

Let $u = x^2 + 1$; then,

$$du = \frac{d}{dx}(x^2 + 1)\, dx = 2x\, dx \qquad \boxed{\begin{array}{l} u = x^2 + 1 \\ du = 2x\, dx \end{array}}$$

Use this substitution to transform both the integrand and the limits of integration. Note that if $x = 1$, then $u = 1^2 + 1 = 2$; and if $x = 0$, then $u = 0^2 + 1 = 1$.

$$\int_1^0 x(x^2 + 1)^2\, dx = \int_{1^2+1}^{0^2+1} u^2 \frac{du}{2}$$

$$= \frac{1}{2} \int_2^1 u^2\, du$$

$$= \frac{1}{2} \cdot \frac{u^3}{3}\bigg|_2^1$$

$$= \frac{1^3}{6} - \frac{2^3}{6}$$

$$= \frac{1}{6} - \frac{8}{6}$$

$$= -\frac{7}{6}$$

Note that in Example 5, the definite integral is negative. There are no restrictions on the value of a definite integral. The choice of upper and lower limits depends on the application of the definite integral. One can show, however, that

$$\int_a^b f(x)\,dx = -\int_b^a f(x)\,dx$$

EXAMPLE 6

Evaluate

$$\int_0^1 \frac{2x+3}{(x^2+3x-7)^2}\,dx$$

$$\int_0^1 \frac{2x+3}{(x^2+3x-7)^2}\,dx = \int_{0^2+3(0)-7}^{1^2+3(1)-7} \frac{du}{u^2}$$

$$\boxed{\begin{aligned} u &= x^2+3x-7 \\ du &= (2x+3)\,dx \end{aligned}}$$

$$= \int_{-7}^{-3} u^{-2}\,du$$

$$= -u^{-1}\Big|_{-7}^{-3}$$

$$= -\frac{1}{u}\Big|_{-7}^{-3}$$

$$= -\frac{1}{-3} - \left(-\frac{1}{-7}\right)$$

$$= \frac{1}{3} - \frac{1}{7}$$

$$= \frac{4}{21}$$

Using a calculator, we have

2nd 7 $(2x+3)/(x^2+3x-7)^2,x,0,1)$ **ENTER**

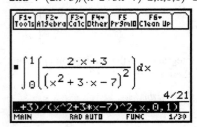

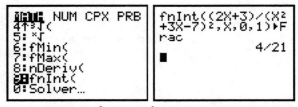

MATH 9 $(2x+3)/(x\ x^2+3x-7)\ x^2,x,0,1)$ **MATH 1 ENTER**

Exercises 5.4

Evaluate each definite integral.

1. $\displaystyle\int_0^1 5x\,dx$

2. $\displaystyle\int_0^1 x^4\,dx$

3. $\displaystyle\int_1^2 (x^2+3)\,dx$

4. $\displaystyle\int_2^4 (3x^2+x-1)\,dx$

5. $\displaystyle\int_2^0 (x^3+1)\,dx$

6. $\displaystyle\int_1^0 (3x^4-8)\,dx$

7. $\displaystyle\int_{-1}^{1} (x^2 + x + 2)\, dx$ **8.** $\displaystyle\int_{-2}^{0} (2x^3 - 4x)\, dx$ **9.** $\displaystyle\int_{4}^{9} (3x^{1/2} + x^{-1/2})\, dx$

10. $\displaystyle\int_{8}^{27} (5x^{2/3} + 4x^{-1/3})\, dx$ **11.** $\displaystyle\int_{1}^{9} \frac{x + 3}{\sqrt{x}}\, dx$ **12.** $\displaystyle\int_{1}^{4} \frac{x^2 + 3x - 2}{\sqrt{x}}\, dx$

13. $\displaystyle\int_{1}^{2} (3x + 4)^4\, dx$ **14.** $\displaystyle\int_{0}^{1} (2x + 1)^5\, dx$ **15.** $\displaystyle\int_{0}^{16} \sqrt{2x + 4}\, dx$

16. $\displaystyle\int_{1}^{44} \sqrt[3]{5x - 4}\, dx$ **17.** $\displaystyle\int_{1}^{2} 4x(x^2 - 3)^3\, dx$ **18.** $\displaystyle\int_{0}^{1} 6x^2(x^3 + 1)^4\, dx$

19. $\displaystyle\int_{-1}^{0} x(1 - x^2)^{2/3}\, dx$ **20.** $\displaystyle\int_{-2}^{0} x\sqrt{4 - x^2}\, dx$ **21.** $\displaystyle\int_{0}^{1} x\sqrt{x^2 + 1}\, dx$

22. $\displaystyle\int_{0}^{2} x^2\sqrt{x^3 + 2}\, dx$ **23.** $\displaystyle\int_{0}^{4} \frac{6x}{\sqrt{x^2 + 9}}\, dx$ **24.** $\displaystyle\int_{-1}^{1} \frac{16x\, dx}{\sqrt[3]{3x^2 + 5}}$

25. $\displaystyle\int_{1}^{2} \frac{3x^2 + 1}{\sqrt{x^3 + x}}\, dx$ **26.** $\displaystyle\int_{2}^{3} \frac{2x + 1}{\sqrt{x^2 + x - 2}}\, dx$

CHAPTER 5 SUMMARY

1. If $f(x)$ is a function, then $F(x)$ is the *antiderivative* of $f(x)$ if $F'(x) = f(x)$.

2. *Integration formulas:*

(a) $\displaystyle\int x^n\, dx = \frac{x^{n+1}}{n + 1} + C \qquad (n \neq -1)$

(b) $\displaystyle\int [f(x) + g(x)]\, dx = \int f(x)\, dx + \int g(x)\, dx$

(c) $\displaystyle\int k\, f(x)\, dx = k \int f(x)\, dx$, where k is a constant

3. The *area under the curve* $y = f(x)$ in Fig. 5.12 from $x = a$ to $x = b$ is $A = F(b) - F(a)$.

4. Definite integral (The Fundamental Theorem of Calculus): If $f(x)$ is continuous on the interval $a \leq x \leq b$, then

$$\int_{a}^{b} f(x)\, dx = F(b) - F(a), \text{ where } F'(x) = f(x).$$

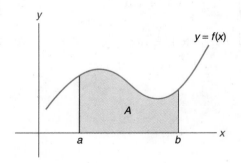

Figure 5.12

CHAPTER 5 REVIEW

Integrate.

1. $\displaystyle\int (5x^2 - x)\, dx$

2. $\displaystyle\int (3x^7 + 2x + 4)\, dx$

3. $\displaystyle\int 6\sqrt{x^7}\, dx$

4. $\displaystyle\int 4x^{2/3}\, dx$

5. $\displaystyle\int \frac{3\, dx}{x^5}$

6. $\displaystyle\int \frac{dx}{\sqrt{x^3}}$

7. $\displaystyle\int (6x^3 + 1)(3x^4 + 2x - 1)^3\, dx$

8. $\displaystyle\int (7x + 4)(7x^2 + 8x + 2)^{3/5}\, dx$

9. $\displaystyle\int \frac{2x + 5}{\sqrt{x^2 + 5x}}\, dx$

10. $\displaystyle\int (15x^2 + 4)(5x^3 + 4x)^{-2/3}\, dx$

11. Find the equation of the curve $y = f(x)$ passing through $(1, -3)$ whose slope is given by $\dfrac{dy}{dx} = 3x^2$.

12. A stone is thrown vertically upward from a cliff 100 ft high with an initial velocity of 25 ft/s. Find the equation describing the altitude of the stone from the ground below ($a = -32$ ft/s²).

13. The rate of change of resistance with respect to temperature of an electric resistor is given by $\dfrac{dR}{dT} = 0.009T^2 + 0.02T - 0.7$. Find the resistance when the temperature is 30°C if $R = 0.2\ \Omega$ when $T = 0$°C.

14. The current in an electric circuit is given by $i = \dfrac{3t^2 + 1}{\sqrt{t^3 + t + 2}}$ amperes. Find the charge (in coulombs) that passes a given point in the circuit after 0.2 s given that $q = 2\sqrt{2}$ at $t = 0$.

Find the area under each curve.

15. $y = x^2 + 1$ from $x = 0$ to $x = 2$

16. $y = 8 - 6x^2$ from $x = 0$ to $x = 1$

17. $y = \dfrac{1}{x^5}$ from $x = 1$ to $x = 2$

18. $y = \dfrac{4x}{(x^2 + 1)^2}$ from $x = 0$ to $x = 1$

19. $y = \sqrt{5x + 6}$ from $x = 0$ to $x = 6$

20. $y = x\sqrt{x^2 + 4}$ from $x = 0$ to $x = 2$

Evaluate each definite integral.

21. $\displaystyle\int_0^1 (x^3 + 2x^2 + x)\, dx$

22. $\displaystyle\int_1^2 (3x^4 - 2x^3 + 7x)\, dx$

23. $\displaystyle\int_0^2 x(x^2 + 1)^2\, dx$

24. $\displaystyle\int_1^2 \frac{5x^2}{(x^3 + 2)^2}\, dx$

25. $\displaystyle\int_1^2 (2x + 1)\sqrt{x^2 + x}\, dx$

26. $\displaystyle\int_0^3 \frac{x^2}{\sqrt{x^3 + 1}}\, dx$

27. $\displaystyle\int_2^1 \left(3x^2 - x + \frac{1}{x^2}\right) dx$

28. $\displaystyle\int_0^{1/2} \frac{3x}{\sqrt{2x^2 + \frac{1}{2}}}\, dx$

6

Applications of Integration

INTRODUCTION

Kurt's basement was flooded with 3.5 ft of water after a heavy rainfall. The amount of *work* required to pump the water out of the basement can be calculated using integrals. In this chapter we study some of the technical applications of integrals.

Objectives

- Find an area bounded by two or more curves.
- Find a volume of revolution.
- Find the center of mass of a linear system.
- Find the centroid of a region bounded by given curves.
- Find moments of inertia.
- Use integration to solve work, fluid pressure, and average value problems.

6.1 AREA BETWEEN CURVES

In Chapter 5 we studied the process of computing the area between a given curve and the *x*-axis. Now consider the problem of finding the area *between* two given curves. First, observe that the area between one given curve $y = f(x)$ and the *x*-axis between $x = a$ and $x = b$ is a definite integral:

$$A = \int_a^b f(x)\, dx = F(b) - F(a)$$

where $F'(x) = f(x)$.

Further recall that definite integration as applied to area is a summation process. That is, the definite integral is the limit of sums of approximating rectangles where the area of a typical rectangle is $f(t)\, \Delta x$ as shown in Fig. 6.1. The typical rectangle, which is shaded, is called an *element* of the area. Note the correspondence between the form of the expression for the area of the element, $f(t)\, \Delta x$, and that for the differential, $f(x)\, dx$, which is to be integrated:

$$f(t)\, \Delta x \leftrightarrow f(x)\, dx$$

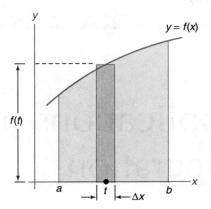

Figure 6.1 Area under the curve $y = f(x)$.

Noting this correspondence will be a visual aid in setting up the appropriate integrals for computing areas between curves. The correct form for $f(x)\,dx$ can be found by finding the appropriate expression $f(t)\,\Delta x$ from viewing a sketch of the area.

Now let's determine the area bounded by the curves $y = f(x)$, $y = g(x)$, $x = a$, and $x = b$ as shown in Fig. 6.2.

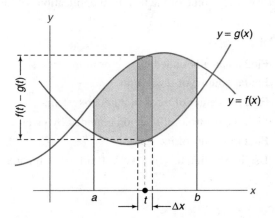

Figure 6.2 Area between two curves.

Between a and b, $g(x) \leq f(x)$, that is, the curve $y = g(x)$ lies below the curve $y = f(x)$. The area of the element shown, used in approximating the area between the two curves, is

$$[f(t) - g(t)]\,\Delta x$$

This corresponds to the differential

$$[f(x) - g(x)]\,dx$$

We therefore use the definite integral

$$\int_a^b [f(x) - g(x)]\,dx$$

to find the desired area.

EXAMPLE 1

Find the area between the curves $y = 8 - x^2$ and $y = x + 2$.

The area is bounded by a parabola and a straight line. First, find the points where the two curves intersect by solving the two equations simultaneously.

$$8 - x^2 = x + 2$$
$$0 = x^2 + x - 6$$
$$0 = (x - 2)(x + 3)$$
$$x = 2 \quad \text{or} \quad x = -3$$

The curves intersect at the points $(-3, -1)$ and $(2, 4)$. Note that between $x = -3$ and $x = 2$, the line $y = x + 2$ is below the parabola $y = 8 - x^2$. The length of the element shown in Fig. 6.3 is the difference between the upper curve $y = 8 - x^2$ and the lower curve $y = x + 2$ at a given value of x.

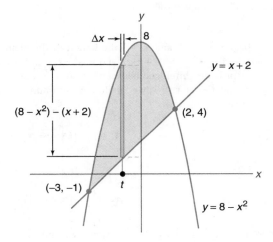

Figure 6.3

The area A between the curves is the value of the definite integral.

$$A = \int_{-3}^{2} [(8 - x^2) - (x + 2)] \, dx$$
$$= \int_{-3}^{2} (6 - x - x^2) \, dx$$
$$= \left(6x - \frac{x^2}{2} - \frac{x^3}{3} \right) \Bigg|_{-3}^{2}$$
$$= \left(12 - 2 - \frac{8}{3} \right) - \left(-18 - \frac{9}{2} + 9 \right) = 20\frac{5}{6}$$

The limits of integration are determined by the points where the curves intersect. The lower limit is the smallest value of x where the curves intersect, and the upper limit is the largest value of x where the curves intersect.

EXAMPLE 2

Find the area between the line $y = -x + 2$ and the parabola $x = 4 - y^2$.

The points of intersection of these two curves are $(0, 2)$ and $(3, -1)$. In this example, we run into a problem. If we use vertical elements to approximate the area as in Fig. 6.4, then

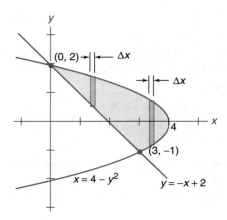

Figure 6.4

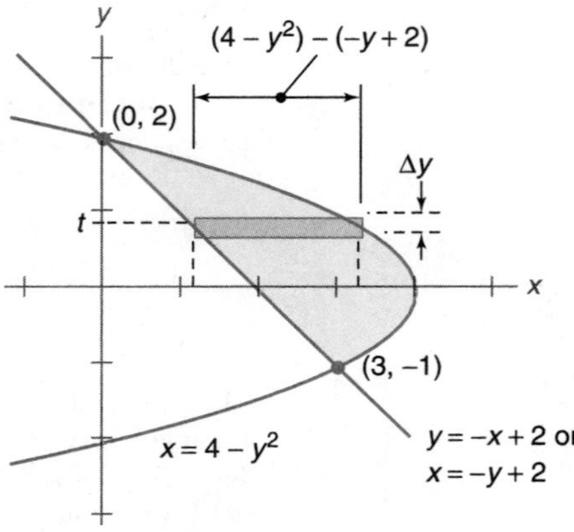

Figure 6.5

between $x = 0$ and $x = 3$ the height of the element is the difference between the curves $x = 4 - y^2$ $(y = \sqrt{4 - x})$ and $y = -x + 2$; between $x = 3$ and $x = 4$ the height of the element is the difference between $y = \sqrt{4 - x}$ and $y = -\sqrt{4 - x}$. Because of the change in boundaries at $x = 3$, we would have to find the desired area A by separately computing the areas

$$A_1 = \int_0^3 [(\sqrt{4 - x}) - (-x + 2)]\, dx$$

and

$$A_2 = \int_3^4 [(\sqrt{4 - x}) - (-\sqrt{4 - x})]\, dx$$

Then $A = A_1 + A_2$. By integrating, we find $A_1 = \frac{19}{6}$ and $A_2 = \frac{4}{3}$. So

$$A = \frac{19}{6} + \frac{4}{3} = \frac{9}{2}$$

Sometimes, as in this example, it is easier to set up the problem using horizontal elements as in Fig. 6.5. Then express the given curves as functions of y instead of x: $x = 4 - y^2$ and $x = -y + 2$; and integrate with respect to the y variable and use limits of integration based on the y-coordinates of the points of intersection: $y = -1$ and $y = 2$. With respect to *the y-axis*, the curve $x = 4 - y^2$ lies above $x = -y + 2$ from $y = -1$ to $y = 2$. The length of a typical horizontal element is then $(4 - y^2) - (-y + 2)$.

$$A = \int_{-1}^2 [(4 - y^2) - (-y + 2)]\, dy$$

$$= \int_{-1}^2 (2 + y - y^2)\, dy$$

$$= \left(2y + \frac{y^2}{2} - \frac{y^3}{3}\right)\Bigg|_{-1}^2$$

$$= \left(4 + 2 - \frac{8}{3}\right) - \left(-2 + \frac{1}{2} + \frac{1}{3}\right) = \frac{9}{2}$$

Note: Using horizontal elements and working in terms of dy is usually simpler than using vertical elements and working in terms of dx when one of the curves does not represent a function (contains a y^2-term, for instance).

In summary, to find the area between two given curves between $x = a$ and $x = b$:

1. Find the points of intersection of the two curves, if necessary.
2. Sketch the two curves:
   (a) Determine whether to use vertical elements with the curves expressed as functions of x or horizontal elements with curves expressed as functions of y.
   (b) Determine which curve lies above the other.
3. Find the height of a typical element based on Step 2(b).
4. Write the definite integral:

$$\int_a^b [f(x) - g(x)]\, dx$$

where $f(x) - g(x)$ is the length of vertical elements between $x = a$ and $x = b$ with $a < b$, or

$$\int_c^d [f(y) - g(y)]\, dy$$

where $f(y) - g(y)$ is the length of horizontal elements between $y = c$ and $y = d$ with $c < d$.

Note that the choice of using vertical or horizontal elements depends on the difficulty of the resulting definite integral. Also, the curves do not need to lie above the x- or y-axis in order to find the area between them.

EXAMPLE 3

Find the area between the curves $x = y^3$ and $x = -y^2$.

The points of intersection are $(0, 0)$ and $(-1, -1)$. We could use either vertical or horizontal elements. We will use horizontal elements as in Fig. 6.6. Since the curve $x = y^3$ lies *above* $x = -y^2$ (*in the positive direction along the x-axis*) from $y = -1$ to $y = 0$, we have

$$A = \int_{-1}^{0} [y^3 - (-y^2)]\, dy$$

$$= \left(\frac{y^4}{4} + \frac{y^3}{3}\right)\Bigg|_{-1}^{0}$$

$$= 0 - \left(\frac{1}{4} - \frac{1}{3}\right) = \frac{1}{12}$$

Using a calculator, we have

2nd 7 y^3-(-y^2),y,-1,0) **ENTER**

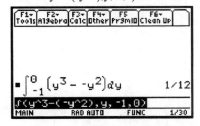

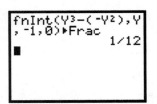

MATH 9 ALPHA Y MATH 3 -(-ALPHA Y x²), ALPHA Y ,-1,0) MATH 1 ENTER

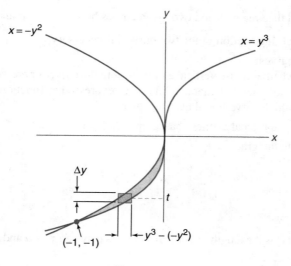

Figure 6.6

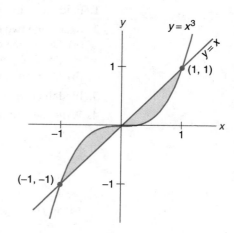

Figure 6.7

EXAMPLE 4

Find the area between the curves $y = x$ and $y = x^3$.

There are three points of intersection: $(-1, -1)$, $(0, 0)$, and $(1, 1)$. Between $x = -1$ and $x = 0$, $y = x^3$ lies above $y = x$. Between $x = 0$ and $x = 1$, $y = x$ lies above $y = x^3$. We need to compute the two areas as in Fig. 6.7.

$$A_1 = \int_{-1}^{0} (x^3 - x)\, dx \qquad \text{and} \quad A_2 = \int_{0}^{1} (x - x^3)\, dx$$

$$A_1 = \left(\frac{x^4}{4} - \frac{x^2}{2} \right) \Big|_{-1}^{0} = \frac{1}{4} \quad \text{and} \quad A_2 = \left(\frac{x^2}{2} - \frac{x^4}{4} \right) \Big|_{0}^{1} = \frac{1}{4}$$

The desired area $A = A_1 + A_2 = \frac{1}{4} + \frac{1}{4} = \frac{1}{2}$.

Using the symmetry of the two areas, note that $A_1 = A_2$. We could also compute

$$A = 2 \int_{0}^{1} (x - x^3)\, dx$$

EXAMPLE 5

Find the area between the x-axis and $y = x^2 - 4$.

The desired region lies between $x = -2$ and $x = 2$. Note that in this region the curve $y = x^2 - 4$ lies below the x-axis in Fig. 6.8. Since the x-axis is the curve $y = 0$, we have

$$A = \int_{-2}^{2} [0 - (x^2 - 4)]\, dx$$

$$= \int_{-2}^{2} (4 - x^2)\, dx$$

$$= \left(4x - \frac{x^3}{3} \right) \Big|_{-2}^{2}$$

$$= \left(8 - \frac{8}{3} \right) - \left(-8 + \frac{8}{3} \right) = \frac{32}{3}$$

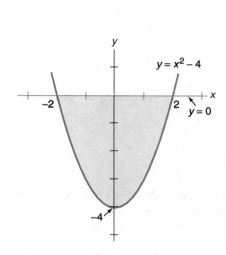

Figure 6.8

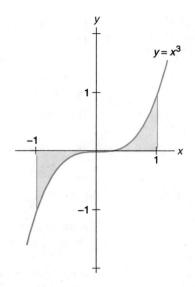

Figure 6.9

EXAMPLE 6

Find the area between the x-axis and $y = x^3$ from $x = -1$ to $x = 1$.

You may be tempted to simply form the integral $\int_{-1}^{1} x^3\, dx$. But

$$\int_{-1}^{1} x^3\, dx = \frac{x^4}{4}\Big|_{-1}^{1} = \frac{1}{4} - \frac{1}{4} = 0$$

We have incorrectly obtained the value zero since we failed to observe that at $x = 0$ the curve $y = x^3$ crosses the x-axis as in Fig. 6.9. To the left of $x = 0$ the curve is below the x-axis, but to the right of $x = 0$ the curve is above the x-axis. We must therefore separate the computation into two integrals as in Example 4:

$$
\begin{aligned}
A &= \int_{-1}^{0} [0 - (x^3)]\, dx + \int_{0}^{1} [(x^3) - 0]\, dx \\
&= -\int_{-1}^{0} x^3\, dx + \int_{0}^{1} x^3\, dx \\
&= -\left(\frac{x^4}{4}\right)\Big|_{-1}^{0} + \frac{x^4}{4}\Big|_{0}^{1} \\
&= -\left(-\frac{1}{4}\right) + \frac{1}{4} = \frac{1}{2}
\end{aligned}
$$

Exercises 6.1

Find each area bounded by the curves.

1. $y = x^2$, $y = 0$, and $x = 1$

2. $y = x^2$, $y = 0$, $x = 1$, and $x = 2$

3. $y = 1 - x$, $x = 0$, and $y = 0$

4. $y = 2x$, $y = 0$, $x = 1$, and $x = 2$

5. $y = 2 - x^2$ and $y + x = 0$

6. $y = x^2 - 2x$ and $y = 3$

7. $y^2 = x$ and $x = 4$

8. $y^2 = 4x$, $x = 0$, $y = -1$, and $y = 4$

9. $y = x^2$ and $y = x$

10. $y = 2x^2$ and $y^2 = 4x$

11. $x = y^2 - 2y$ and $y = x$

12. $y = x^3, y = 2 - x^2, x = 0$, and $x = 1$

13. $y = x^3 - x, y = 0, x = -1$, and $x = 1$

14. $y^3 = x, y = 1$, and $x = -1$

15. $x = y + 1$ and $x = 3 - y^2$

16. $x = y^2$ and $x = y + 2$

17. $y = 4 - 4x^2$ and $y = 1 - x^2$

18. $y = x^2$ and $y = 8 - x^2$

19. $x = y^4$ and $x = 2 - y^2$

20. $x = y^2$ and $x = 4 + 2y - y^2$

21. $y = x^2 - 3x - 4$ and $y = 6$

22. $y = x^2$ and $y = \sqrt{x}$

23. $x^2y = 8, y = x, x = 5$, and $y = 0$

24. $y = x, x + y = 6$, and $2y = x$

25. $y = x(x - 1)(x - 3)$ and the x-axis

26. $y = x(x + 3)(x - 2)$ and the x-axis

6.2   VOLUMES OF REVOLUTION: DISK METHOD

Another application of integration is finding the volume of a solid resulting from rotating an area about an axis. For example, consider the region bounded by the curves $y = f(x), x = a, x = b$, and the x-axis. Revolving this region about the x-axis determines a solid figure as in Fig. 6.10(a).

The area ΔA of a typical rectangle used in Chapter 5 to approximate the area under the curve $y = f(x)$ is $\Delta A = f(t)\,\Delta x$, where t is a point at the base of the rectangle, Δx is the width, and $f(t)$ is the height. If we now rotate this area about the x-axis as in Fig. 6.10(b), we obtain a cylindrical disk with volume

$$\Delta V = \pi r^2 h$$

where the radius r is $f(t)$ and the thickness h is the width Δx. So

$$\Delta V = \pi [f(t)]^2 \,\Delta x$$

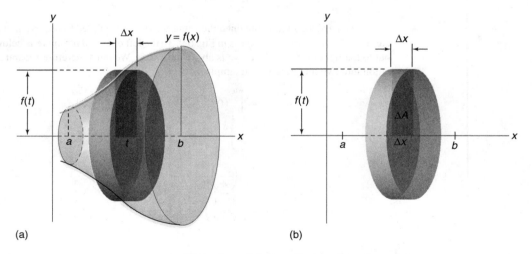

(a)   (b)

Figure 6.10   Disk of a solid of revolution about the x-axis.

By a method similar to approximating the area under a curve by rectangles, we approximate the volume of revolution by using the sum of the volumes of differential disks (see Fig. 6.11).

For areas, the integral

$$A = \int_a^b f(x)\,dx$$

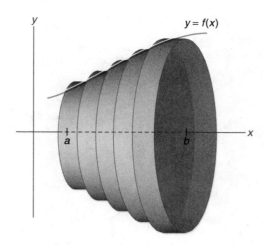

Figure 6.11 Approximating the volume of revolution about the *x*-axis by using the sum of the volumes of differential disks.

gives the exact area for a region that is approximated by summing the areas of rectangles:

$$\Delta A = f(t) \, \Delta x$$

In a similar manner, the integral

$$V = \pi \int_a^b [f(x)]^2 \, dx = \pi \int_a^b y^2 \, dx$$

gives the exact volume for the solid of revolution about the *x*-axis which is approximated by summing the volumes of disks: $\Delta V = \pi [f(t)]^2 \, \Delta x$. This method of computing the volume of a solid is called the *disk method*.

CIRCULAR DISK METHOD

$V =$ sum of circular disks

$$\overset{\text{radius}^2}{\downarrow} \quad \overset{\text{thickness}}{\downarrow}$$

$$V = \pi \int_a^b [f(x)]^2 \quad dx \qquad \text{(revolved about } x\text{-axis)}$$

$$V = \pi \int_c^d [f(y)]^2 \quad dy \qquad \text{(revolved about } y\text{-axis)}$$

EXAMPLE 1

Find the volume of the solid formed by revolving the curve $y = x$ from $x = 0$ to $x = 2$ about the *x*-axis.

The area rotated about the *x*-axis is a triangle as in Fig. 6.12(a). The resulting solid is a cone. The volume of a typical differential disk in Fig. 6.12(b) is

$$\Delta V = \pi [f(t)]^2 \, \Delta x = \pi (t)^2 \, \Delta x$$

So, the integral giving the exact volume is

$$V = \pi \int_a^b [f(x)]^2 \, dx$$

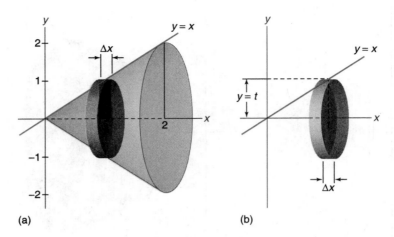

(a)   (b)

Figure 6.12

$$= \pi \int_0^2 x^2 \, dx \qquad (y = x)$$

$$= \pi \left. \frac{x^3}{3} \right|_0^2$$

$$= \pi \left[\frac{8}{3} - \frac{0}{3} \right]$$

$$= \frac{8\pi}{3}$$

This same volume could also be found using the formula for the volume of a cone from geometry, $V = \frac{1}{3}\pi r^2 h$. In this example, $r = 2$ (radius of the base of the cone) and $h = 2$ (the altitude). So,

$$V = \frac{1}{3}\pi(2)^2(2) = \frac{8\pi}{3}$$

Although this problem could also be solved using a geometrical formula, this is not always the case. In the following example, integration provides the only solution.

EXAMPLE 2

Find the volume of the solid obtained by revolving the region bounded by the curves $y = x^2$, $y = 0$, and $x = 2$ about the x-axis.

The volume of a differential disk in Fig. 6.13 is

$$\Delta V = \pi[f(t)]^2 \, \Delta x = \pi[t^2]^2 \, \Delta x$$

The exact volume is then

$$V = \pi \int_a^b [f(x)]^2 \, dx = \pi \int_0^2 (x^2)^2 \, dx \qquad (y = x^2)$$

$$= \pi \int_0^2 x^4 \, dx$$

$$= \pi \left. \frac{x^5}{5} \right|_0^2$$

$$= \frac{32\pi}{5}$$

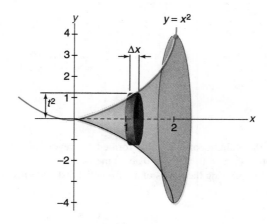

Figure 6.13

When a solid is formed by revolving an area about the y-axis, the integral giving the volume is

$$V = \pi \int_c^d [f(y)]^2 \, dy = \pi \int_c^d x^2 \, dy$$

Here, express the radius of a differential disk as a distance x from the y-axis and the width of the disk as an increment of y, Δy (see Fig. 6.14).

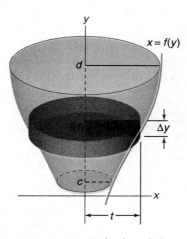

Figure 6.14   Disk of a solid of revolution about the y-axis.

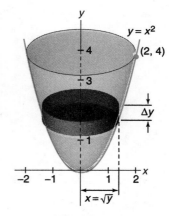

Figure 6.15

EXAMPLE 3

Find the volume of the solid obtained by revolving the region bounded by the curves $y = x^2$, $x = 0$, and $y = 4$ about the y-axis.

When revolving the area about the y-axis as in Fig. 6.15, the boundary curve ($y = x^2$) must be determined in a manner that expresses x as a function of y. That is,

$$x = \sqrt{y} \qquad \text{(for } 0 \leq y \leq 4\text{)}$$

Note that the boundary curve determines the radius of the differential disks.

The volume of the solid is then given by

$$V = \pi \int_c^d [f(y)]^2 \, dy = \pi \int_0^4 (\sqrt{y})^2 \, dy \qquad (x = \sqrt{y})$$

$$= \pi \int_0^4 y \, dy$$

$$= \pi \frac{y^2}{2} \Big|_0^4 = \pi \left(\frac{16}{2} - 0 \right)$$

$$= 8\pi$$

EXAMPLE 4

Find the volume of the solid formed by revolving the region bounded by the curves $y = 4 - x^2$, $x = 0$, and $y = 0$ about the y-axis.

Expressing the radius of a differential disk in terms of x, we have

$$y = 4 - x^2$$

$$x^2 = 4 - y$$

$$x = \sqrt{4 - y}$$

The desired volume in Fig. 6.16 is then

$$V = \pi \int_c^d [f(y)]^2 \, dy$$

$$= \pi \int_0^4 (\sqrt{4 - y})^2 \, dy \qquad (x = \sqrt{4 - y})$$

$$= \pi \int_0^4 (4 - y) \, dy$$

$$= \pi \left(4y - \frac{y^2}{2} \right) \Big|_0^4$$

$$= \pi \left[\left(16 - \frac{16}{2} \right) - (0) \right]$$

$$= 8\pi$$

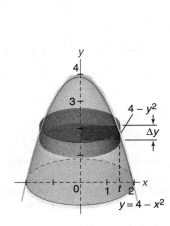

Figure 6.16

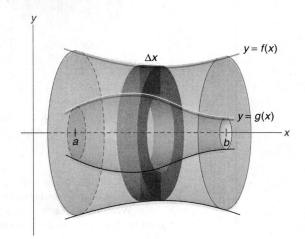

Figure 6.17 Washer-type solid of revolution about the x-axis.

Washer Method

When the region between two curves is rotated as shown in Fig. 6.17 about the x-axis, the rotation results in a *washer*-type solid. If $y = f(x)$ is the outer radius and $y = g(x)$

is the inner radius of the region being revolved, the volume of the resulting solid is

$$V = \pi \int_a^b \{[f(x)]^2 - [g(x)]^2\}\, dx$$

EXAMPLE 5

Find the volume of the solid formed by revolving the region bounded by $y = x^2$ and $y = x$ about the x-axis.

From Fig. 6.18, we have

$$V = \pi \int_0^1 [(x)^2 - (x^2)^2]\, dx$$

$$= \pi \int_0^1 (x^2 - x^4)\, dx$$

$$= \pi \left(\frac{x^3}{3} - \frac{x^5}{5} \right) \Bigg|_0^1$$

$$= \pi \left[\left(\frac{1}{3} - \frac{1}{5} \right) - (0) \right]$$

$$= \frac{2\pi}{15}$$

EXAMPLE 6

Drill a hole of radius 3 in. through the center of a metal sphere of radius 5 in. Find the volume of the resulting ring.

First, rotate the shaded portion of the circle $x^2 + y^2 = 25$ about the x-axis as shown in Fig. 6.19. Its outer radius is $y = \sqrt{25 - x^2}$ and its inner radius (radius of hole) is $y = 3$. Thus,

$$V = \pi \int_{-4}^4 [(\sqrt{25 - x^2})^2 - (3)^2]\, dx$$

$$= \pi \int_{-4}^4 (16 - x^2)\, dx$$

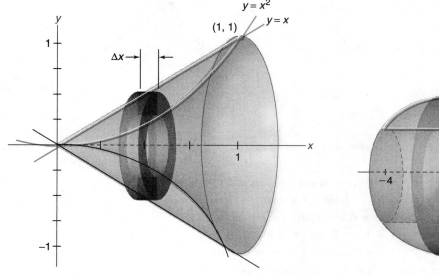

Figure 6.18   Figure 6.19

$$= \pi \left(16x - \frac{x^3}{3} \right) \Big|_{-4}^{4}$$

$$= \pi \left[\left(64 - \frac{64}{3} \right) - \left(-64 + \frac{64}{3} \right) \right]$$

$$= \frac{256\pi}{3} \, in^3$$

EXAMPLE 7

Find the volume of the solid obtained by revolving the region bounded by the curves $y = x^2$, $x = 2$, and the x-axis about the line $x = 2$.

Note that the radius of the differential disk in Fig. 6.20(b) is $2 - x$ and its thickness is Δy with $0 \le y \le 4$.

$$V = \pi \int_{0}^{4} (2 - x)^2 \, dy$$

$$= \pi \int_{0}^{4} (4 - 4x + x^2) \, dy$$

$$= \pi \int_{0}^{4} (4 - 4\sqrt{y} + y) \, dy \qquad (x^2 = y \text{ and } x = \sqrt{y})$$

$$= \pi \left(4y - \frac{8}{3} y^{3/2} + \frac{y^2}{2} \right) \Big|_{0}^{4}$$

$$= \pi \left[\left(16 - \frac{8}{3} \cdot 8 + 8 \right) - (0) \right]$$

$$= \frac{8\pi}{3}$$

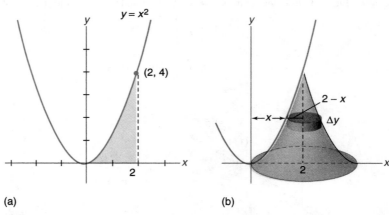

(a)   (b)   Figure 6.20

Exercises 6.2

Find the volume of each solid formed by revolving the region bounded by the given curves about the given line.

1. $y = x + 1$, $y = 0$, $x = 0$, and $x = 2$ about the x-axis
2. $y = x$, $y = 0$, $x = 2$, and $x = 4$ about the x-axis
3. $y = x^2 + 1$, $y = 0$, $x = 1$, and $x = 2$ about the x-axis
4. $y = \sqrt{x}$, $y = 0$, $x = 1$, and $x = 4$ about the x-axis
5. $y = x - 1$, $x = 0$, and $y = 1$ about the y-axis
6. $y^2 = 2x$, $x = 0$, and $y = 2$ about the y-axis
7. $y = 4x^2$, $x = 0$, and $y = 4$ about the y-axis

8. $y = 4 - x^2$, $x = 0$, $y = 1$, and $y = 2$ about the y-axis

9. $y = x$, $x = 1$, and $y = 0$ about $x = 1$

10. $y = x^2$, $x = 2$, and $y = 0$ about $x = 2$

11. $y = x$, $x = 1$, $x = 2$, and $y = 1$ about $y = 1$

12. $y = x^2$, $x = 1$, $x = 2$, and $y = 1$ about $y = 1$

13. $4y = x^2$, $y = 0$, and $x = 2$ about the y-axis

14. $y^2 = x$, $y = 0$, and $x = 4$ about the y-axis

15. $y^2 = x$, $y = 0$, and $x = 4$ about the x-axis

16. $y = x^3$ and $y = x$ from $x = 0$ to $x = 1$ about the x-axis

17. $y = x^3$ and $y = x$ from $x = 0$ to $x = 1$ about the y-axis

18. $y = 2 - x^2$, $y = x$, and $x = 0$ about the x-axis

19. $y = 2 - x^2$, $y = x$, and $x = 0$ about the y-axis

20. $2y = x$ and $y^2 = x$ about the y-axis

21. $2y = x$ and $y^2 = x$ about the x-axis

22. $x = y^2$ and $x = 2 - y^2$ about the y-axis

23. $y = 3 - x^2$ and $y = x^2 + 1$ about the x-axis

24. $x = 2y^2 + 1$ and $x = 4 - y^2$ about the y-axis

25. The area bounded by the first and second quadrants of the ellipse $9x^2 + 25y^2 = 225$ is revolved about the x-axis. Find the volume.

26. The area bounded by the first and fourth quadrants of the ellipse $9x^2 + 25y^2 = 225$ is revolved about the y-axis. Find the volume.

27. Drill a hole of radius 2 in. through the center of the solid (along the x-axis) described in Exercise 25. Find the volume of the resulting solid.

28. Drill a hole of radius 2 in. through the center of the solid (along the y-axis) described in Exercise 26. Find the volume of the resulting solid.

29. Use the disk method to verify that the volume of a sphere of radius r is $V = \frac{4}{3}\pi r^3$.

30. Use the disk method to verify that the volume of a right circular cone is $V = \frac{1}{3}\pi r^2 h$, where r is the radius of the base and h is the height.

6.3 VOLUMES OF REVOLUTION: SHELL METHOD

A second method of obtaining the volume of a solid uses cylindrical shells instead of disks. Let's use this method to find the volume of the solid described in Example 4 of Section 6.2.

The volume ΔV of a typical shell in Fig. 6.21(a) is

$$\Delta V = \pi r_2^2 h - \pi r_1^2 h$$

where

$$r_1 = t \qquad \text{(radius of inside wall of the shell)}$$
$$r_2 = t + \Delta x \qquad \text{(radius of outside wall of the shell)}$$

Now

$$\begin{aligned}
\Delta V &= \pi r_2^2 h - \pi r_1^2 h \\
&= \pi h (r_2^2 - r_1^2) \\
&= \pi h (r_2 + r_1)(r_2 - r_1) \\
&= 2\pi h \left(\frac{r_2 + r_1}{2}\right)(r_2 - r_1) \qquad \text{(Multiply numerator and denominator by 2.)}
\end{aligned}$$

$\underset{\uparrow}{}$———average radius

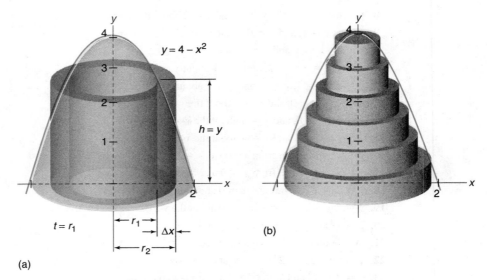

Figure 6.21 Shell method about the *y*-axis.

or

$$\Delta V = 2\pi y \left(\frac{2t + \Delta x}{2} \right)(\Delta x) \qquad [r_2 + r_1 = (t + \Delta x) + t = 2t + \Delta x]$$

$$= 2\pi y \left(t + \frac{\Delta x}{2} \right) \Delta x$$

$$= 2\pi f(x)\, x\, \Delta x \qquad \left(\text{where we let } x = t + \frac{\Delta x}{2} \right)$$

This expression for ΔV is the product of the circumference of the shell of radius x, its height $f(x)$, and its thickness Δx. By taking the sum of the volumes of all such approximating shells as in Fig. 6.21(b), we obtain another approximation for the desired volume.

Again using the methods of Chapter 5, we find that this approximation leads to the integral

$$V = 2\pi \int_a^b x f(x)\, dx$$

which gives the exact volume of the solid.

Expressing y as a function of x, we have $y = f(x) = 4 - x^2$ and

$$V = 2\pi \int_0^2 x(4 - x^2)\, dx$$

$$= 2\pi \int_0^2 (4x - x^3)\, dx$$

$$= 2\pi \left(2x^2 - \frac{x^4}{4} \right) \Big|_0^2 = 2\pi[(8 - 4) - (0)] = 8\pi$$

This method of computing the volume of a solid is called the *shell method*.

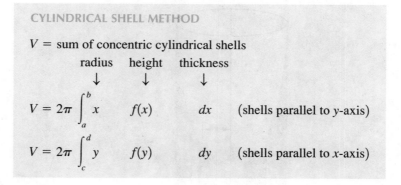

CYLINDRICAL SHELL METHOD

V = sum of concentric cylindrical shells

radius   height   thickness

$$V = 2\pi \int_a^b x \quad f(x) \quad dx \quad \text{(shells parallel to } y\text{-axis)}$$

$$V = 2\pi \int_c^d y \quad f(y) \quad dy \quad \text{(shells parallel to } x\text{-axis)}$$

EXAMPLE 1

Find the volume of the solid formed by the region under $y = x^2 + 1$ from $x = 0$ to $x = 2$ revolved about the y-axis. Note that the disk method would not readily solve this problem (some pieces would be disks and others would be washers, so there is no typical unit of volume for that approach). Instead, revolve vertical rectangles about the y-axis to form cylindrical shells (see Fig. 6.22).

$$\Delta V = 2\pi(x)(y)\Delta x$$

where x is the radius of the shell, y is the height, and Δx is the thickness. The integral for the volume is

$$V = 2\pi \int_0^2 x\, y\, dx$$

$$= 2\pi \int_0^2 x(x^2 + 1)\, dx$$

$$= 2\pi \int_0^2 (x^3 + x)\, dx$$

$$= 2\pi\left(\frac{x^4}{4} + \frac{x^2}{2}\right)\Big|_0^2$$

$$= 2\pi\left(\frac{2^4}{4} + \frac{2^2}{2} - 0\right) = 12\pi$$

The volume is 12π cubic units.

EXAMPLE 2

Find the volume of the solid formed by revolving the region bounded by $y = x^2$, $y = 0$, and $x = 1$ about the line $x = 1$.

In this example the shell method is more convenient than the disk method. The volume of a typical shell in Fig. 6.23 is

$$\Delta V = 2\pi(1 - x)y\,\Delta x$$

where $1 - x$ is the radius of the shell, y is the height, and Δx is its thickness. The integral for V then becomes

$$V = 2\pi \int_0^1 (1 - x)y\, dx$$

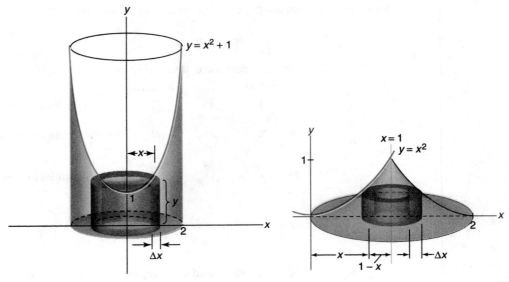

Figure 6.22   Figure 6.23

$$V = 2\pi \int_0^1 (1 - x)(x^2)\, dx \qquad (y = x^2)$$

$$= 2\pi \int_0^1 (x^2 - x^3)\, dx$$

$$= 2\pi \left(\frac{x^3}{3} - \frac{x^4}{4} \right) \Bigg|_0^1$$

$$= 2\pi \left[\left(\frac{1}{3} - \frac{1}{4} \right) - (0) \right]$$

$$= \frac{\pi}{6}$$

EXAMPLE 3

Find the volume of the solid formed by revolving the region bounded by $y = x^2$ and $y = x$ about the x-axis.

The volume of a typical shell in Fig. 6.24 is

$$\Delta V = 2\pi y(x_2 - x_1)\, \Delta y$$

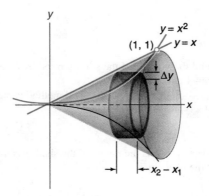

Figure 6.24

where y is the radius of the shell, $x_2 - x_1$ is the height of the shell, and Δy is its thickness. The height of the shell, $x_2 - x_1$, is found by subtracting the curve $x_1 = f(y) = y$ from the curve $x_2 = g(y) = \sqrt{y}$.

The integral for V then becomes

$$V = 2\pi \int_c^d y[g(y) - f(y)]\, dy$$

$$= 2\pi \int_0^1 y(x_2 - x_1)\, dy$$

$$= 2\pi \int_0^1 y(\sqrt{y} - y)\, dy$$

$$= 2\pi \int_0^1 (y^{3/2} - y^2)\, dy$$

$$= 2\pi \left(\frac{2}{5}y^{5/2} - \frac{y^3}{3}\right)\Big|_0^1$$

$$= 2\pi \left[\left(\frac{2}{5} - \frac{1}{3}\right) - (0)\right]$$

$$= \frac{2\pi}{15}$$

Exercises 6.3

Find the volume of each solid formed by revolving the region bounded by the given curves about the given line using the shell method.

1. $y = 4x^2$, $x = 0$, and $y = 4$ about the y-axis

2. $y = 4x^2$, $x = 0$, and $y = 4$ about the x-axis

3. $4y = x^2$, $y = 0$, and $x = 2$ about the y-axis

4. $y^2 = x$, $y = 0$, and $x = 4$ about the y-axis

5. $y^2 = 2x$, $x = 0$, and $y = 2$ about the x-axis

6. $y = x^3$, $y = 0$, and $x = 2$ about the y-axis

7. $y = x^3$, $y = 0$, and $x = 2$ about the x-axis

8. $y = \sqrt{x}$, $x = 0$, and $y = 2$ about the x-axis

9. $y = 2x - x^2$ and the x-axis about the y-axis

10. $x = 3y - y^2$ and the y-axis about the x-axis

11. $y = x$, $x = 1$, and $y = 0$ about $x = 1$

12. $y = x^2$, $x = 2$, and $y = 0$ about $x = 2$

13. $x = y^2$, $y = 1$, and $x = 0$ about $y = 2$

14. $y = x^2$ and $y = 4$ about $y = -2$

15. $y = x^3$ and $y = x$ from $x = 0$ to $x = 1$ about the x-axis

16. $y = x^3$ and $y = x$ from $x = 0$ to $x = 1$ about the y-axis

17. $y = x^2 - 3x + 2$ and $y = 0$ about the y-axis

18. $x = y^2 - 6y + 8$ and $x = 0$ about the x-axis

19. $y = x(x - 2)^2$ and $y = 0$ about $x = 2$

20. $y = x(x - 2)^2$ and $y = 0$ about the y-axis

6.4 CENTER OF MASS OF A SYSTEM OF PARTICLES

The next application of integration involves finding the center of mass, which is discussed in the next two sections. We find the center of mass of a system of particles in this section and the center of mass of a thin plate and of a solid of revolution in the next section. Finding the center of mass is of fundamental importance in the study of mechanics. The *center of mass or center of gravity* of an object or system of objects is the point at which the object or system balances or at which the entire mass can be considered to be concentrated.

Before finding the center of mass of a system of particles, we must first introduce the concept of a moment. The *moment* about a point P produced by some mass m is given by

$$\text{moment} = md$$

where d is the length of the *moment arm,* which is the distance between the mass and point P (see Fig. 6.25).

Suppose we have a 15-kg sign hanging from a support 0.8 m from a building as shown in Fig. 6.26. The length of the moment arm is 0.8 m, the distance from the mass to P. The mass is 15 kg. Therefore,

$$\text{moment} = md = (15 \text{ kg})(0.8 \text{ m}) = 12 \text{ kg m}$$

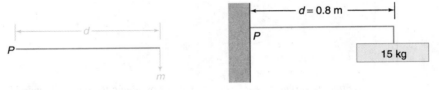

Figure 6.25   Length of moment arm.

Figure 6.26

Consider the mobile that is balanced by the five weights as shown in Fig. 6.27. Let the masses m_1, m_2, m_3, m_4, and m_5 be at distances d_1, d_2, d_3, d_4, and d_5, respectively, from a point P. The moment of the system about P is

$$\text{moment} = m_1 d_1 + m_2 d_2 + m_3 d_3 + m_4 d_4 + m_5 d_5$$

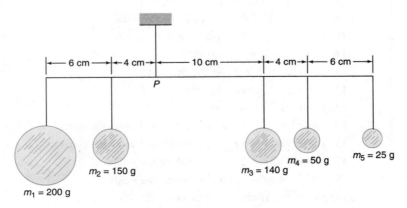

Figure 6.27

If we let P be the origin of the x-axis, $d_1 = -10$, $d_2 = -4$, $d_3 = 10$, $d_4 = 14$, and $d_5 = 20$. Then the moment about P is

$$\text{moment} = (200)(-10) + (150)(-4) + (140)(10) + (50)(14) + (25)(20)$$
$$= -2000 - 600 + 1400 + 700 + 500$$
$$= 0$$

If the moment is zero, the system is in equilibrium, that is, the mobile balances.

Note: Point P may be any point from which the lengths of the moment arms are measured. We usually choose point P to be the center of mass or the pivot point.

MOMENT IN A LINEAR SYSTEM ALONG THE X-AXIS

Let $\bar{x}$ be the center of mass or balancing point of a linear system along the x-axis with n masses. That is, $\bar{x}$ is the point where all the mass seems to be concentrated. So

$$(m_1 + m_2 + m_3 + \cdots + m_n)\bar{x} = m_1 x_1 + m_2 x_2 + m_3 x_3 + \cdots + m_n x_n$$

Then

$$\bar{x} = \frac{m_1 x_1 + m_2 x_2 + m_3 x_3 + \cdots + m_n x_n}{m_1 + m_2 + m_3 + \cdots + m_n}$$

If we let M_0 be the moment about the origin, $\bar{x}$ be the center of mass, and m be the total mass of the system, then

$$\bar{x} = \frac{M_0}{m}$$

EXAMPLE 1

Find the center of mass of the linear system $m_1 = 10$, $x_1 = -4$; $m_2 = 25$, $x_2 = 2$; $m_3 = 40$, $x_3 = 5$; $m_4 = 15$, $x_4 = 10$.

The moment about the origin is

$$M_0 = m_1 x_1 + m_2 x_2 + m_3 x_3 + m_4 x_4$$
$$= (10)(-4) + (25)(2) + (40)(5) + (15)(10)$$
$$= -40 + 50 + 200 + 150 = 360$$

The total mass of the system is

$$m = 10 + 25 + 40 + 15 = 90$$

The center of mass is

$$\bar{x} = \frac{M_0}{m} = \frac{360}{90} = 4$$

We extend these concepts to two dimensions as in Fig. 6.28:

MOMENTS OF A TWO-DIMENSIONAL SYSTEM

Consider n masses $m_1, m_2, \ldots, m_n$ located in the xy-plane at points $(x_1, y_1)(x_2, y_2), \ldots, (x_n, y_n)$, respectively. Their moments with respect to the x-axis and the y-axis are defined as follows: The moment about the y-axis M_y is

$$M_y = m_1 x_1 + m_2 x_2 + \cdots + m_n x_n$$

and the moment about the x-axis M_x is

$$M_x = m_1 y_1 + m_2 y_2 + \cdots + m_n y_n$$

If we let m be the total mass of the system, the center of mass $(\bar{x}, \bar{y})$ is given by

$$\bar{x} = \frac{M_y}{m} \quad \text{and} \quad \bar{y} = \frac{M_x}{m}$$

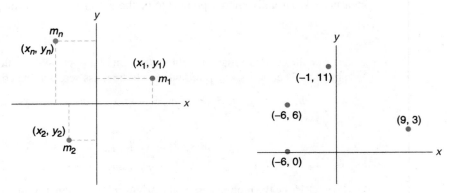

Figure 6.28 Moments of a two-dimensional system.

Figure 6.29

The quantities $m\bar{x}$ and $m\bar{y}$ are regarded as the moments about the y-axis and the x-axis, respectively, of a mass m located at $(\bar{x}, \bar{y})$. That is, $(\bar{x}, \bar{y})$ is the point where the total mass that would give the same moments M_y and M_x seems to be concentrated.

EXAMPLE 2

Find the center of mass of the system $m_1 = 10$ at $(9, 3)$, $m_2 = 6$ at $(-1, 11)$, $m_3 = 8$ at $(-6, 6)$, and $m_4 = 12$ at $(-6, 0)$.

From Fig. 6.29,

$$m = 10 + 6 + 8 + 12 = 36$$
$$M_y = (10)(9) + (6)(-1) + (8)(-6) + (12)(-6) = -36$$
$$M_x = (10)(3) + (6)(11) + (8)(6) + (12)(0) = 144$$

Then,

$$\bar{x} = \frac{M_y}{m} = \frac{-36}{36} = -1$$

$$\bar{y} = \frac{M_x}{m} = \frac{144}{36} = 4$$

So, the center of mass of this system is $(-1, 4)$.

Exercises 6.4

Find the center of mass of each linear system.

1. $m_1 = 3, x_1 = -5; m_2 = 7, x_2 = 3; m_3 = 4, x_3 = 6$

2. $m_1 = 6, x_1 = -12; m_2 = 3, x_2 = -3; m_3 = 10, x_3 = 0; m_4 = 5, x_4 = 9$

3. $m_1 = 24, x_1 = -15; m_2 = 15, x_2 = -9; m_3 = 12, x_3 = 3; m_4 = 9, x_4 = 6$

4. $m_1 = 8, x_1 = -15; m_2 = 15, x_2 = -9; m_3 = 7, x_3 = -1; m_4 = 20, x_4 = 8; m_5 = 24, x_5 = 12$

5. There is a mass of 6 at $(9, 0)$ and a mass of 18 at $(-2, 0)$. Find where a mass of 3 should be placed on the x-axis so that the origin is the center of mass.

6. There is a mass of 30 at $(-4, 0)$, a mass of 9 at $(2, 0)$, and a mass of 15 at $(8, 0)$. Find where a mass of 3 should be placed on the x-axis so that the origin is the center of mass.

7. There is a mass of 24 at $(-8, 0)$ and a mass of 36 at $(12, 0)$. Find where a mass of 9 should be placed on the x-axis so that $(3, 0)$ is the center of mass.

8. There is a mass of 15 at $(-8, 0)$, a mass of 5 at $(-4, 0)$, and a mass of 12 at $(3, 0)$. Find where a mass of 8 should be placed on the x-axis so that $(-3, 0)$ is the center of mass.

9. There is a mass of 6 at $(-3, 0)$ and a mass of 9 at $(12, 0)$. Find what mass should be placed at $(-6, 0)$ so that the origin is the center of mass.

10. There is a mass of 4 at $(-5, 0)$, a mass of 16 at $(3, 0)$, and a mass of 24 at $(8, 0)$. Find what mass should be placed at $(-4, 0)$ so that the origin is the center of mass.

11. There is a mass of 25 at $(-6, 0)$, a mass of 45 at $(8, 0)$, and a mass of 40 at $(10, 0)$. Find what mass should be placed at $(-4, 0)$ so that $(3, 0)$ is the center of mass.

12. There is a mass of 18 at $(3, 0)$, a mass of 54 at $(9, 0)$, a mass of 24 at $(12, 0)$, and a mass of 36 at $(15, 0)$. Find what mass should be placed at $(4, 0)$ so that $(6, 0)$ is the center of mass.

13. A straight road connects Flatville (population 75,000), Pleasant Hill (population 50,000), and Harristown (population 25,000). Pleasant Hill is 18 mi north of Flatville and Harristown is 30 mi north of Flatville. Where is the best place to locate an airport to serve these three communities?

14. A straight road connects Leadville (population 1750), Branburg (population 2800), Princeton (population 970), and Four Oaks (population 480). The distance from Leadville to Branburg is 4 mi, to Princeton is 10 mi, and to Four Oaks is 13 mi. Where is the best place to locate a hospital to serve these four communities?

Find the center of mass of each two-dimensional system.

15. $m_1 = 6$ at $(1, 4)$, $m_2 = 3$ at $(6, 2)$, $m_3 = 12$ at $(3, 3)$

16. $m_1 = 20$ at $(-5, 10)$, $m_2 = 15$ at $(-10, -15)$, $m_3 = 40$ at $(0, -5)$

17. $m_1 = 8$ at $(8, 12)$, $m_2 = 16$ at $(-12, 8)$, $m_3 = 20$ at $(-16, -4)$, $m_4 = 36$ at $(4, -20)$

18. $m_1 = 9$ at $(3, 6)$, $m_2 = 12$ at $(-6, 12)$, $m_3 = 18$ at $(0, -9)$, $m_4 = 30$ at $(15, 0)$, $m_5 = 15$ at $(-12, -9)$

19. There is a mass of 6 at $(4, 2)$ and a mass of 9 at $(-5, 8)$. Find where a mass of 10 should be placed so that the origin is the center of mass.

20. There is a mass of 18 at $(-4, 6)$, a mass of 12 at $(1, -2)$, and a mass of 9 at $(8, 0)$. Find where a mass of 6 should be placed so that $(2, -3)$ is the center of mass.

21. There is a mass of 15 at $(10, 3)$, a mass of 25 at $(-6, -1)$, and a mass of 40 at $(8, -2)$. Find what mass should be placed at $(-5, -3)$ so that $(-1, -2)$ is the center of mass.

22. There is a mass of 4 at $(-5, -3)$, a mass of 16 at $(-4, 3)$, and a mass of 12 at $(6, -4)$. Find what mass should be placed at $(2, 2)$ so that the origin is the center of mass.

23. Three towns plan to build a new health clinic to serve all three communities. Town B (population 8200) is 6 mi east and 3 mi south of Town A (population 12,500). Town C (population 5200) is 2 mi west and 8 mi south of Town A. Find the best location for the new health clinic. Do not consider new roads in determining the best location.

24. Four cities plan to build a new airport to serve all four communities. City B (population 180,000) is 4 mi north and 3 mi west of City A (population 75,000). City C (population 240,000) is 6 mi east and 12 mi south of City A. City D (population 105,000) is 15 mi due south of City A. Find the best location for the airport. Do not consider new roads in determining the best location.

6.5 CENTER OF MASS OF CONTINUOUS MASS DISTRIBUTIONS

As we saw in Section 6.4, the center of mass of any system of finite particles may be found arithmetically by summing the moments and the masses and dividing. Recall that the center of mass of a linear system along the x-axis with n masses is given by

$$\bar{x} = \frac{M_0}{m} = \frac{m_1 x_1 + m_2 x_2 + m_3 x_3 + \cdots + m_n x_n}{m_1 + m_2 + m_3 + \cdots + m_n}$$

For a continuous mass distribution, the center of mass is found by integration. For example, to find the center of mass of a straight thin wire of constant density ρ, place the wire on the x-axis as shown in Fig. 6.30. Then, subdivide the wire into n equal lengths, each of length Δx and mass Δm. The mass of the ith length is

$$\text{mass} = (\text{density})(\text{length})$$
$$m = \rho \qquad \Delta x$$

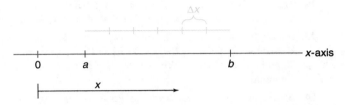

Figure 6.30 Center of mass of a straight thin wire of constant density.

The total mass of the wire is the integral

$$m = \rho \int_a^b dx$$

Next, find the moment of the ith length:

$$\text{moment} = (\text{mass})(\text{length of moment arm})$$
$$= (\rho \, \Delta x)(x)$$

So, the moment of the entire wire about the origin is the integral

$$M_0 = \rho \int_a^b x \, dx$$

Then, the center of mass is given as follows:

CENTER OF MASS OF A CONTINUOUS THIN UNIFORM MASS

$$\bar{x} = \frac{M_0}{m} = \frac{\displaystyle\int_a^b x \, dx}{\displaystyle\int_a^b dx}$$

Note: The density ρ cancels in all such cases when it is constant or uniform. For any homogeneous mass distribution having constant density (constant mass per unit length, per unit area, or per unit volume), the *centroid* is the same as the center of mass. The centroid often refers to the geometric center.

EXAMPLE 1

Find the center of mass of a straight wire 12 cm long and of uniform density.

$$\bar{x} = \frac{\displaystyle\int_a^b x\,dx}{\displaystyle\int_a^b dx} = \frac{\displaystyle\int_0^{12} x\,dx}{\displaystyle\int_0^{12} dx} = \frac{\left.\dfrac{x^2}{2}\right|_0^{12}}{\left.x\right|_0^{12}} = \frac{72}{12} = 6$$

This result should be no surprise. For a uniform linear object, the center of mass is at its center, the point at which the object can be supported. For example, a metre stick is supported on one's finger at the 50-cm mark as in Fig. 6.31.

Figure 6.31 The center of mass, or centroid, of a metre stick is the 50-cm mark, the point at which it can be balanced on one's finger.

For a nonuniform object, the center of mass is usually not at its geometric center, but at the point at which it can be supported in equilibrium by a single force or the point about which it spins if allowed to spin freely in space as in Fig. 6.32.

When the density of a continuous thin mass is not uniform, the center of mass is found as follows:

CENTER OF MASS OF A CONTINUOUS THIN MASS OF VARIABLE DENSITY

$$\bar{x} = \frac{M_0}{m} = \frac{\displaystyle\int_a^b \rho(x)\,x\,dx}{\displaystyle\int_a^b \rho(x)\,dx}$$

where $\rho(x)$ is the density expressed as a function of x. Density is mass per unit length.

EXAMPLE 2

Find the center of mass of a straight wire 16 cm long and whose density is given by $\rho(x) = 4\sqrt{x}$, where x is the distance from one end of the wire.

$$\bar{x} = \frac{M_0}{m} = \frac{\displaystyle\int_a^b \rho(x)\,x\,dx}{\displaystyle\int_a^b \rho(x)\,dx} = \frac{\displaystyle\int_0^{16} 4\sqrt{x}\,x\,dx}{\displaystyle\int_0^{16} 4\sqrt{x}\,dx} = \frac{\displaystyle\int_0^{16} x^{3/2}\,dx}{\displaystyle\int_0^{16} x^{1/2}\,dx} = \frac{\left.\dfrac{2}{5}x^{5/2}\right|_0^{16}}{\left.\dfrac{2}{3}x^{3/2}\right|_0^{16}}$$

$$= \frac{\frac{2}{5}[16^{5/2} - 0]}{\frac{2}{3}[16^{3/2} - 0]} = \frac{\frac{2}{5}(1024)}{\frac{2}{3}(64)} = \frac{48}{5} = 9.6 \text{ cm from the lighter end}$$

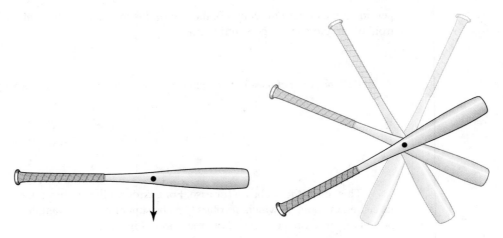

Figure 6.32 The center of mass of any object is the point about which it spins freely in space.

The center of mass of a two-dimensional thin plate is the point at which the plate can be supported as in Fig. 6.33.

If the thin plate is in a regular geometric shape, its center of mass is its geometric center because of its symmetry. Examples of four common geometric figures with each corresponding center of mass are shown in Fig. 6.34.

The center of mass of a more complex but uniformly thin object can be found by subdividing the object into combinations of simpler figures. Find the center of each simpler figure. Consider the mass of each simpler figure to be concentrated at its center and proceed using the method for moments of a two-dimensional system used in Example 2 of Section 6.4.

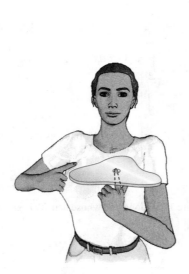

Figure 6.33 The center of mass, or centroid, of a thin plate is the point at which the plate can be supported.

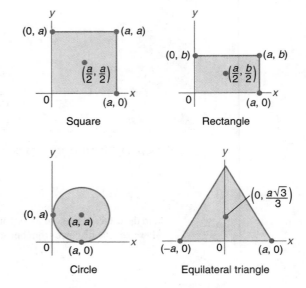

Figure 6.34 Centers of mass, or centroids, of some common geometric shapes placed in the xy-plane.

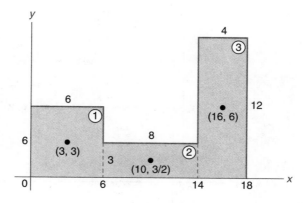

Figure 6.35

EXAMPLE 3

Find the center of mass of the uniform thin plate in Fig. 6.35.

The center of region 1 (square) is (3, 3), of region 2 (rectangle) is $(10, \frac{3}{2})$, and of region 3 (rectangle) is (16, 6). Since the plate is uniform, the mass in each region is proportional to its area. The area of region 1 is 36 units, of region 2 is 24 units, and of region 3 is 48 units. So

$$m = 36 + 24 + 48 = 108$$
$$M_y = m_1 x_1 + m_2 x_2 + m_3 x_3$$
$$= (36)(3) + (24)(10) + (48)(16)$$
$$= 1116$$
$$M_x = m_1 y_1 + m_2 y_2 + m_3 y_3$$
$$= (36)(3) + (24)(\tfrac{3}{2}) + (48)(6)$$
$$= 432$$

Then

$$\bar{x} = \frac{M_y}{m} = \frac{1116}{108} = 10\tfrac{1}{3}$$

$$\bar{y} = \frac{M_x}{m} = \frac{432}{108} = 4$$

The center of mass of the plate is $(10\tfrac{1}{3}, 4)$.

Note that in Example 3 the center of mass is not on the surface of the plate.

Next, let's find the centroid of an irregular-shaped area (or thin plate) of constant density ρ between the curves shown in Fig. 6.36. First divide the area into n rectangles, each of width Δx. Let (x_i, y_i) be the center of mass of the ith rectangle. The y-value of the geometric center of the ith rectangle is

$$y_i = \frac{f(x_i) + g(x_i)}{2}$$

The area of the ith rectangle is $[f(x_i) - g(x_i)]\, \Delta x$. The mass of the ith rectangle is

$$\text{mass} = (\text{density})(\text{area})$$
$$= \rho[f(x_i) - g(x_i)]\, \Delta x$$

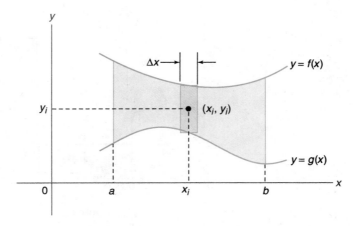

Figure 6.36 Finding the centroid of an irregular-shaped area or thin plate of constant density.

The total mass is the integral

$$m = \rho \int_a^b [f(x) - g(x)] \, dx = \rho A$$

where A is the area of the region.

Next, find the moment of the ith rectangle about the x-axis:

$$\text{moment} = (\text{mass})(\text{moment arm})$$
$$= \rho[f(x_i) - g(x_i)] \, \Delta x \cdot y_i$$
$$= \rho[f(x_i) - g(x_i)] \, \Delta x \cdot \frac{f(x_i) + g(x_i)}{2}$$
$$= \frac{\rho}{2} \{[f(x_i)]^2 - [g(x_i)]^2\} \, \Delta x$$

The moment about the x-axis is the integral

$$M_x = \frac{\rho}{2} \int_a^b \{[f(x)]^2 - [g(x)]^2\} \, dx$$

Similarly, the moment about the y-axis is the integral

$$M_y = \rho \int_a^b x[f(x) - g(x)] \, dx$$

MOMENTS AND CENTER OF MASS OF A PLANE AREA OR THIN PLATE

Let $g(x) \le f(x)$ be continuous functions on $a \le x \le b$ for the area of uniform density ρ bounded by $y = f(x)$, $y = g(x)$, $x = a$, and $x = b$. The moments about the x-axis and the y-axis are, respectively,

$$M_x = \frac{\rho}{2} \int_a^b \{[f(x)]^2 - [g(x)]^2\} \, dx \quad \text{and} \quad M_y = \rho \int_a^b x[f(x) - g(x)] \, dx$$

Its mass is given by

$$m = \rho \int_a^b [f(x) - g(x)]\, dx$$

and its center of mass is $(\bar{x}, \bar{y})$, where

$$\bar{x} = \frac{M_y}{m} \quad \text{and} \quad \bar{y} = \frac{M_x}{m}$$

EXAMPLE 4

Find the center of mass of the uniformly thin plate of density ρ bounded by $y = x^2$ and $y = x + 2$.

First, graph the equations and find the points of intersection as in Fig. 6.37.

$$x^2 = x + 2$$
$$x^2 - x - 2 = 0$$
$$(x - 2)(x + 1) = 0$$
$$x = 2, -1$$

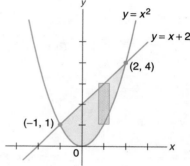

Figure 6.37

$$M_x = \frac{\rho}{2} \int_a^b \{[f(x)]^2 - [g(x)]^2\}\, dx$$

$$= \frac{\rho}{2} \int_{-1}^{2} [(x + 2)^2 - (x^2)^2]\, dx$$

$$= \frac{\rho}{2} \int_{-1}^{2} [x^2 + 4x + 4 - x^4]\, dx$$

$$= \frac{\rho}{2}\left(\frac{x^3}{3} + 2x^2 + 4x - \frac{x^5}{5} \right)\Big|_{-1}^{2}$$

$$= \frac{\rho}{2}\left[\left(\frac{8}{3} + 8 + 8 - \frac{32}{5} \right) - \left(-\frac{1}{3} + 2 - 4 + \frac{1}{5} \right) \right]$$

$$= \frac{\rho}{2}\left(\frac{72}{5} \right)$$

$$= \frac{36\rho}{5}$$

$$M_y = \rho \int_a^b x[f(x) - g(x)]\, dx$$

$$= \rho \int_{-1}^{2} x(x + 2 - x^2)\, dx$$

$$= \rho \int_{-1}^{2} (x^2 + 2x - x^3)\, dx$$

$$= \rho\left(\frac{x^3}{3} + x^2 - \frac{x^4}{4} \right)\Big|_{-1}^{2}$$

$$= \rho\left[\left(\frac{8}{3} + 4 - 4\right) - \left(-\frac{1}{3} + 1 - \frac{1}{4}\right)\right]$$

$$= \frac{9\rho}{4}$$

$$m = \rho \int_a^b [f(x) - g(x)]\, dx$$

$$= \rho \int_{-1}^2 (x + 2 - x^2)\, dx$$

$$= \rho\left(\frac{x^2}{2} + 2x - \frac{x^3}{3}\right)\Big|_{-1}^2$$

$$= \rho\left[\left(2 + 4 - \frac{8}{3}\right) - \left(\frac{1}{2} - 2 + \frac{1}{3}\right)\right]$$

$$= \frac{9\rho}{2}$$

Then

$$\bar{x} = \frac{M_y}{m} = \frac{9\rho/4}{9\rho/2} = \frac{1}{2}$$

$$\bar{y} = \frac{M_x}{m} = \frac{36\rho/5}{9\rho/2} = \frac{8}{5}$$

The center of mass is $(\frac{1}{2}, \frac{8}{5})$.

Note that the density ρ cancels in both $\bar{x}$ and $\bar{y}$. That is, the center of mass of a thin plate or area of uniform density depends only on its shape and not its density. Thus we may find the centroid as follows:

CENTROID OF A PLANE REGION OR THIN PLATE

Let $g(x) \leq f(x)$ be continuous functions on $a \leq x \leq b$. The centroid $(\bar{x}, \bar{y})$ of the region bounded by $y = f(x)$, $y = g(x)$, $x = a$, and $y = b$ is

$$\bar{x} = \frac{\displaystyle\int_a^b x[f(x) - g(x)]\, dx}{A}$$

and

$$\bar{y} = \frac{\dfrac{1}{2}\displaystyle\int_a^b \{[f(x)]^2 - [g(x)]^2\}\, dx}{A}$$

where A is the area of the region.

EXAMPLE 5

Find the centroid of the region bounded by $y = x^4$ and $y = x$.

First, graph the equations and find the points of intersection (see Fig. 6.38).

$$A = \int_0^1 (x - x^4)\,dx$$

$$= \left(\frac{x^2}{2} - \frac{x^5}{5}\right)\Big|_0^1$$

$$= \left(\frac{1}{2} - \frac{1}{5}\right) - (0) = \frac{3}{10}$$

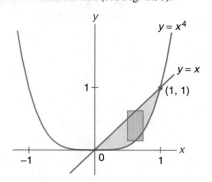

Figure 6.38

$$\bar{x} = \frac{\displaystyle\int_a^b x[f(x) - g(x)]\,dx}{A}$$

$$= \frac{\displaystyle\int_0^1 x(x - x^4)\,dx}{3/10}$$

$$= \frac{10}{3} \int_0^1 (x^2 - x^5)\,dx$$

$$= \frac{10}{3}\left(\frac{x^3}{3} - \frac{x^6}{6}\right)\Big|_0^1$$

$$= \frac{10}{3}\left[\left(\frac{1}{3} - \frac{1}{6}\right) - (0)\right]$$

$$= \frac{10}{3}\left(\frac{1}{6}\right) = \frac{5}{9}$$

$$\bar{y} = \frac{\dfrac{1}{2}\displaystyle\int_a^b \{[f(x)]^2 - [g(x)]^2\}\,dx}{A}$$

$$= \frac{\dfrac{1}{2}\displaystyle\int_0^1 [(x)^2 - (x^4)^2]\,dx}{3/10}$$

$$= \frac{5}{3} \int_0^1 (x^2 - x^8)\,dx$$

$$= \frac{5}{3}\left(\frac{x^3}{3} - \frac{x^9}{9}\right)\Big|_0^1$$

$$= \frac{5}{3}\left[\left(\frac{1}{3} - \frac{1}{9}\right) - (0)\right]$$

$$= \frac{5}{3}\left(\frac{2}{9}\right)$$

$$= \frac{10}{27}$$

The centroid is $\left(\frac{5}{9}, \frac{10}{27}\right)$.

The most general case of finding the center of mass of a two-dimensional mass distribution requires double integration and is not treated in this text.

A solid of revolution of constant density has its centroid on its axis of revolution. Let the area bounded by $y = f(x)$, $x = a$, and $x = b$ be revolved about the x-axis. We have drawn a typical disk in Fig. 6.39. Its center of mass is x units from the y-axis; therefore, the length of its moment arm is x. Its volume is $\pi y^2\,dx$. Since the solid is of constant density ρ, its mass is proportional to its volume, that is, $m = \rho\pi y^2\,dx$. Thus the moment about the y-axis is

$$md = (\rho\pi y^2\,dx)x = \rho\pi xy^2\,dx$$

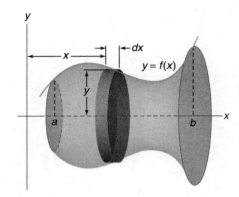

Figure 6.39   Finding the center of mass, or centroid, of a solid of revolution about the x-axis.

The sum of the moments of all such disks may be expressed by the integral

$$M_y = \rho\pi \int_a^b xy^2\,dx$$

The mass of the solid may be expressed by the integral

$$m = \rho\pi \int_a^b y^2\,dx$$

CENTROID OF A SOLID OF REVOLUTION ABOUT THE X-AXIS

$$\bar{x} = \frac{M_y}{m} = \frac{\displaystyle\int_a^b xy^2\,dx}{\displaystyle\int_a^b y^2\,dx} \quad \text{and} \quad \bar{y} = 0$$

Note: The ρ and π factors cancel.
In a similar manner, we can show:

CENTROID OF A SOLID OF REVOLUTION ABOUT THE Y-AXIS

$$\bar{y} = \frac{M_x}{m} = \frac{\displaystyle\int_c^d yx^2\,dy}{\displaystyle\int_c^d x^2\,dy} \quad \text{and} \quad \bar{x} = 0$$

EXAMPLE 6

Find the centroid of the solid formed by revolving the region bounded by $y = x^2$, $x = 1$, and $y = 0$ about the x-axis (see Fig. 6.40).

$$\bar{x} = \frac{\displaystyle\int_a^b xy^2\,dx}{\displaystyle\int_a^b y^2\,dx}$$

$$= \frac{\displaystyle\int_0^1 x(x^2)^2\,dx}{\displaystyle\int_0^1 (x^2)^2\,dx}$$

$$= \frac{\displaystyle\int_0^1 x^5\,dx}{\displaystyle\int_0^1 x^4\,dx}$$

$$= \frac{\left.\dfrac{x^6}{6}\right|_0^1}{\left.\dfrac{x^5}{5}\right|_0^1} = \frac{\dfrac{1}{6}}{\dfrac{1}{5}} = \frac{5}{6}$$

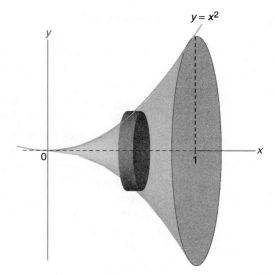

Figure 6.40

The centroid is $\left(\frac{5}{6}, 0\right)$.

EXAMPLE 7

Find the centroid of the solid formed by revolving the region bounded by $y = 4 - x^2$, $x = 0$, and $y = 0$ about the y-axis (see Fig. 6.41).

$$\bar{y} = \frac{\displaystyle\int_c^d yx^2\,dy}{\displaystyle\int_c^d x^2\,dy}$$

$$= \frac{\displaystyle\int_0^4 y(4 - y)\,dy}{\displaystyle\int_0^4 (4 - y)\,dy} \qquad (Note: x^2 = 4 - y.)$$

$$= \frac{\displaystyle\int_0^4 (4y - y^2)\,dy}{\displaystyle\int_0^4 (4 - y)\,dy}$$

$$= \frac{\left.\left(2y^2 - \dfrac{y^3}{3}\right)\right|_0^4}{\left.\left(4y - \dfrac{y^2}{2}\right)\right|_0^4} = \frac{\left(32 - \dfrac{64}{3}\right) - (0)}{(16 - 8) - (0)} = \frac{32/3}{8} = \frac{4}{3}$$

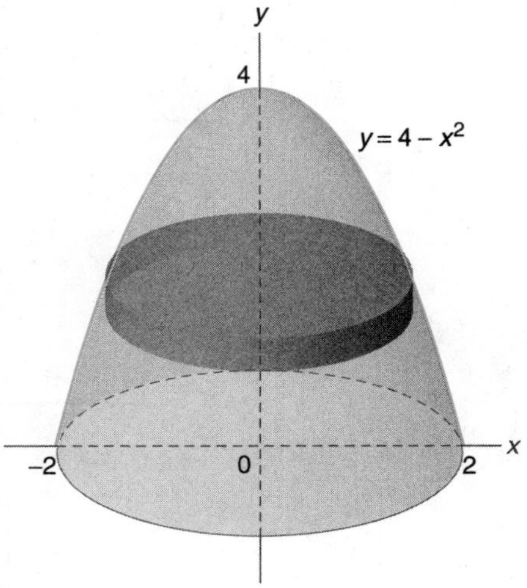

Figure 6.41

The centroid is $\left(0, \frac{4}{3}\right)$.

The most general case of finding the center of mass of a three-dimensional mass distribution requires triple integration and is not treated in this text.

Exercises 6.5

1. Find the center of mass of a straight wire 20 cm long and of uniform density.

2. Show that the center of mass of a straight wire of length L and of uniform density is at its midpoint.

3. Find the center of mass measured from the lighter end of a straight wire 10 cm long whose density is given by $\rho(x) = 0.1x$, where x is the distance from one end.

4. Find the center of mass measured from the lighter end of a straight wire 8 cm long whose density is given by $\rho(x) = 0.1x^2$, where x is the distance from one end.

5. Find the center of mass measured from the lighter end of a straight wire 12 cm long whose density is given by $\rho(x) = 4 + x^2$, where x is the distance from one end.

6. Find the center of mass measured from the lighter end of a straight wire 9 cm long whose density is given by $\rho(x) = 3 - \sqrt{x}$, where x is the distance from one end.

7. The density of a straight wire 6 cm long is directly proportional to the distance from one end. Find its center of mass.

8. The density of a straight wire 9 cm long varies inversely as the square root of the distance from one end. Find its center of mass.

Find the center of mass of each uniform thin plate.

9.
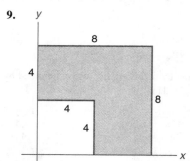

10.
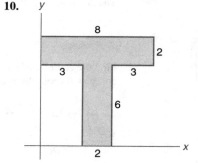

11.
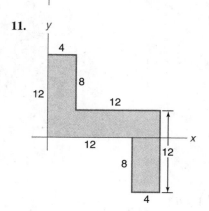

12.
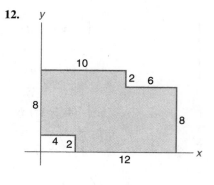

13.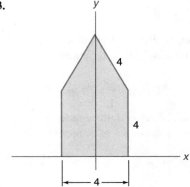

14.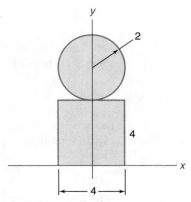

Find the centroid of each region bounded by the given curves.

15. $y = \sqrt{x}$, $y = 0$, and $x = 9$

16. $y = x^2$ and $y = 4$

17. $y = x^2 - 2x$ and $y = 0$

18. $y = 4 - x^2$ and $y = x^2 - 4$

19. $y = 4 - x^2$ and $y = 0$

20. $y = 4 - x^2$ and $y = x + 2$

21. $y = x^3$ and $y = x$ (first quadrant)

22. $y = x^3$, $x = 0$, and $y = 1$

23. Find the centroid of the semicircle of radius 1 with center at the origin lying in the first and second quadrants.

24. Find the centroid of the quarter circle of radius 1 with center at the origin lying in the first quadrant.

Find the centroid of the solid formed by revolving each region bounded by the given curves about the given axis.

25. $y = x^3$, $y = 0$, and $x = 1$ about the x-axis

26. $y = x^3$, $y = 0$, and $x = 1$ about the y-axis

27. $y = 3 - x$, $x = 0$, and $y = 0$ about the x-axis

28. $y = 3 - 2x$, $x = 0$, and $y = 0$ about the y-axis

29. $y = x^2$, $x = 1$, and $y = 0$ about the y-axis

30. $x^2 + y^2 = 1$, $x = 0$, and $y = 0$ about the x-axis

6.6 MOMENTS OF INERTIA

In Sections 6.4 and 6.5 we used moments to find centers of mass and centroids. Each moment was the product of the mass and its distance from some line. This case is called the first moment.

The second moment, called the *moment of inertia* about a line, is defined as the product of a mass m and the square of its distance d from a given line, that is,

$$I = md^2$$

Inertia is a property of an object that resists a change in its motion. That is, inertia is a property of an object that causes it to remain at rest if it is at rest or to continue moving with constant velocity.

MOMENT OF INERTIA OF A SYSTEM

Let masses $m_1, m_2, m_3, \ldots, m_n$ be at distances $d_1, d_2, d_3, \ldots, d_n$, respectively, from some axis about which they are rotating. The moment of inertia I of the system is

$$I = m_1 d_1^2 + m_2 d_2^2 + m_3 d_3^2 + \cdots + m_n d_n^2$$

Let m be the sum of all the masses in the systems and let R be the distance from the axis of rotation that gives the same total moment of inertia. Then

$$I = mR^2 = m_1 d_1^2 + m_2 d_2^2 + m_3 d_3^2 + \cdots + m_n d_n^2$$

R is called the *radius* of *gyration*. It tells how far from the axis of rotation the entire mass would be concentrated to have the same moment of inertia. This is a convenient way to express the moment of inertia of the mass of a body in terms of its mass and a length.

EXAMPLE 1

Find the moment of inertia and the radius of gyration about the y-axis of the system $m_1 = 8$ at $(2, -4)$, $m_2 = 3$ at $(-9, 8)$, and $m_3 = 6$ at $(-5, 2)$.

$$I_y = m_1 x_1^2 + m_2 x_2^2 + m_3 x_3^2$$
$$I_y = 8(2)^2 + 3(-9)^2 + 6(-5)^2 = 425$$
$$m = m_1 + m_2 + m_3 = 8 + 3 + 6 = 17$$
$$I_y = mR^2$$
$$R = \sqrt{\frac{I_y}{m}} = \sqrt{\frac{425}{17}} = 5$$

Now, let's find the moment of inertia of an area of constant density ρ about the y-axis as shown in Fig. 6.42. First, divide the area into n rectangles, each of width Δx. Let (x_i, y_i) be the center of mass of the ith rectangle. As we saw in the preceding sections, the y-value

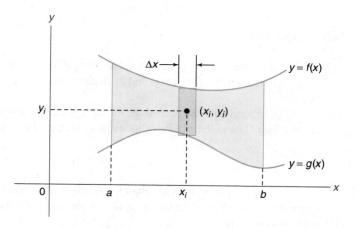

Figure 6.42 Finding the moment of inertia of an area of constant density about the y-axis.

of the geometric center of the ith rectangle is

$$y_i = \frac{f(x_i) + g(x_i)}{2}$$

Its area is $[f(x_i) - g(x_i)] \, \Delta x$ and its mass is $\rho[f(x_i) - g(x_i)] \, \Delta x$. The total mass is the integral

$$m = \rho \int_a^b [f(x) - g(x)]dx = \rho A$$

where A is the area of the region.

The distance of the center of the ith rectangle from the y-axis is x_i. Its moment of inertia, its second moment, is then

$$(\text{mass})(\text{moment arm})^2 = \rho[f(x_i) - g(x_i)] \, \Delta x \cdot (x_i)^2$$

Summing the moments of all such rectangles, we obtain the moment of inertia of the region about the y-axis as the integral

$$I_y = \rho \int_a^b x^2[f(x) - g(x)] \, dx$$

Similarly, the moment of inertia of an area about the x-axis is

$$I_x = \rho \int_c^d y^2[f(y) - g(y)] \, dy$$

The radius of gyration for each moment is as follows:

About y-axis	About x-axis
$I_y = mR^2$	$I_x = mR^2$
$R = \sqrt{\dfrac{I_y}{m}}$	$R = \sqrt{\dfrac{I_x}{m}}$

MOMENTS OF INERTIA OF AN AREA OF CONSTANT DENSITY ABOUT THE x- AND y-AXES

Let $g(x) \le f(x)$ be continuous functions on $a \le x \le b$ for the area of constant density ρ bounded by $y = f(x)$, $y = g(x)$, $x = a$, and $x = b$. The moment of inertia about the y-axis is

$$I_y = \rho \int_a^b x^2[f(x) - g(x)] \, dx \qquad \left(R = \sqrt{\frac{I_y}{m}}\right)$$

Similarly, the moment of inertia about the x-axis is

$$I_x = \rho \int_c^d y^2[f(y) - g(y)] \, dy \qquad \left(R = \sqrt{\frac{I_x}{m}}\right)$$

EXAMPLE 2

Find the moment of inertia and the radius of gyration about the y-axis of the region bounded by $y = x^2$, $y = 0$, and $x = 3$, where the region has a constant density of 5 (see Fig. 6.43).

$$I_y = \rho \int_a^b x^2[f(x) - g(x)]\, dx$$

$$= 5 \int_0^3 x^2[x^2 - 0]\, dx$$

$$= 5 \int_0^3 x^4\, dx$$

$$= 5 \cdot \left. \frac{x^5}{5} \right|_0^3$$

$$= 243$$

$$m = \rho \int_a^b [f(x) - g(x)]\, dx$$

$$= 5 \int_0^3 (x^2 - 0)\, dx$$

$$= 5 \cdot \left. \frac{x^3}{3} \right|_0^3$$

$$= 45$$

$$R = \sqrt{\frac{I_y}{m}} = \sqrt{\frac{243}{45}} = 2.32$$

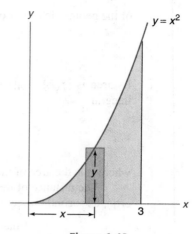

Figure 6.43

EXAMPLE 3

Find the moment of inertia and the radius of gyration about the x-axis of the region described in Example 2 (see Fig. 6.44).

$$I_x = \rho \int_c^d y^2[f(y) - g(y)]\, dy$$

$$= 5 \int_0^9 y^2[3 - \sqrt{y}]\, dy \qquad (3 - x = 3 - \sqrt{y})$$

$$= 5 \int_0^9 [3y^2 - y^{5/2}]\, dy$$

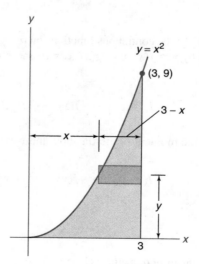

Figure 6.44

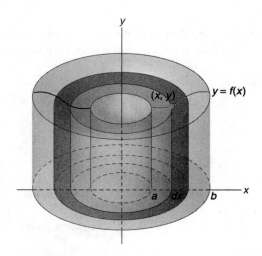

Figure 6.45 Finding the moment of inertia of a solid of revolution with respect to its *y*-axis of revolution.

$$= 5\left[y^3 - \frac{y^{7/2}}{7/2}\right]\Big|_0^9$$

$$= 5\left[9^3 - \frac{9^{7/2}}{7/2}\right] - 5[0] = 521 \qquad \text{(three significant digits)}$$

$$R = \sqrt{\frac{I_x}{m}} = \sqrt{\frac{521}{45}} = 3.40$$

To find the moment of inertia of a solid of revolution with respect to its axis of revolution, it is most convenient to use the shell method. Let the area bounded by $y = f(x)$, $y = 0$, $x = a$, and $x = b$ be revolved about the *y*-axis. We have drawn a typical shell in Fig. 6.45. The mass of the solid is proportional to its volume, $m = \rho V$:

$$m = 2\pi\rho \int_a^b x f(x)\, dx$$

and x^2 is the square of its distance from the *y*-axis. Summing all such shells gives the following results:

MOMENTS OF INERTIA OF A SOLID OF REVOLUTION

The moment of inertia of a solid of revolution about the *y*-axis is given by the integral

$$I_y = 2\pi\rho \int_a^b x^3 f(x)\, dx$$

Similarly, let the area bounded by $x = f(y)$, $x = 0$, $y = c$, and $y = d$ be revolved about the *x*-axis as in Fig. 6.46. Its moment of inertia about the *x*-axis is given by the integral

$$I_x = 2\pi\rho \int_c^d y^3 f(y)\, dy$$

Note: $f(x)$ and $f(y)$ correspond to the height of the shell.

Each radius of gyration is found in a similar way as that for a plane region, that is,

$$R = \sqrt{\frac{I_y}{m}} \quad \text{or} \quad R = \sqrt{\frac{I_x}{m}}$$

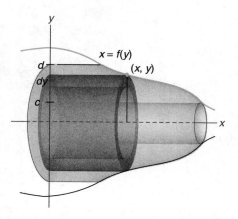

Figure 6.46 Finding the moment of inertia of a solid of revolution with respect to its x-axis of revolution.

EXAMPLE 4

Find the moment of inertia and the radius of gyration of the solid formed by revolving the region bounded by $y = 2x$, $y = 0$, and $x = 3$ about the y-axis. Assume that $\rho = 5$ (see Fig. 6.47).

$$I_y = 2\pi\rho \int_a^b x^3 f(x)\, dx$$

$$= 2\pi(5) \int_0^3 x^3 (2x)\, dx$$

$$= 20\pi \int_0^3 x^4\, dx$$

$$= 20\pi \cdot \frac{x^5}{5}\Big|_0^3 = 972\pi$$

$$m = 2\pi\rho \int_a^b x f(x)\, dx$$

$$= 2\pi(5) \int_0^3 x(2x)\, dx$$

$$= 20\pi \int_0^3 x^2\, dx$$

$$= 20\pi \cdot \frac{x^3}{3}\Big|_0^3 = 180\pi$$

$$R = \sqrt{\frac{I_y}{m}} = \sqrt{\frac{927\pi}{180\pi}} = 2.32$$

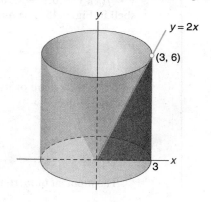

Figure 6.47

EXAMPLE 5

Find the moment of inertia and the radius of gyration of the solid formed by revolving the region bounded by $y = x^2$, $y = 0$, and $x = 2$ about the x-axis. Assume that $\rho = 1$ (see Fig. 6.48).

$$I_x = 2\pi\rho \int_c^d y^3 f(y)\, dy$$

$$= 2\pi(1) \int_0^4 y^3(2 - \sqrt{y})\, dy \qquad (2 - x = 2 - \sqrt{y})$$

$$= 2\pi \int_0^4 (2y^3 - y^{7/2})\, dy$$

$$= 2\pi\left(\frac{y^4}{2} - \frac{y^{9/2}}{9/2}\right)\Big|_0^4$$

$$= 2\pi\left(128 - \frac{1024}{9}\right) = \frac{256\pi}{9}$$

$$m = 2\pi\rho \int_c^d y f(y)\, dy$$

$$= 2\pi(1) \int_0^4 y(2 - \sqrt{y})\, dy$$

$$= 2\pi \int_0^4 (2y - y^{3/2})\, dy$$

$$= 2\pi\left(y^2 - \frac{y^{5/2}}{5/2}\right)\Big|_0^4$$

$$= 2\pi\left(16 - \frac{64}{5}\right) = \frac{32\pi}{5}$$

$$R = \sqrt{\frac{I_x}{m}} = \sqrt{\frac{256\pi/9}{32\pi/5}} = 2.11$$

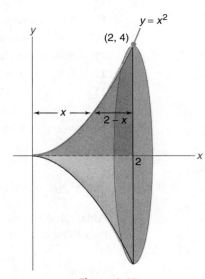

Figure 6.48

Exercises 6.6

Find the moment of inertia and the radius of gyration about the y-axis of each system.

1. $m_1 = 9$ at $(3, -2)$, $m_2 = 12$ at $(5, 4)$, $m_3 = 15$ at $(3, 7)$
2. $m_1 = 3$ at $(-6, 2)$, $m_2 = 9$ at $(-5, 8)$, $m_3 = 8$ at $(7, -2)$
3. $m_1 = 15$ at $(3, -9)$, $m_2 = 10$ at $(6, -4)$, $m_3 = 18$ at $(9, 2)$, $m_4 = 12$ at $(1, 3)$
4. $m_1 = 24$ at $(-6, 3)$, $m_2 = 36$ at $(7, -9)$, $m_3 = 15$ at $(4, 4)$, $m_4 = 12$ at $(-2, -5)$, $m_5 = 18$ at $(8, 6)$

Find the moment of inertia and the radius of gyration about the x-axis of each system.

5. The system in Exercise 1
6. $m_1 = 8$ at $(-3, 9)$, $m_2 = 16$ at $(8, -6)$, $m_3 = 14$ at $(4, 2)$
7. $m_1 = 9$ at $(-5, -9)$, $m_2 = 5$ at $(8, -2)$, $m_3 = 8$ at $(5, 0)$, $m_4 = 10$ at $(-3, 1)$
8. The system in Exercise 4

Find the moment of inertia and the radius of gyration of each region bounded by the given curves about the given axis.

9. $y = x^2$, $x = 0$, and $y = 4$ about the y-axis ($\rho = 5$)
10. Region of Exercise 9 about the x-axis

11. $y = x^2$, $y = x$, and $x > 0$ about the x-axis ($\rho = 4$)

12. Region of Exercise 11 about the y-axis

13. $y = 5 - x^2$, $y = 1$, and $x = 0$ about the y-axis ($\rho = 3$)

14. $x = 1 + y^2$, $x = 10$, and $y = 0$ about the x-axis ($\rho = 5$)

15. $y = 1/x^2$, $y = 0$, $x = 1$, and $x = 2$ about the y-axis ($\rho = 2$)

16. $y = 4x - x^2$ and $y = 0$ about the y-axis ($\rho = 15$)

Find the moment of inertia and the radius of gyration of the solid formed by revolving the region bounded by the given curves about the given axis.

17. $y = 3x$, $y = 0$, and $x = 2$ about the y-axis ($\rho = 15$)

18. Region of Exercise 17 about the x-axis

19. $y = 4x^2$, $y = 0$, and $x = 2$ about the x-axis ($\rho = 1$)

20. Region of Exercise 19 about the y-axis

21. $y = 9 - x^2$, $y = 0$, and $x = 0$ about the y-axis ($\rho = 12$)

22. $x = 4 - y^2$, $y = 0$, and $x = 0$ about the x-axis ($\rho = 6$)

23. $y = 4x - x^2$ and $y = 0$ about the y-axis ($\rho = 15$)

24. $y = 1/x^3$, $x = 0$, $y = 1$, and $y = 8$ about the x-axis ($\rho = 2$)

6.7 WORK, FLUID PRESSURE, AND AVERAGE VALUE

Although there are still many more technical applications of the integral, we will consider only three more in this section: work, fluid pressure, and average value.

Work

When a constant force F is applied to an object, moving it through a distance s, the technical term *work* is defined to be the product $F \cdot s$. That is, work W is the product of the force and the distance through which the force acts.

EXAMPLE 1

A 70-lb container is lifted 8 ft above the floor. Find the work done.

$$W = F \cdot s$$
$$= (70 \text{ lb})(8 \text{ ft})$$
$$= 560 \text{ ft-lb}$$

This formula for work is appropriate when the force remains constant. However, if an object is moved from a to b by a variable force F, then we can approximate the work done as follows: Divide the interval from a to b into intervals, each of width Δx. Let F_k represent the value of the force acting on the object somewhere in the kth interval (see Fig. 6.49).

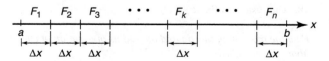

Figure 6.49 The work done by a variable force in moving an object from a to b is the sum of the work done in each interval of width Δx.

Then $\Delta W_k = F_k \cdot \Delta x$ is an approximation for the work done in the kth interval. If there are n intervals, each of width Δx, from a to b, then

$$W_{\text{approx}} = F_1 \cdot \Delta x + F_2 \cdot \Delta x + F_3 \cdot \Delta x + \cdots + F_n \cdot \Delta x$$

is an approximation for the work done moving the object from a to b. If the variable force can be expressed as a function of the distance traveled by the object, then it is possible to use integration techniques to find the actual work done. Suppose that $F = f(x)$ expresses the force as a function of the distance traveled by the object. Then

$$W_{\text{approx}} = f(x_1) \cdot \Delta x + f(x_2) \cdot \Delta x + f(x_3) \cdot \Delta x + \cdots + f(x_k) \cdot \Delta x + \cdots + f(x_n) \cdot \Delta x$$

is an approximation for W, the actual work done, where x_k is a number in the kth interval.

The smaller we choose Δx, the better approximation we obtain for W_{approx}. In fact, if we let Δx approach 0, then W_{approx} approaches the actual work done W. Then

WORK

$$W = \int_a^b f(x)\, dx$$

since this is how the definite integral of $f(x)$ from a to b was described in Chapter 5.

Note that work is the integral of force with respect to the displacement x. Thus, in setting up a work calculation, the force must be modeled as a function of the displacement. The reason for this comment is that work is not the only application that involves the integral of a force function. In physics, for example, *impulse* is defined as the integral of force with respect to the time variable t.

EXAMPLE 2

Find the work done by a force F moving an object from $x = 1$ to $x = 2$ according to $F = f(x) = x^2$.

$$W = \int_1^2 x^2\, dx$$

$$= \frac{x^3}{3}\bigg|_1^2 = \frac{8}{3} - \frac{1}{3} = \frac{7}{3}$$

EXAMPLE 3

Hooke's law states that the force required to stretch a spring is directly proportional to the amount that it is stretched. Find the work done in stretching a spring 3 in. if it requires 12 lb of force to stretch it 10 in.

Let x represent the distance stretched by the force $F = f(x)$. Then, by Hooke's law

$$f(x) = kx$$

At $x = 10$ we know that $f(10) = 12$, so

$$12 = k(10)$$

$$k = \frac{6}{5}$$

Then,

$$f(x) = \frac{6}{5}x$$

and

$$W = \int_a^b f(x)\, dx$$

$$= \int_0^3 \frac{6}{5} x \, dx$$

$$= \frac{6}{5} \left(\frac{x^2}{2} \right) \Big|_0^3 = \frac{6}{5} \left(\frac{9}{2} - 0 \right)$$

$$= \frac{27}{5} \text{ in.-lb}$$

EXAMPLE 4

Two charged particles separated by a distance x (in metres) attract each other with a force $F = 4.65 \times 10^{-20} x^{-2}$ newton (N). Find the work done (in joules) in separating them over an interval from $x = 0.01$ m to $x = 0.1$ m.

$$W = \int_{0.01}^{0.1} 4.65 \times 10^{-20} x^{-2} \, dx$$

$$= 4.65 \times 10^{-20} \int_{0.01}^{0.1} x^{-2} \, dx$$

$$= 4.65 \times 10^{-20} \left(\frac{x^{-1}}{-1} \Big|_{0.01}^{0.1} \right)$$

$$= 4.65 \times 10^{-20} \left(\frac{-1}{x} \Big|_{0.01}^{0.1} \right)$$

$$= 4.65 \times 10^{-20} \left(\frac{-1}{0.1} - \frac{-1}{0.01} \right)$$

$$= 4.65 \times 10^{-20} (-10 + 100)$$

$$= 4.19 \times 10^{-18} \text{ N m}$$

$$= 4.19 \times 10^{-18} \text{ J}$$

Note: The metric system unit of work is the joule (J). 1 J = 1 N m.

EXAMPLE 5

A chain 50 ft long and weighing 4 lb/ft is hanging from a pulley. (a) How much work is needed to pull 30 ft of the chain to the top? (b) How much work is needed to pull all of the chain to the top?

The force needed to lift the chain at any one time equals the weight of the chain hanging down at that time. If x feet of chain are hanging down and the chain weighs 4 lb/ft, the force is

$$f(x) = F = 4x$$

(a) $W = \displaystyle\int_{20}^{50} 4x \, dx$ \qquad (b) $W = \displaystyle\int_{0}^{50} 4x \, dx$

$\quad = 2x^2 \Big|_{20}^{50} = 4200 \text{ ft-lb}$ \qquad $= 2x^2 \Big|_{0}^{50} = 5000 \text{ ft-lb}$

EXAMPLE 6

A cylindrical tank 10 ft in diameter and 12 ft high is full of water. How much work is needed to pump all the water out over the top? The density of water $\rho = 62.4$ lb/ft³.

First, divide the tank into n layers, each of thickness Δx as in Fig. 6.50. Let x be the distance that each layer travels as it is pumped to the top. The force is the weight of each layer of water. $F = \rho V$.

Each layer is in the shape of a cylinder, whose volume is given by

$$V = \pi r^2 h$$

So,

$$F = \rho V = 62.4\pi (5^2) \, \Delta x$$

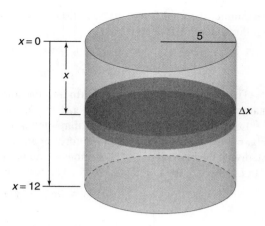

Figure 6.50

is the force of each layer. Since each layer travels a distance of x feet, the work needed to move one layer to the top is

$$W = F \cdot s = 62.4\pi (5^2)\Delta x \cdot x$$
$$= 1560\pi x\, \Delta x$$

Summing the work of such layers gives

$$W = \int_0^{12} 1560\pi x\, dx$$
$$= 780\pi\, x^2 \Big|_0^{12}$$
$$= 112{,}320\pi \text{ ft-lb}$$

Fluid Pressure

As a body goes deeper under water, the pressure on it increases because the water's weight increases with depth. Fluids are different in this respect from solids in that, where solids exert only a downward force due to gravity, the force exerted by fluids is the same in all directions. *Hydrostatic pressure* is the pressure at any given depth in a fluid due to its weight and may be expressed by

$$p = \rho g h$$

where p is the pressure, ρ is the mass density of the fluid, g is the force of gravity, and h is the height or depth of the fluid. For example, if you are in a swimming pool 12 ft below the surface, the pressure you feel is

$$p = \rho g h$$
$$p = (62.4 \text{ lb/ft}^3)(12 \text{ ft}) \qquad (\rho g = 62.4 \text{ lb/ft}^3)$$
$$= 748.8 \text{ lb/ft}^2$$

The total force is given by

$$F = pA$$

One main interest in fluid pressure is determining the total force exerted by a fluid on the walls of its container. If the container has vertical sides, it is simple to calculate the total force on the *bottom* of the container, that is,

$$F = \rho g h A$$

For example, the total force on the bottom of a rectangular swimming pool 12 ft × 30 ft when the water is 8 ft deep is

$$F = (62.4 \text{ lb/ft}^3)(8 \text{ ft})(12 \text{ ft} \times 30 \text{ ft})$$
$$F = 180,000 \text{ lb (approx.)}$$

The more difficult problem is finding the total force against the *vertical sides* of a container because the pressure is not constant. The pressure increases as the depth increases.

Let a vertical plane region be submerged into a fluid of constant density ρ as shown in Fig. 6.51. We need to find the total force against this region from depth $h - a$ to $h - b$. First, divide the interval $a \leq y \leq b$ into n rectangles each of width Δy. The ith rectangle has length L_i, area $L_i \Delta y$, and depth $h - y_i$. The force on the ith rectangle is

$$\Delta F_i = \rho g(h - y_i)L_i \Delta y$$

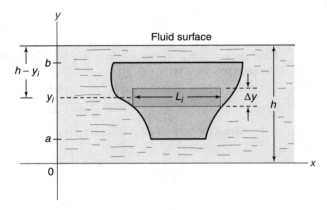

Figure 6.51   Finding the force exerted by a fluid against a submerged vertical plane.

Summing the forces on all such rectangles gives the following integral:

FORCE EXERTED BY A FLUID

The force F exerted by a fluid of constant mass density ρ against a submerged vertical plane region from $y = a$ to $y = b$ is given by

$$F = \rho g \int_a^b (h - y)L \, dy$$

where h is the total depth of the fluid and L is the horizontal length of the region at y.

Note: In the metric system, the mass density ρ must be known and $g = 9.80 \text{ m/s}^2$. In the English system, the weight density ρg must be known.

EXAMPLE 7

A vertical gate in a dam is in the shape of an isosceles trapezoid 12 ft across the top and 8 ft across the bottom, with a height of 10 ft. Find the total force against the gate if the water surface is at the top of the gate.

The solution can be simplified if we position the trapezoid in the plane as shown in Fig. 6.52. The equation of the line through $(4, 0)$ and $(6, 10)$ is

$$y - 0 = 5(x - 4)$$
$$x = \frac{y + 20}{5}$$

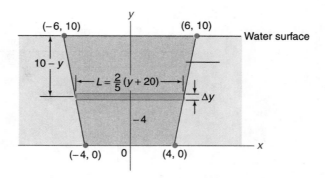

Figure 6.52

The width of the ith rectangle is Δy; its length L may be written as

$$L = 2x = 2\left(\frac{y + 20}{5}\right) = \frac{2}{5}(y + 20)$$

and its depth is $10 - y$. So

$$F = \rho g \int_a^b (h - y)L \, dy$$

$$F = 62.4 \int_0^{10} (10 - y)\frac{2}{5}(y + 20) \, dy$$

$$= 24.96 \int_0^{10} (10 - y)(y + 20) \, dy$$

$$= 24.96 \int_0^{10} (200 - 10y - y^2) \, dy$$

$$= 24.96\left(200y - 5y^2 - \frac{y^3}{3}\right)\Big|_0^{10}$$

$$= 24.96\left(2000 - 500 - \frac{1000}{3}\right)$$

$$= 29{,}120 \text{ lb}$$

EXAMPLE 8

A vertical gate in a dam is semicircular and has a diameter of 8 m. Find the total force against the gate if the water level is 1 m from the top of the gate.

Here place the semicircle with center at the origin as in Fig. 6.53. Its equation is $x^2 + y^2 = 16$. Other positions make the integration more difficult.

$$L = 2x = 2\sqrt{16 - y^2}$$

The depth of the rectangle is $0 - y$, or $-y$; $\rho = 1000 \text{ kg/m}^3$; and $g = 9.80 \text{ m/s}^2$.

$$F = \rho g \int_a^b (h - y) L \, dy$$

$$F = 9800 \int_{-4}^{-1} (-y) 2\sqrt{16 - y^2} \, dy$$

$$= -19{,}600 \int_{-4}^{-1} y(16 - y^2)^{1/2} \, dy$$

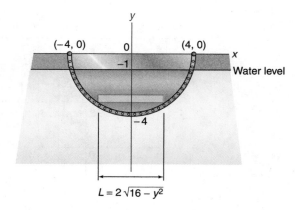

$$L = 2\sqrt{16 - y^2}$$

Figure 6.53

$$= -19{,}600 \int y u^{1/2} \frac{du}{-2y}$$

$$\boxed{\begin{aligned} u &= 16 - y^2 \\ du &= -2y\,dy \end{aligned}}$$

$$= 9800 \int u^{1/2}\,du$$

$$= 9800 \cdot \frac{u^{3/2}}{3/2} + C$$

$$= \frac{19{,}600}{3}(16 - y^2)^{3/2}\Big|_{-4}^{-1}$$

$$= \frac{19{,}600}{3}(15^{3/2} - 0)$$

$$= 379{,}600 \text{ N} \qquad \text{(4 significant digits)}$$

EXAMPLE 9

A swimming pool is 15 ft wide and 20 ft long. The bottom is flat but sloped so that the water is 4 ft deep at one end and 12 ft deep at the other end. Find the force of the water on one 20-ft side.

First, let's position the vertical side in the plane as shown in Fig. 6.54. Notice that the right ends of the horizontal strips sometimes are on the vertical line $x = 20$ and sometimes on the line through $(0, 0)$ and $(20, 8)$, whose equation is $y = 2x/5$. Thus we need two integrals. For each integral $L = x$.

$$F = 62.4 \int_0^8 (12 - y)x\,dy + 62.4 \int_8^{12} (12 - y)x\,dy$$

$$= 62.4 \int_0^8 (12 - y)\left(\frac{5}{2}y\right)dy + 62.4 \int_8^{12} (12 - y)(20)\,dy$$

$$= 156 \int_0^8 (12y - y^2)\,dy + 1248 \int_8^{12} (12 - y)\,dy$$

$$= 156\left(6y^2 - \frac{y^3}{3}\right)\Big|_0^8 + 1248\left(12y - \frac{y^2}{2}\right)\Big|_8^{12}$$

$$= 33{,}280 + 9984$$

$$= 43{,}264 \text{ lb}$$

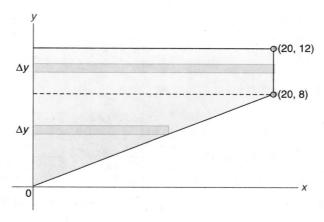

Figure 6.54

Note: The position of the vertical side in the *xy*-plane has no effect on the final result. You should repeat this problem using other positions.

Average Value

Finding the average value of a function y_{av} is another application of integration. The sum

$$y_{av} = \frac{f(x_1) + f(x_2) + f(x_3) + \cdots + f(x_n)}{n}$$

is the average value of a function for the given values of x: $x_1, x_2, x_3, \ldots, x_n$.

For example, if $f(x_1) = 3, f(x_2) = 5$, and $f(x_3) = 4$, then

$$y_{av} = \frac{3 + 5 + 4}{3} = 4$$

is the average of the three given values.

Now,

$$
\begin{aligned}
y_{av} &= \frac{f(x_1) + f(x_2) + f(x_3) + \cdots + f(x_n)}{n} \\
&= \frac{[f(x_1) + f(x_2) + f(x_3) + \cdots + f(x_n)] \, \Delta x}{n \, \Delta x} \qquad \text{(Multiply numerator and denominator by } \Delta x.\text{)} \\
&= \frac{1}{n \, \Delta x} [f(x_1) \, \Delta x + f(x_2) \, \Delta x + f(x_3) \, \Delta x + \cdots + f(x_n) \, \Delta x]
\end{aligned}
$$

In Fig. 6.55, $n \, \Delta x = b - a$, so that

$$y_{av} = \frac{1}{b - a} [f(x_1) \, \Delta x + f(x_2) \, \Delta x + f(x_3) \, \Delta x + \cdots + f(x_n) \, \Delta x]$$

As we let Δx approach 0, the right-hand factor approaches the integral

$$\int_a^b f(x) \, dx$$

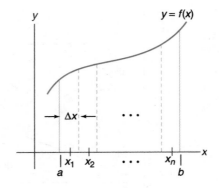

Figure 6.55   The average value of $y = f(x)$.

We then have the following result:

AVERAGE VALUE

The *average value* of the function $y = f(x)$ over the interval $x = a$ to $x = b$ is

$$y_{av} = \frac{1}{b - a} \int_a^b f(x)\, dx$$

A geometrical interpretation can be given to y_{av} as the height of a rectangle with base $b - a$ having the same area as the area bounded by the curve $y = f(x)$, $x = a$, $x = b$, and the x-axis as shown in Fig. 6.56.

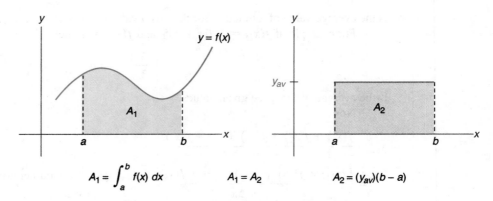

$$A_1 = \int_a^b f(x)\, dx \qquad A_1 = A_2 \qquad A_2 = (y_{av})(b - a)$$

Figure 6.56   Geometrically, y_{av} is the height of a rectangle with base $b - a$ having the same area as the area under the curve $y = f(x)$ from $x = a$ to $x = b$.

EXAMPLE 10

Find the average value of the function $y = 4 - x^2$ from $x = 0$ to $x = 2$.

$$y_{av} = \frac{1}{b - a} \int_a^b f(x)\, dx = \frac{1}{2 - 0} \int_0^2 (4 - x^2)\, dx$$

$$= \frac{1}{2}\left(4x - \frac{x^3}{3}\right)\Big|_0^2 = \frac{1}{2}\left[\left(8 - \frac{8}{3}\right) - (0)\right] = \frac{8}{3}$$

A rectangle with height $\frac{8}{3}$ and width 2 has area also equal to A: $\left(\frac{8}{3}\right)(2) = \frac{16}{3}$ (see Fig. 6.57).

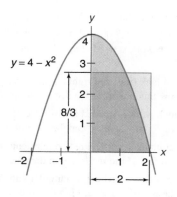

Figure 6.57

EXAMPLE 11

The power developed in a resistor is given by $p = 0.5i^3$. Find the average power (in watts) as the current changes from 1 A to 3 A.

$$p_{av} = \frac{1}{3-1} \int_1^3 0.5i^3 \, di$$

$$= \frac{0.5}{2} \cdot \frac{i^4}{4} \Big|_1^3$$

$$= \frac{0.5}{2} \left(\frac{81}{4} - \frac{1}{4} \right)$$

$$= 5.0 \text{ W}$$

Exercises 6.7

1. A force moves an object from $x = 0$ to $x = 3$ according to $F = x^3 - x$. Find the work done.

2. A force moves an object from $x = 1$ to $x = 100$ according to $F = \sqrt{x}$. Find the work done.

3. Find the work done in stretching a spring 5 in. if it requires a 20-lb force to stretch it 10 in.

4. Find the work done in stretching a spring 12 in. if it requires a 10-lb force to stretch it 8 in.

5. A spring with a natural length of 8 cm measures 12 cm after a 150-N weight is attached. Find the work required to stretch the spring 6 cm from its natural length.

6. A spring with a natural length of 10 cm measures 14 cm after a 60-N weight is attached. Find the work done in stretching the spring 10 cm from its natural length.

7. Two charged particles separated by a distance x attract each other with a force $F = 3.62 \times 10^{-16}x^{-2}$ N. Find the work done (in joules) in separating them over an interval from $x = 0.01$ m to $x = 0.05$ m.

8. Two charged particles separated by a distance x attract each other with a force $F = 4.52 \times 10^{-18}x^{-2}$ N. Find the work done (in joules) in separating them over an interval from $x = 0.02$ m to $x = 0.08$ m.

9. A chain 50 ft long and weighing 2 lb/ft is hanging over a pulley. How much work is needed to pull (a) 10 ft of the chain to the top? (b) half of the chain to the top? (c) all of the chain to the top?

10. Find the amount of work done in winding all of a 300-ft hanging cable that weighs 120 lb.

11. A cylindrical tank 8 ft in diameter and 12 ft high is full of water. How much work is needed to pump all the water out over the top?

12. How much work is needed in Exercise 11 to pump half the water out over the top of the tank?

13. Suppose that the tank in Exercise 11 is placed on a 10-ft platform. How much work is needed to fill the tank from the ground when the water is pumped in through a hole in the bottom of the tank?

14. How much work is needed to fill the tank in Exercise 13 if the water is pumped into the top of the tank?

15. A conical tank (inverted right circular cone) filled with water is 10 ft across the top and 12 ft high. How much work is needed to pump all the water out over the top?

16. How much work is needed in Exercise 15 to pump 4 ft of water out over the top (a) when the tank is full? (b) when the tank has 4 ft of water in it?

17. A dam contains a vertical rectangular gate 10 ft high and 8 ft wide. The top of the gate is at the water's surface. Find the force on the gate.

18. A dam contains a vertical rectangular gate 6 ft high and 8 ft wide. The top of the gate is 4 ft below the water's surface. Find the force on the gate.

19. A rectangular tank is 8 m wide and 4 m deep. If the tank is $\frac{3}{4}$ full of water, find the force against the side.

20. A cylindrical tank is lying on its side and is half-filled with water. If its diameter is 6 m, find the force against an end.

21. A cylindrical tank of oil is half full of oil ($\rho = 870$ kg/m^3) and lying on its side. If the diameter of the tank is 10 m, find the force on an end of the tank.

22. A rectangular porthole on a vertical side of a ship is 1 ft square. Find the total force on the porthole if its top is 20 ft below the water's surface.

23. A trough is 12 ft long and 2 ft high. Vertical cross sections are isosceles right triangles with the hypotenuse horizontal. Find the force on one end if the trough is filled with water.

24. A trough is 12 m long and 1 m high. Vertical cross sections are equilateral triangles with the top side horizontal. Find the force on one end if the trough is filled with alcohol ($\rho = 790$ kg/m^3).

25. A dam has a vertical gate in the shape of an isosceles trapezoid with upper base 10 ft, lower base 16 ft, and height 6 ft. Find the force on the gate if the upper base is 8 ft below the water's surface.

26. Find the force on the gate in Exercise 25 if the gate is inverted.

27. A swimming pool is 12 ft wide and 18 ft long. The bottom is flat but sloped so that the water is 3 ft deep at one end and 9 ft deep at the other end. Find the force on one 18-ft side.

28. A dam is in the shape of a parabola 12 ft high and 8 ft across its top. Find the force on it when the water's surface is at the top.

Find the average value of each function.

29. $y = x^2$ from $x = 1$ to $x = 3$

30. $y = \sqrt{x}$ from $x = 1$ to $x = 4$

31. $y = \dfrac{1}{\sqrt{x-1}}$ from $x = 5$ to $x = 10$

32. $y = x^2 - 1/x^2$ from $x = 1$ to $x = 3$

33. The electric current for a certain circuit is given by $i = 6t - t^2$. Find the average value of the current (in amperes) over the interval from $t = 0.1$ s to $t = 0.5$ s.

34. The power developed in a resistor is given by $P = 0.28i^3$. Find the average power (in watts) as the current changes from 1 A to 4 A.

CHAPTER 6 SUMMARY

1. The *area between two curves* $y = f(x)$ and $y = g(x)$ between $x = a$ and $x = b$ is

$$\int_a^b [f(x) - g(x)]\, dx$$

for $f(x) \geq g(x)$ and $a \leq x \leq b$. The *area between two curves* $x = f(y)$ and $x = g(y)$ between $y = c$ and $y = d$ is

$$\int_c^d [f(y) - g(y)] \, dy$$

for $f(y) \geq g(y)$ and $c \leq y \leq d$.

2. *Volume of revolution, disk method:*

$$V = \pi \int_a^b \underset{\underset{\text{radius}^2}{\uparrow}}{[f(x)]^2} \quad \underset{\underset{\text{thickness}}{\uparrow}}{dx} \qquad \text{(revolved about } x\text{-axis)}$$

$$V = \pi \int_c^d [f(y)]^2 \qquad dy \qquad \text{(revolved about } y\text{-axis)}$$

$$V = \pi \int_a^b \{[f(x)]^2 - [g(x)]^2\} \quad dx \qquad \text{(washer revolved about } x\text{-axis)}$$

3. *Volume of revolution, shell method:*

$$V = 2\pi \int_a^b \underset{\underset{\text{radius}}{\uparrow}}{x} \quad \underset{\underset{\text{height}}{\uparrow}}{f(x)} \quad \underset{\underset{\text{thickness}}{\uparrow}}{dx} \qquad \text{(shells parallel to } y\text{-axis)}$$

$$V = 2\pi \int_c^d y \quad f(y) \quad dy \qquad \text{(shells parallel to } x\text{-axis)}$$

4. *Moment in a linear system along the x-axis:* Let $\bar{x}$ be the center of mass of a linear system along the x-axis with n masses; then,

$$\bar{x} = \frac{m_1 x_1 + m_2 x_2 + m_3 x_3 + \cdots + m_n x_n}{m_1 + m_2 + m_3 + \cdots + m_n}$$

If we let M_0 be the moment about the origin and m be the total mass of the system, then

$$\bar{x} = \frac{M_0}{m}$$

5. *Moments of a two-dimensional system:* Consider n masses $m_1, m_2, \ldots, m_n$ located at points $(x_1, y_1), (x_2, y_2), \ldots, (x_n, y_n)$, respectively. The moment about the y-axis M_y is

$$M_y = m_1 x_1 + m_2 x_2 + \cdots + m_n x_n$$

and the moment about the x-axis M_x is

$$M_x = m_1 y_1 + m_2 y_2 + \cdots + m_n y_n.$$

If we let m be the total mass of the system, the center of mass $(\bar{x}, \bar{y})$ is

$$\bar{x} = \frac{M_y}{m} \quad \text{and} \quad \bar{y} = \frac{M_x}{m}$$

6. *Center of mass of a continuous thin mass of variable density* from $x = a$ to $x = b$ is given by

$$\bar{x} = \frac{M_0}{m} = \frac{\displaystyle\int_a^b \rho(x)\,x\,dx}{\displaystyle\int_a^b \rho(x)\,dx}$$

where $\rho(x)$ is the density expressed as a function of x. If the density is constant, ρ will cancel.

7. *Moments and center of mass of a plane area or thin plate:* Let $g(x) \leq f(x)$ be continuous functions on $a \leq x \leq b$ for the area of uniform density ρ bounded by $y = f(x)$, $y = g(x)$, $x = a$, and $x = b$; the moments about the x-axis and the y-axis are

$$M_x = \frac{\rho}{2}\int_a^b \{[f(x)]^2 - [g(x)]^2\}\,dx \quad \text{and} \quad M_y = \rho\int_a^b x[f(x) - g(x)]\,dx$$

Its mass is given by

$$m = \rho\int_a^b [f(x) - g(x)]\,dx$$

and its center of mass is $(\bar{x}, \bar{y})$, where

$$\bar{x} = \frac{M_y}{m} \quad \text{and} \quad \bar{y} = \frac{M_x}{m}$$

8. *Centroid of a plane region or thin plate:* Let $g(x) \leq f(x)$ be continuous functions on $a \leq x \leq b$. The centroid $(\bar{x}, \bar{y})$ of the region bounded by $y = f(x)$, $y = g(x)$, $x = a$, and $x = b$ is

$$\bar{x} = \frac{\displaystyle\int_a^b x[f(x) - g(x)]\,dx}{A} \quad \text{and} \quad \bar{y} = \frac{\dfrac{1}{2}\displaystyle\int_a^b \{[f(x)]^2 - [g(x)]^2\}\,dx}{A}$$

where A is the area of the region.

9. *Centroid of a solid of revolution:*

$$\bar{x} = \frac{M_y}{m} = \frac{\displaystyle\int_a^b xy^2\,dx}{\displaystyle\int_a^b y^2\,dx} \quad \text{and} \quad \bar{y} = 0 \qquad \text{(revolved about x-axis)}$$

$$\bar{y} = \frac{M_x}{m} = \frac{\displaystyle\int_c^d yx^2\,dy}{\displaystyle\int_c^d x^2\,dy} \quad \text{and} \quad \bar{x} = 0 \qquad \text{(revolved about y-axis)}$$

10. *Moment of inertia of a system:* Let masses $m_1, m_2, m_3, \ldots, m_n$ be at distances $d_1, d_2, d_3, \ldots, d_n$, respectively, rotating about some axis. The moment of inertia I of the system is

$$I = m_1 d_1^2 + m_2 d_2^2 + m_3 d_3^2 + \cdots + m_n d_n^2$$

Let m be the sum of all the masses in the system and let R be the distance from the axis of rotation that gives the same total moment of inertia:

$$I = mR^2$$

R is called the radius of gyration.

11. *Moments of inertia of an area of constant density about the x- and y-axes:* Let $g(x) \leq f(x)$ be continuous functions on $a \leq x \leq b$ for the area of constant density ρ bounded by $y = f(x)$, $y = g(x)$, $x = a$, and $x = b$. The moment of inertia about the y-axis is

$$I_y = \rho \int_a^b x^2[f(x) - g(x)]\, dx \quad \text{and} \quad R = \sqrt{\frac{I_y}{m}}$$

Similarly, the moment of inertia about the x-axis is

$$I_x = \rho \int_c^d y^2[f(y) - g(y)]\, dy \quad \text{and} \quad R = \sqrt{\frac{I_x}{m}}$$

12. *Moment of inertia of a solid of revolution:* Let the area bounded by $y = f(x)$, $y = 0$, $x = a$, and $x = b$ be revolved about the y-axis. The moment of inertia about the y-axis is

$$I_y = 2\pi\rho \int_a^b x^3 f(x)\, dx$$

Its radius of gyration is $R = \sqrt{\dfrac{I_y}{m}}$, where $m = 2\pi\rho \displaystyle\int_a^b x f(x)\, dx$.

Similarly, let the area bounded by $x = f(y)$, $x = 0$, $y = c$, and $y = d$ be revolved about the x-axis. Its moment of inertia about the x-axis is

$$I_x = 2\pi\rho \int_c^d y^3 f(y)\, dy$$

Its radius of gyration is $R = \sqrt{\dfrac{I_x}{m}}$, where $m = 2\pi\rho \displaystyle\int_c^d y f(y)\, dy$.

Note: $f(x)$ and $f(y)$ correspond to the height of the shell.

13. *Work of a variable force $f(x)$ acting through the distance from $x = a$ to $x = b$:*

$$W = \int_a^b f(x)\, dx$$

14. *Force exerted by a fluid:* The force F exerted by a fluid of constant density ρ against a submerged vertical plane region from $y = a$ to $y = b$ is

$$F = \rho g \int_a^b (h - y) L\, dy$$

where h is the total depth of the fluid and L is the horizontal length of the region at y.

15. *Average value:* The average value of the function $y = f(x)$ over the interval $x = a$ to $x = b$ is

$$y_{av} = \frac{1}{b - a} \int_a^b f(x)\, dx$$

Find each area bounded by the curves.

1. $y = x^2 + 3$, $y = 0$, $x = 1$, and $x = 2$

2. $y = 1 - x^2$, $y = 0$, and $x = 0$

3. $x = y^2 - y^3$ and the y-axis

4. $y = 3x^2 - 12x + 9$, $y = 0$, $x = 0$, and $x = 4$

5. $x = y^4 - 2y^2$ and $x = 2y^2$

6. $x = y^2$ and $x = 9$

Find the volume of each solid formed by revolving the region bounded by the given curves about the given line.

7. $y = \sqrt{x}$, $y = 0$, and $x = 4$ about the x-axis (shell method)

8. $y = \sqrt{x}$, $y = 0$, and $x = 4$ about the x-axis (disk method)

9. $y = x - x^2$ and $y = 0$ about the x-axis

10. $y = x$ and $y = 3x - x^2$ about the y-axis

11. $y = 3x^2 - x^3$ and $y = 0$ about the y-axis

12. $y = x^2 + 1$, $y = 0$, $x = 0$, and $x = 3$ about the y-axis

13. $x = y^2$ and $x = 4$ about the y-axis

14. $x = 4y - y^2$, $x = 0$, and $y = 3$ about the x-axis

15. Find the center of mass of the linear system $m_1 = 12$, $x_1 = -4$; $m_2 = 20$, $x_2 = 9$; $m_3 = 24$, $x_3 = 12$.

16. Find the center of mass of the system $m_1 = 24$ at $(11, -3)$; $m_2 = 36$ at $(-4, -15)$; $m_3 = 30$ at $(-7, 0)$.

17. Find the center of mass of the uniform thin plate in Fig. 6.58.

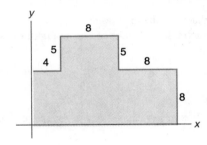

Figure 6.58

Find the centroid of each region bounded by the given curves.

18. $y = 5x$, $x = 4$, and $y = 0$

19. $y = 6x - x^2$ and $y = 3x$

20. $y = x^2 - 6x$ and $y = 0$

Find the centroid of the solid formed by revolving each region bounded by the given curves about the given axis.

21. $y = 2x$, $x = 0$, and $y = 2$ about the y-axis

22. $y = x^2$, $x = 0$, and $y = 1$ about the x-axis

23. $x = y^2 - 4y$ and $x = 0$ about the y-axis

24. Find the moment of inertia and the radius of gyration about the x-axis of the system $m_1 = 10$ at $(3, 2)$, $m_2 = 6$ at $(5, 7)$, and $m_3 = 8$ at $(8, -4)$.

Find the moment of inertia and the radius of gyration of each region bounded by the given curves about the given axis.

25. $y = 3x$, $x = 4$, and $y = 0$ about the y-axis $(\rho = 1)$

26. Region in Exercise 25 about the x-axis

27. $x = 1 - y^2$, $y = 0$, and $x = 0$ about the x-axis ($\rho = 4$)

Find the moment of inertia and the radius of gyration of the solid formed by revolving the region bounded by the given curves about the given axis.

28. $y = x^3$, $y = 0$, and $x = 1$ about the x-axis ($\rho = 4$)

29. Region of Exercise 28 about the y-axis

30. $y = 1/x$, $y = 0$, $x = 1$, and $x = 4$ about the y-axis ($\rho = 3$)

31. Find the work done in stretching a spring 10 in. if it requires a 16-lb force to stretch it 4 in.

32. Two charged particles separated by a distance x attract each other with a force $F = 5.24 \times 10^{-18}x^{-2}$ N. Find the work done (in joules) in separating them over an interval from $x = 0.01$ m to $x = 0.02$ m.

33. A cable weighs 4 lb/ft and has a 250-lb weight attached in a hole 200 ft below the ground. Find the amount of work needed to pull the cable and weight to ground level.

34. A dam contains a vertical rectangular gate 8 ft high and 10 ft wide. The top of the gate is 6 ft below the water's surface. Find the force on the gate.

35. A cylindrical tank 10 m in diameter is lying on its side and is half full of water. Find the force against an end.

36. Find the average value of the voltage V_{av} in an electric circuit from $t = 0$ s to $t = 3$ s if $V = t^2 + 3t + 2$.

37. Find the average value of the current i_{av} in an electric circuit from $t = 4$ s to $t = 9$ s if $i = 4t^{3/2}$.

38. The power in a circuit varies according to $p = 2t^3$. Find the average power p_{av} (in watts) from $t = 1$ s to $t = 3$ s.

Weights and Measures

TABLE 1   U.S. Weights and Measures

Units of length	Units of weight
Standard unit–inch (in. or ″)	Standard unit–pound (lb)
12 inches = 1 foot (ft or ′)	16 ounces (oz) = 1 pound
3 feet = 1 yard (yd)	2000 pounds = 1 ton (T)
$5\frac{1}{2}$ yards or $16\frac{1}{2}$ feet = 1 rod (rd)	
5280 feet = 1 mile (mi)	

Volume measure

Liquid

16 ounces (fl oz) = 1 pint (pt)
2 pints = 1 quart (qt)
4 quarts = 1 gallon (gal)

Dry

2 pints (pt) = 1 quart (qt)
8 quarts = 1 peck (pk)
4 pecks = 1 bushel (bu)

TABLE 2 Conversion Tables

Length

	cm	m	km	in.	ft	mi
1 centimetre	1	10^{-2}	10^{-5}	0.394	3.28×10^{-2}	6.21×10^{-6}
1 metre	100	1	10^{-3}	39.4	3.28	6.21×10^{-4}
1 kilometre	10^5	1000	1	3.94×10^4	3280	0.621
1 inch	2.54	2.54×10^{-2}	2.54×10^{-5}	1	8.33×10^{-2}	1.58×10^{-5}
1 foot	30.5	0.305	3.05×10^{-4}	12	1	1.89×10^{-4}
1 mile	1.61×10^5	1610	1.61	6.34×10^4	5280	1

Area

Metric	U.S.
$1 \text{ m}^2 = 10{,}000 \text{ cm}^2$	$1 \text{ ft}^2 = 144 \text{ in}^2$
$= 1{,}000{,}000 \text{ mm}^2$	$1 \text{ yd}^2 = 9 \text{ ft}^2$
$1 \text{ cm}^2 = 100 \text{ mm}^2$	$1 \text{ rd}^2 = 30.25 \text{ yd}^2$
$= 0.0001 \text{ m}^2$	$1 \text{ acre} = 160 \text{ rd}^2$
$1 \text{ km}^2 = 1{,}000{,}000 \text{ m}^2$	$= 4840 \text{ yd}^2$
$1 \text{ ha} = 10{,}000 \text{ m}^2$	$= 43{,}560 \text{ ft}^2$
	$1 \text{ mi}^2 = 640 \text{ acres}$

	m^2	cm^2	ft^2	in^2
1 m^2	1	10^4	10.8	1550
1 cm^2	10^{-4}	1	1.08×10^{-3}	0.155
1 ft^2	9.29×10^{-2}	929	1	144
1 in^2	6.45×10^{-4}	6.45	6.94×10^{-3}	1

$1 \text{ mi}^2 = 2.79 \times 10^7 \text{ ft}^2 = 640 \text{ acres}$

$1 \text{ circular mil} = 5.07 \times 10^{-6} \text{ cm}^2 = 7.85 \times 10^{-7} \text{ in}^2$

$1 \text{ hectare} = 2.47 \text{ acres}$

Volume

	Metric	U.S.
	$1 \text{ m}^3 = 10^6 \text{ cm}^3$	$1 \text{ ft}^3 = 1728 \text{ in}^3$
	$1 \text{ cm}^3 = 10^{-6} \text{ m}^3$	$1 \text{ yd}^3 = 27 \text{ ft}^3$
	$= 10^3 \text{ mm}^3$	

	m^3	cm^3	L	ft^3	in^3
1 m³	1	10^6	1000	35.3	6.10×10^4
1 cm³	10^{-6}	1	1.00×10^{-3}	3.53×10^{-5}	6.10×10^{-2}
1 L	1.00×10^{-3}	1000	1	3.53×10^{-2}	61.0
1 ft³	2.83×10^{-2}	2.83×10^4	28.3	1	1728
1 in³	1.64×10^{-5}	16.4	1.64×10^{-2}	5.79×10^{-4}	1

1 U.S. fluid gallon = 4 U.S. fluid quarts = 8 U.S. pints = 128 U.S. fluid ounces = 231 in³ = 0.134 ft³ = 3.79 litres

1 L = 1000 cm³ = 1.06 qt

Other useful conversion factors

1 newton (N) = 0.225 lb
1 pound (lb) = 4.45 N
1 slug = 14.6 kg
1 joule (J) = 0.738 ft-lb
$\qquad = 2.39 \times 10^{-4}$ kcal
1 calorie (cal) = 4.185 J
1 kilocalorie (kcal) = 4185 J
1 foot-pound (ft-lb) = 1.36 J
1 watt (W) = 1 J/s = 0.738 ft-lb/s
1 kilowatt (kW) = 1000 W
$\qquad = 1.34$ hp
1 hp = 550 ft-lb/s = 746 W

1 atm = 101.32 kpa
$\qquad = 14.7$ lb/in²
1 Btu = 0.252 kcal
1 kcal = 3.97 Btu
$F = \frac{9}{5}C + 32°$
$C = \frac{5}{9}(F - 32°)$
1 kg = 2.20 lb (on the
$\qquad$ earth's surface)
1 lb = 454 g
$\qquad = 16$ oz
1 metric ton = 1000 kg
$\qquad = 2200$ lb

Table of Integrals

1. $\int u^n \, du = \dfrac{u^{n+1}}{n+1} + C \qquad (n \neq -1)$

2. $\int \dfrac{du}{a+bu} = \dfrac{1}{b} \ln |a+bu| + C$

3. $\int \dfrac{u}{a+bu} \, du = \dfrac{1}{b^2}[(a+bu) - a \ln|a+bu|] + C$

4. $\int \dfrac{u^2 \, du}{a+bu} = \dfrac{1}{b^3}\left[\dfrac{1}{2}(a+bu)^2 - 2a(a+bu) + a^2 \ln|a+bu|\right] + C$

5. $\int \dfrac{du}{u(a+bu)} = \dfrac{1}{a} \ln \left|\dfrac{u}{a+bu}\right| + C$

6. $\int \dfrac{du}{u^2(a+bu)} = -\dfrac{1}{au} + \dfrac{b}{a^2} \ln \left|\dfrac{a+bu}{u}\right| + C$

7. $\int \dfrac{u \, du}{(a+bu)^2} = \dfrac{1}{b^2}\left(\ln|a+bu| + \dfrac{a}{a+bu}\right) + C$

8. $\int \dfrac{u^2 \, du}{(a+bu)^2} = \dfrac{1}{b^3}\left(a+bu - \dfrac{a^2}{a+bu} - 2a \ln|a+bu|\right) + C$

9. $\int \dfrac{du}{u(a+bu)^2} = \dfrac{1}{a(a+bu)} + \dfrac{1}{a^2} \ln \left|\dfrac{u}{a+bu}\right| + C$

10. $\int \dfrac{du}{u^2(a+bu)^2} = -\dfrac{a+2bu}{a^2u(a+bu)} + \dfrac{2b}{a^3} \ln \left|\dfrac{a+bu}{u}\right| + C$

Forms containing $\sqrt{a+bu}$

---

11. $\int u\sqrt{a+bu} \, du = -\dfrac{2(2a - 3bu)(a+bu)^{3/2}}{15b^2} + C$

12. $\int u^2\sqrt{a+bu} \, du = \dfrac{2(8a^2 - 12abu + 15b^2u^2)(a+bu)^{3/2}}{105b^3} + C$

13. $\int \dfrac{u \, du}{\sqrt{a+bu}} = -\dfrac{2(2a - bu)\sqrt{a+bu}}{3b^2} + C$

14. $\int \dfrac{u^2 \, du}{\sqrt{a+bu}} = \dfrac{2(3b^2u^2 - 4abu + 8a^2)\sqrt{a+bu}}{15b^3} + C$

15. $\int \dfrac{du}{u\sqrt{a+bu}} = \dfrac{1}{\sqrt{a}} \ln \left|\dfrac{\sqrt{a+bu} - \sqrt{a}}{\sqrt{a+bu} + \sqrt{a}}\right| + C \qquad (a > 0)$

16. $\displaystyle \int \frac{du}{u\sqrt{a + bu}} = \frac{2}{\sqrt{-a}} \arctan \sqrt{\frac{a + bu}{-a}} + C \qquad (a < 0)$

17. $\displaystyle \int \frac{\sqrt{a + bu}\, du}{u} = 2\sqrt{a + bu} + a \int \frac{du}{u\sqrt{a + bu}} + C$

Rational forms containing $a^2 \pm u^2$ and $u^2 \pm a^2$

---

18. $\displaystyle \int \frac{du}{a^2 + u^2} = \frac{1}{a} \arctan \frac{u}{a} + C$

19. $\displaystyle \int \frac{du}{a^2 - u^2} = \frac{1}{2a} \ln \left| \frac{a + u}{a - u} \right| + C \qquad (a^2 > u^2)$

20. $\displaystyle \int \frac{du}{u^2 - a^2} = \frac{1}{2a} \ln \left| \frac{u - a}{u + a} \right| + C \qquad (a^2 < u^2)$

Irrational forms containing $\sqrt{a^2 - u^2}$

---

21. $\displaystyle \int (a^2 - u^2)^{1/2} \, du = \frac{u}{2} \sqrt{a^2 - u^2} + \frac{a^2}{2} \arcsin \frac{u}{a} + C$

22. $\displaystyle \int \frac{du}{(a^2 - u^2)^{1/2}} = \arcsin \frac{u}{a} + C \qquad (a > 0)$

23. $\displaystyle \int \frac{du}{(a^2 - u^2)^{3/2}} = \frac{u}{a^2 \sqrt{a^2 - u^2}} + C$

24. $\displaystyle \int \frac{u^2 \, du}{(a^2 - u^2)^{1/2}} = -\frac{u}{2} \sqrt{a^2 - u^2} + \frac{a^2}{2} \arcsin \frac{u}{a} + C$

25. $\displaystyle \int \frac{u^2 \, du}{(a^2 - u^2)^{3/2}} = \frac{u}{\sqrt{a^2 - u^2}} - \arcsin \frac{u}{a} + C$

26. $\displaystyle \int \frac{du}{u(a^2 - u^2)^{1/2}} = -\frac{1}{a} \ln \left| \frac{a + \sqrt{a^2 - u^2}}{u} \right| + C$

27. $\displaystyle \int \frac{du}{u^2(a^2 - u^2)^{1/2}} = -\frac{\sqrt{a^2 - u^2}}{a^2 u} + C$

28. $\displaystyle \int \frac{(a^2 - u^2)^{1/2} \, du}{u} = \sqrt{a^2 - u^2} - a \ln \left| \frac{a + \sqrt{a^2 - u^2}}{u} \right| + C$

29. $\displaystyle \int \frac{(a^2 - u^2)^{1/2} \, du}{u^2} = -\frac{\sqrt{a^2 - u^2}}{u} - \arcsin \frac{u}{a} + C$

Irrational forms containing $\sqrt{u^2 \pm a^2}$

---

30. $\displaystyle \int \sqrt{u^2 \pm a^2} \, du = \tfrac{1}{2}\left(u\sqrt{u^2 \pm a^2} \pm a^2 \ln|u + \sqrt{u^2 \pm a^2}|\right) + C$

31. $\displaystyle \int u^2 \sqrt{u^2 \pm a^2} \, du = \tfrac{1}{8} u(2u^2 \pm a^2)\sqrt{u^2 \pm a^2} - \tfrac{1}{8} a^4 \ln|u + \sqrt{u^2 \pm a^2}| + C$

32. $\displaystyle \int \frac{\sqrt{u^2 + a^2}}{u} \, du = \sqrt{u^2 + a^2} - a \ln \left| \frac{a + \sqrt{u^2 + a^2}}{u} \right| + C$

33. $\displaystyle \int \frac{\sqrt{u^2 - a^2}}{u} \, du = \sqrt{u^2 - a^2} - a \arccos \frac{a}{u} + C$

34. $\displaystyle \int \frac{\sqrt{u^2 \pm a^2}}{u^2} \, du = -\frac{\sqrt{u^2 \pm a^2}}{u} + \ln|u + \sqrt{u^2 \pm a^2}| + C$

35. $\displaystyle\int \frac{du}{\sqrt{u^2 \pm a^2}} = \ln|u + \sqrt{u^2 \pm a^2}| + C$

36. $\displaystyle\int \frac{du}{u\sqrt{u^2 - a^2}} = \frac{1}{a}\arccos\frac{a}{u} + C$

37. $\displaystyle\int \frac{du}{u\sqrt{u^2 + a^2}} = \frac{1}{a}\ln\left|\frac{u}{a + \sqrt{u^2 + a^2}}\right| + C$

38. $\displaystyle\int \frac{u^2\,du}{\sqrt{u^2 \pm a^2}} = \frac{1}{2}\left(u\sqrt{u^2 \pm a^2} \pm a^2\ln|u + \sqrt{u^2 \pm a^2}|\right) + C$

39. $\displaystyle\int \frac{du}{u^2\sqrt{u^2 \pm a^2}} = -\frac{\pm\sqrt{u^2 \pm a^2}}{a^2 u} + C$

40. $\displaystyle\int \frac{du}{(u^2 \pm a^2)^{3/2}} = \frac{\pm u}{a^2\sqrt{u^2 \pm a^2}} + C$

41. $\displaystyle\int \frac{u^2\,du}{(u^2 \pm a^2)^{3/2}} = \frac{-u}{\sqrt{u^2 \pm a^2}} + \ln|u + \sqrt{u^2 \pm a^2}| + C$

Forms containing $a + bu \pm cu^2$ $\quad(c > 0)$

42. $\displaystyle\int \frac{du}{a + bu + cu^2} = \frac{2}{\sqrt{4ac - b^2}}\arctan\frac{2cu + b}{\sqrt{4ac - b^2}} + C \quad (b^2 < 4ac)$

43. $\displaystyle\int \frac{du}{a + bu + cu^2} = \frac{1}{\sqrt{b^2 - 4ac}}\ln\left|\frac{2cu + b - \sqrt{b^2 - 4ac}}{2cu + b + \sqrt{b^2 - 4ac}}\right| + C \quad (b^2 > 4ac)$

44. $\displaystyle\int \frac{du}{a + bu - cu^2} = \frac{1}{\sqrt{b^2 + 4ac}}\ln\left|\frac{\sqrt{b^2 + 4ac} + 2cu - b}{\sqrt{b^2 + 4ac} - 2cu + b}\right| + C$

45. $\displaystyle\int \sqrt{a + bu + cu^2}\,du = \frac{2cu + b}{4c}\sqrt{a + bu + cu^2} - \frac{b^2 - 4ac}{8c^{3/2}}\ln|2cu + b + 2\sqrt{c}\sqrt{a + bu + cu^2}| + C$

46. $\displaystyle\int \sqrt{a + bu - cu^2}\,du = \frac{2cu - b}{4c}\sqrt{a + bu - cu^2} + \frac{b^2 + 4ac}{8c^{3/2}}\arcsin\left(\frac{2cu - b}{\sqrt{b^2 + 4ac}}\right) + C$

47. $\displaystyle\int \frac{du}{\sqrt{a + bu + cu^2}} = \frac{1}{\sqrt{c}}\ln|2cu + b + 2\sqrt{c}\sqrt{a + bu + cu^2}| + C$

48. $\displaystyle\int \frac{du}{\sqrt{a + bu - cu^2}} = \frac{1}{\sqrt{c}}\arcsin\left(\frac{2cu - b}{\sqrt{b^2 + 4ac}}\right) + C$

49. $\displaystyle\int \frac{u\,du}{\sqrt{a + bu + cu^2}} = \frac{\sqrt{a + bu + cu^2}}{c} - \frac{b}{2c^{3/2}}\ln|2cu + b + 2\sqrt{c}\sqrt{a + bu + cu^2}| + C$

50. $\displaystyle\int \frac{u\,du}{\sqrt{a + bu - cu^2}} = -\frac{\sqrt{a + bu - cu^2}}{c} + \frac{b}{2c^{3/2}}\arcsin\left(\frac{2cu - b}{\sqrt{b^2 + 4ac}}\right) + C$

Exponential and logarithmic forms

51. $\displaystyle\int e^u\,du = e^u + C$

52. $\displaystyle\int a^u\,du = \frac{a^u}{\ln a} + C \quad (a > 0, a \neq 1)$

53. $\displaystyle\int ue^{au}\,du = \frac{e^{au}}{a^2}(au - 1) + C$

54. $\displaystyle\int u^n e^{au}\,du = \frac{u^n e^{au}}{a} - \frac{n}{a}\int u^{n-1}e^{au}\,du$

55. $\displaystyle\int \frac{e^{au}}{u^n}\,du = -\frac{e^{au}}{(n-1)u^{n-1}} + \frac{a}{n-1}\int \frac{e^{au}}{u^{n-1}}\,du$

56. $\displaystyle\int \ln u\,du = u\ln u - u + C$

57. $\displaystyle\int u^n \ln u\,du = \frac{u^{n+1}\ln u}{n+1} - \frac{u^{n+1}}{(n+1)^2} + C$

58. $\displaystyle\int \frac{du}{u\ln u} = \ln|\ln u| + C$

59. $\displaystyle\int e^{au}\sin nu\,du = \frac{e^{au}(a\sin nu - n\cos nu)}{a^2 + n^2} + C$

60. $\displaystyle\int e^{au}\cos nu\,du = \frac{e^{au}(n\sin nu + a\cos nu)}{a^2 + n^2} + C$

Trigonometric forms

---

61. $\displaystyle\int \sin u\,du = -\cos u + C$

62. $\displaystyle\int \cos u\,du = \sin u + C$

63. $\displaystyle\int \tan u\,du = -\ln|\cos u| + C = \ln|\sec u| + C$

64. $\displaystyle\int \cot u\,du = \ln|\sin u| + C$

65. $\displaystyle\int \sec u\,du = \ln|\sec u + \tan u| + C$

66. $\displaystyle\int \csc u\,du = \ln|\csc u - \cot u| + C$

67. $\displaystyle\int \sec^2 u\,du = \tan u + C$

68. $\displaystyle\int \csc^2 u\,du = -\cot u + C$

69. $\displaystyle\int \sec u\tan u\,du = \sec u + C$

70. $\displaystyle\int \csc u\cot u\,du = -\csc u + C$

71. $\displaystyle\int \sin^2 u\,du = \tfrac{1}{2}u - \tfrac{1}{4}\sin 2u + C$

72. $\displaystyle\int \cos^2 u\,du = \tfrac{1}{2}u + \tfrac{1}{4}\sin 2u + C$

73. $\displaystyle\int \cos^n u\sin u\,du = -\frac{\cos^{n+1} u}{n+1} + C$

74. $\displaystyle\int \sin^n u\cos u\,du = \frac{\sin^{n+1} u}{n+1} + C$

75. $\displaystyle\int \sin mu\sin nu\,du = -\frac{\sin(m+n)u}{2(m+n)} + \frac{\sin(m-n)u}{2(m-n)} + C$

76. $\displaystyle\int \cos mu\cos nu\,du = \frac{\sin(m+n)u}{2(m+n)} + \frac{\sin(m-n)u}{2(m-n)} + C$

77. $\displaystyle\int \sin mu \, \cos nu \, du = -\frac{\cos(m+n)u}{2(m+n)} - \frac{\cos(m-n)u}{2(m-n)} + C$

78. $\displaystyle\int e^{au} \sin nu \, du = \frac{e^{au}(a \sin nu - n \cos nu)}{a^2 + n^2} + C$

79. $\displaystyle\int e^{au} \cos nu \, du = \frac{e^{au}(n \sin nu + a \cos nu)}{a^2 + n^2} + C$

80. $\displaystyle\int u \sin u \, du = \sin u - u \cos u + C$

81. $\displaystyle\int u \cos u \, du = \cos u + u \sin u + C$

82. $\displaystyle\int \sin^m u \cos^n u \, du = \frac{\sin^{m+1} u \cos^{n-1} u}{m+n} + \frac{n-1}{m+n} \int \sin^m u \cos^{n-2} u \, du$

83. $\displaystyle\int \sin^n u \, du = -\frac{1}{n} \sin^{n-1} u \cos u + \frac{n-1}{n} \int \sin^{n-2} u \, du$

84. $\displaystyle\int \cos^n u \, du = \frac{1}{n} \cos^{n-1} u \sin u + \frac{n-1}{n} \int \cos^{n-2} u \, du$

85. $\displaystyle\int \tan^n u \, du = \frac{\tan^{n-1} u}{n-1} - \int \tan^{n-2} u \, du$

86. $\displaystyle\int \cot^n u \, du = -\frac{\cot^{n-1} u}{n-1} - \int \cot^{n-2} u \, du$

87. $\displaystyle\int \sec^n u \, du = \frac{\sec^{n-2} u \tan u}{n-1} + \frac{n-2}{n+1} \int \sec^{n-2} u \, du$

88. $\displaystyle\int \csc^n u \, du = -\frac{\csc^{n-2} u \cot u}{n-1} + \frac{n-2}{n-1} \int \csc^{n-2} u \, du$

Answers to Odd-Numbered Exercises and Chapter Reviews

CHAPTER 1

Exercises 1.1, Page 7

	Function	Domain	Range
1.	Yes	$\{2, 3, 9\}$	$\{2, 4, 7\}$
3.	No	$\{1, 2, 7\}$	$\{1, 3, 5\}$
5.	Yes	$\{-2, 2, 3, 5\}$	$\{2\}$
7.	Yes	Real numbers	Real numbers
9.	Yes	Real numbers	Real numbers where $y \geq 1$
11.	No	Real numbers where $x \geq -2$	Real numbers
13.	Yes	Real numbers where $x \geq -3$	Real numbers where $y \geq 0$
15.	Yes	Real numbers where $x \geq 4$	Real numbers where $y \geq 6$

17. (a) 20 **(b)** -12 **(c)** -28 **19. (a)** 35 **(b)** 15 **(c)** -25 **21. (a)** 95 **(b)** 0 **(c)** 4

23. (a) 2 **(b)** $\frac{2}{3}$ **(c)** 0 is not in the domain of $f(t)$.   **25. (a)** $6a + 8$ **(b)** $24a + 8$ **(c)** $6c^2 + 8$

27. (a) $4x^2 + 4x - 8$ **(b)** $4x^2 - 36x + 72$ **(c)** $16x^2 - 8x - 8$

29. (a) $x^2 - 3x$ **(b)** $-x^2 + 9x - 2$ **(c)** $3x^3 - 19x^2 + 9x - 1$ **(d)** $3x + 3h - 1$ **31.** All real numbers $x \neq 2$

33. All real numbers $t \neq 6$ or $t \neq -3$ **35.** All real numbers $x < 5$

Exercises 1.2, Pages 14–16

1.

$y = 2x + 1$

3. $y = 2x + 1$

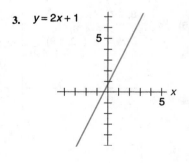

5.

$y = x^2 - 9$

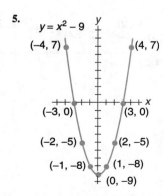

7.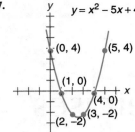
$y = x^2 - 5x + 4$

9.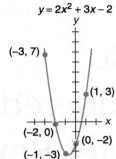
$y = 2x^2 + 3x - 2$

11.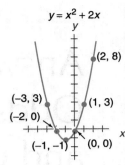
$y = x^2 + 2x$

13.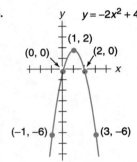
$y = -2x^2 + 4x$

15.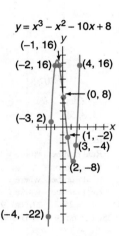
$y = x^3 - x^2 - 10x + 8$

17.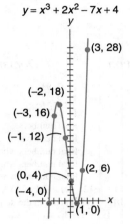
$y = x^3 + 2x^2 - 7x + 4$

19.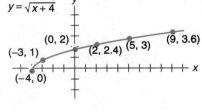
$y = \sqrt{x + 4}$

21.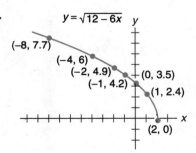
$y = \sqrt{12 - 6x}$

23. 3 and −3; 2 and −2; 3.3 and −3.3   **25.** 1 and 4; 4.5 and 0.5; no solution

27. −2 and $\frac{1}{2}$; 1 and −2.5; 1.3 and −2.8   **29.** 0 and −2; 1 and −3; 1.7 and −3.7

31. 0 and 2; no solution; 2.7 and −0.7; 2.3 and −0.3   **33.** 3.3, −3.1, 0.8; 3.4, −3.0, 0.6; 3.2, −3.2, 1.0

35. −4, 1; −3.8, 0, 1.8; −3.6, −0.5, 2.1

37. −4 and 1; −5 and 2; 0.5 and −3.5   **39.** 2 and −2; no solution; 3.5 and −3.5   **41.** 2.9, −0.5, 0.7; 2.5, −0.9, 1.3; 2.8, −0.6, 0.8

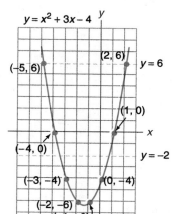
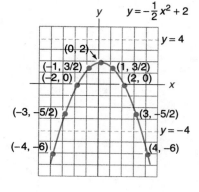
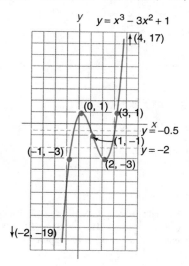

43. 2.6 ms, 4 ms, 5.5 ms   **45.** 0.27 ms, 0.48 ms, 0.94 ms
47. 2.7 s, 3.1 s   **49.** $A(1.18, -1.62)$, $B(2.35, -3.24)$, $C(3.53, -4.85)$

Exercises 1.3, Pages 22–23

1. 1   **3.** −4   **5.** 0   **7.** $\frac{5}{8}$
9.   **11.**   **13.**   **15.**

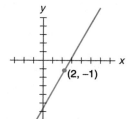
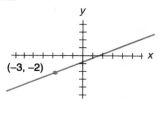
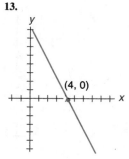
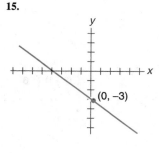

17. $3x + y - 2 = 0$ **19.** $x - 2y - 5 = 0$ **21.** $x + y - 5 = 0$ **23.** $x + 2y + 10 = 0$
25. $y = -5x - 2$ **27.** $y = 2x + 7$ **29.** $y = 5$ **31.** $x = -2$ **33.** $y = -3$ **35.** $x = -7$
37. $m = -\frac{1}{4}$, $b = 3$ **39.** $m = 2$, $b = 7$ **41.** $m = 0$, $b = 6$
43.   **45.**   **47.**   **49.**

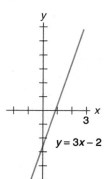
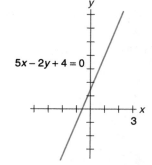
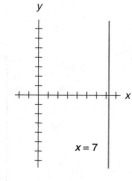
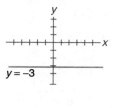

51.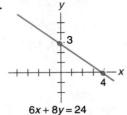

$6x + 8y = 24$

53.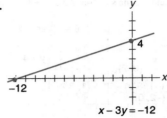

$x - 3y = -12$

55. $\frac{1}{350}$

Exercises 1.4, Page 27

1. Perpendicular   **3.** Neither   **5.** Parallel   **7.** $2x - y + 7 = 0$ **9.** $5x + y + 31 = 0$ **11.** $3x - 4y = 0$
13. $3x - 2y = 18$ **15.** $y = 8$ **17.** $x = 7$ **19.** **(a)** Yes, slopes of opposite sides are equal.   **(b)** No, slopes of adjacent sides are not negative reciprocals.

Exercises 1.5, Pages 29–30

1. 15   **3.** 7   **5.** $4\sqrt{2}$ **7.** 7   **9.** $(3\frac{1}{2}, 5)$ **11.** $(1\frac{1}{2}, -1)$ **13.** $(0, -2\frac{1}{2})$
15. **(a)** 24   **(b)** Yes   **(c)** No   **(d)** 24   **17.** **(a)** $10 + \sqrt{82} + \sqrt{58}$ or 26.7   **(b)** No   **(c)** No   **19.** $4\sqrt{2}$
21. $x - 2y = 10$ **23.** $x + 2y = 21$

Exercises 1.6, Pages 34–35

1.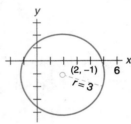

3.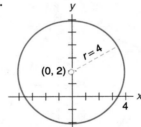

5. $(x - 1)^2 + (y + 1)^2 = 16$ **7.** $(x + 2)^2 + (y + 4)^2 = 34$ **9.** $x^2 + y^2 = 36$ **11.** $(0, 0); r = 4$
13. $(-3, 4); r = 8$ **15.** $(4, -6); r = 2\sqrt{15}$ **17.** $(6, 1); r = 7$ **19.** $(-\frac{7}{2}, -\frac{3}{2}); r = \sqrt{94}/2$
21. $x^2 + y^2 - 2y - 9 = 0; (0, 1); r = \sqrt{10}$ **23.** $x^2 + y^2 + 10x - 40y = 0; (-5, 20); r = 5\sqrt{17}$

Exercises 1.7, Pages 42–43

1.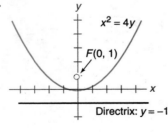

3.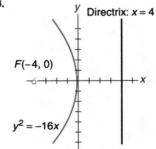

5.

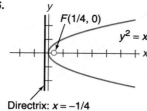

F(1/4, 0)

$y^2 = x$

Directrix: $x = -1/4$

7.

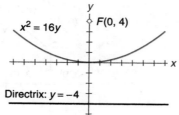

$x^2 = 16y$

F(0, 4)

Directrix: $y = -4$

9.

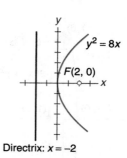

$y^2 = 8x$

F(2, 0)

Directrix: $x = -2$

11. $y^2 = 8x$ **13.** $y^2 = -32x$ **15.** $x^2 = 24y$ **17.** $y^2 = -16x$ **19.** $y^2 - 6y + 8x + 1 = 0$ **21.** 15 m, 7 m

23. $x^2 = 32y$ **25.**

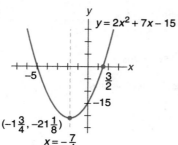

$y = 2x^2 + 7x - 15$

-5

$\frac{3}{2}$

-15

$(-1\frac{3}{4}, -21\frac{1}{8})$

$x = -\frac{7}{4}$

27.

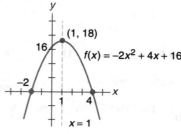

(1, 18)

16

$f(x) = -2x^2 + 4x + 16$

-2

1   4

$x = 1$

29. **(a)** 1024 m;   **(b)** 1024 m   **31.** 3600 m^2

Exercises 1.8, Page 47

Vertices	Foci	Major axis	Minor axis
1. $(5, 0)(-5, 0)$	$(3, 0)(-3, 0)$	10	8
3. $(4, 0)(-4, 0)$	$(\sqrt{7}, 0)(-\sqrt{7}, 0)$	8	6
5. $(0, 6)(0, -6)$	$(0, \sqrt{35})(0, -\sqrt{35})$	12	2
7. $(0, 4)(0, -4)$	$(0, \sqrt{7})(0, -\sqrt{7})$	8	6

1.

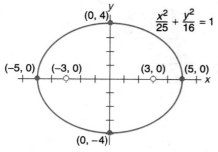

(0, 4)

$\frac{x^2}{25} + \frac{y^2}{16} = 1$

(-5, 0)   (-3, 0)   (3, 0)   (5, 0)

(0, -4)

3.

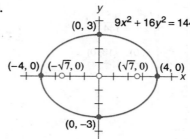

(0, 3) $9x^2 + 16y^2 = 144$

(-4, 0)   (-$\sqrt{7}$, 0)   ($\sqrt{7}$, 0)   (4, 0)

(0, -3)

5.

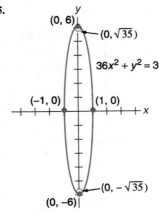

7.

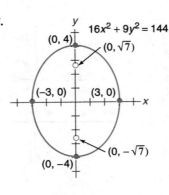

9. $\dfrac{x^2}{16} + \dfrac{y^2}{12} = 1$ or $3x^2 + 4y^2 = 48$ **11.** $\dfrac{x^2}{45} + \dfrac{y^2}{81} = 1$ or $9x^2 + 5y^2 = 405$

13. $\dfrac{x^2}{36} + \dfrac{y^2}{25} = 1$ or $25x^2 + 36y^2 = 900$ **15.** $\dfrac{x^2}{39} + \dfrac{y^2}{64} = 1$ or $64x^2 + 39y^2 = 2496$

17. $\dfrac{x^2}{5600^2} + \dfrac{y^2}{5000^2} = 1$ or $625x^2 + 784y^2 = 1.96 \times 10^{10}$

Exercises 1.9, Pages 52–53

Vertices	Foci	Transverse axis	Conjugate axis	Asymptotes
1. $(5, 0)\,(-5, 0)$	$(13, 0)\,(-13, 0)$	10	24	$y = \pm\dfrac{12}{5}x$
3. $(0, 3)\,(0, -3)$	$(0, 5)\,(0, -5)$	6	8	$y = \pm\dfrac{3}{4}x$
5. $(\sqrt{2}, 0)\,(-\sqrt{2}, 0)$	$(\sqrt{7}, 0)\,(-\sqrt{7}, 0)$	$2\sqrt{2}$	$2\sqrt{5}$	$y = \pm\sqrt{\dfrac{5}{2}}x$
7. $(0, 1)\,(0, -1)$	$(0, \sqrt{5})\,(0, -\sqrt{5})$	2	4	$y = \pm\dfrac{1}{2}x$

1.

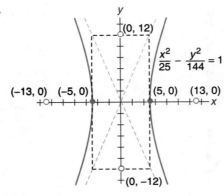

3.

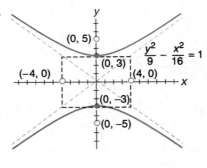

5.

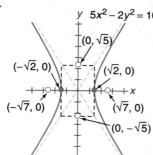

$y \quad 5x^2 - 2y^2 = 10$
$(0, \sqrt{5})$
$(-\sqrt{2}, 0)$ $(\sqrt{2}, 0)$
$(-\sqrt{7}, 0)$ $(\sqrt{7}, 0)$
$(0, -\sqrt{5})$

7.

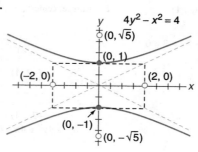

$y \quad 4y^2 - x^2 = 4$
$(0, \sqrt{5})$
$(0, 1)$
$(-2, 0)$ $(2, 0)$
$(0, -1)$
$(0, -\sqrt{5})$

9. $\dfrac{x^2}{16} - \dfrac{y^2}{20} = 1$ or $5x^2 - 4y^2 = 80$ **11.** $\dfrac{y^2}{36} - \dfrac{x^2}{28} = 1$ or $7y^2 - 9x^2 = 252$

13. $\dfrac{x^2}{9} - \dfrac{y^2}{25} = 1$ or $25x^2 - 9y^2 = 225$ **15.** $\dfrac{x^2}{25} - \dfrac{y^2}{11} = 1$ or $11x^2 - 25y^2 = 275$

17.

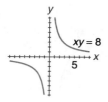

y
$xy = 8$
x
5

Exercises 1.10, Pages 57–58

1. $\dfrac{(x-1)^2}{16} + \dfrac{(y+1)^2}{12} = 1$ **3.** $\dfrac{(y-1)^2}{36} - \dfrac{(x-1)^2}{28} = 1$ **5.** $(y+1)^2 = 8(x-3)$

7. Parabola; vertex: $(2, -3)$ **9.** Hyperbola; center: $(-2, 0)$ **11.** Ellipse; center: $(2, 0)$

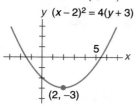

$y \quad (x-2)^2 = 4(y+3)$
5
x
$(2, -3)$

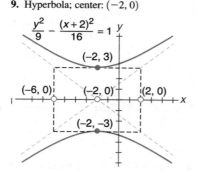

$\dfrac{y^2}{9} - \dfrac{(x+2)^2}{16} = 1$ y
$(-2, 3)$
$(-6, 0)$ $(-2, 0)$ $(2, 0)$
$(-2, -3)$

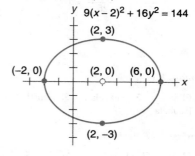

$y \quad 9(x-2)^2 + 16y^2 = 144$
$(2, 3)$
$(-2, 0)$ $(2, 0)$ $(6, 0)$
x
$(2, -3)$

13. Ellipse; center: $(3, 1)$ **15.** Parabola; vertex: $(1, -3)$ **17.** Hyperbola; center: $(-1, -1)$

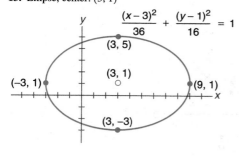

$y \quad \dfrac{(x-3)^2}{36} + \dfrac{(y-1)^2}{16} = 1$
$(3, 5)$
$(3, 1)$
$(-3, 1)$ $(9, 1)$
x
$(3, -3)$

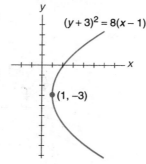

y
$(y+3)^2 = 8(x-1)$
x
$(1, -3)$

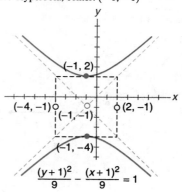

y
$(-1, 2)$
$(-4, -1)$ $(2, -1)$
$(-1, -1)$
x
$(-1, -4)$
$\dfrac{(y+1)^2}{9} - \dfrac{(x+1)^2}{9} = 1$

19. Parabola; vertex: $(2, -1)$

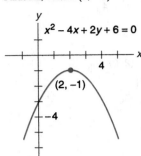

$x^2 - 4x + 2y + 6 = 0$

$(2, -1)$

21. Ellipse; center: $(-2, 1)$

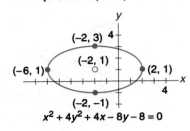

$(-2, 3)$
$(-2, 1)$
$(-6, 1)$ $(2, 1)$
$(-2, -1)$
$x^2 + 4y^2 + 4x - 8y - 8 = 0$

23. Hyperbola; center: $(1, 1)$

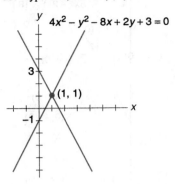

$4x^2 - y^2 - 8x + 2y + 3 = 0$

$(1, 1)$

25. Hyperbola; center: $(-3, 3)$

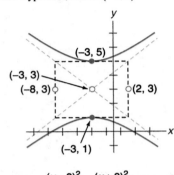

$(-3, 5)$
$(-3, 3)$
$(-8, 3)$ $(2, 3)$
$(-3, 1)$

$$\frac{(y-3)^2}{4} - \frac{(x+3)^2}{25} = 1$$

27. Parabola; vertex: $(-8, -2)$

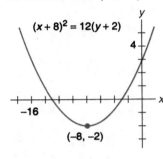

$(x + 8)^2 = 12(y + 2)$

$(-8, -2)$

29. Ellipse; center: $(-6, -2)$

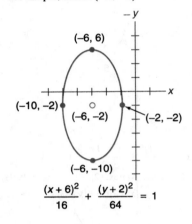

$(-6, 6)$
$(-10, -2)$
$(-6, -2)$ $(-2, -2)$
$(-6, -10)$

$$\frac{(x+6)^2}{16} + \frac{(y+2)^2}{64} = 1$$

Exercises 1.11, Page 59

1. Ellipse   **3.** Parabola   **5.** Hyperbola   **7.** Circle   **9.** Circle   **11.** Ellipse   **13.** Hyperbola
15. Parabola

Exercises 1.12, Page 63

1. $(3, 3)$ **3.** $(1, \sqrt{3}), (1, -\sqrt{3})$ **5.** $(2\sqrt{6}, 6), (-2\sqrt{6}, 6)$ **7.** $(-2, 0), (2, 0)$ **9.** $(-6, 6), (6, 6)$
11. $(-2, 2), (-2, -2)$ **13.** $(2.3, 5.5), (-2.3, 5.5)$ **15.** $(5, 4), (5, -4), (-5, 4), (-5, -4)$
17. $(1, 4), (-1, -4), (4, 1), (-4, -1)$

Exercises 1.13, Pages 69–70

1.

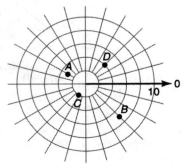

3.

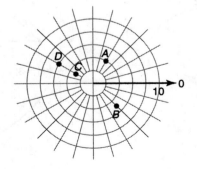

5. $(-3, 240°), (-3, -120°), (3, -300°)$ **7.** $(5, 135°), (-5, -45°), (5, -225°)$
9. $(-4, -315°), (-4, 45°), (4, 225°)$ **11.** $(-3, 7\pi/6), (-3, -5\pi/6), (3, -11\pi/6)$
13. $(9, 5\pi/3), (9, -\pi/3), (-9, -4\pi/3)$ **15.** $(4, -3\pi/4), (-4, \pi/4), (4, 5\pi/4)$
17.

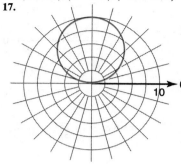

$r = 10 \sin \theta$

19.

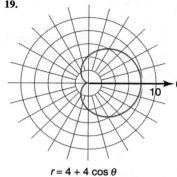

$r = 4 + 4 \cos \theta$

21.

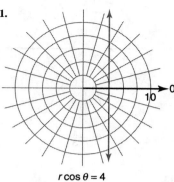

$r \cos \theta = 4$

23.

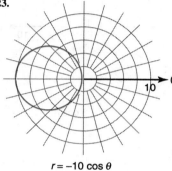

$r = -10 \cos \theta$

25.

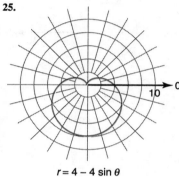

$r = 4 - 4 \sin \theta$

27.

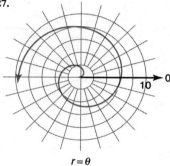

$r = \theta$

29. $(3\sqrt{3}/2, 3/2)$ **31.** $(1, \sqrt{3})$ **33.** $(2\sqrt{3}, -2)$ **35.** $(0, 6)$ **37.** $(2.5, -4.33)$ **39.** $(1.4, 1.4)$
41. $(7.1, 45°)$ **43.** $(4, 90°)$ **45.** $(4, 240°)$ **47.** $(4\sqrt{2}, 3\pi/4)$ **49.** $(2\sqrt{2}, 5\pi/6)$ **51.** $(4, 3\pi/2)$
53. $r \cos \theta = 3$ **55.** $r = 6$ **57.** $r + 2 \cos \theta + 5 \sin \theta = 0$ **59.** $r = 12/(4 \cos \theta - 3 \sin \theta)$
61. $r^2 = 36/(9 - 5 \sin^2 \theta)$ **63.** $r = 4 \sec \theta \tan^2 \theta$ **65.** $y = -3$ **67.** $x^2 + y^2 = 25$ **69.** $y = x$
71. $x^2 + y^2 - 5x = 0$ **73.** $x^2 + y^2 - 3x + 3\sqrt{3}y = 0$ **75.** $y^2 = 3x$ **77.** $xy = 1$
79. $x^4 + 2x^2y^2 + y^4 - 2xy = 0$ **81.** $y^2 = x^2(x^2 + y^2)$ **83.** $x^2 + 6y - 9 = 0$
85. $x^4 + 2x^2y^2 + y^4 + 4y^3 - 12x^2y = 0$ **87.** $x^4 + 2x^2y^2 + y^4 - 8x^2y - 8y^3 - 4x^2 + 12y^2 = 0$ **89.** $\sqrt{13}$
91. $d = \sqrt{r_1^2 + r_2^2 - 2r_1r_2 \cos(\theta_1 - \theta_2)}$

Exercises 1.14, Pages 76–77

1.

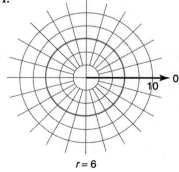

$r = 6$

3.

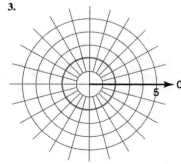

$r = -2$

5.

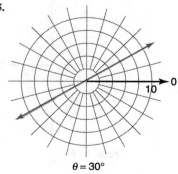

$\theta = 30°$

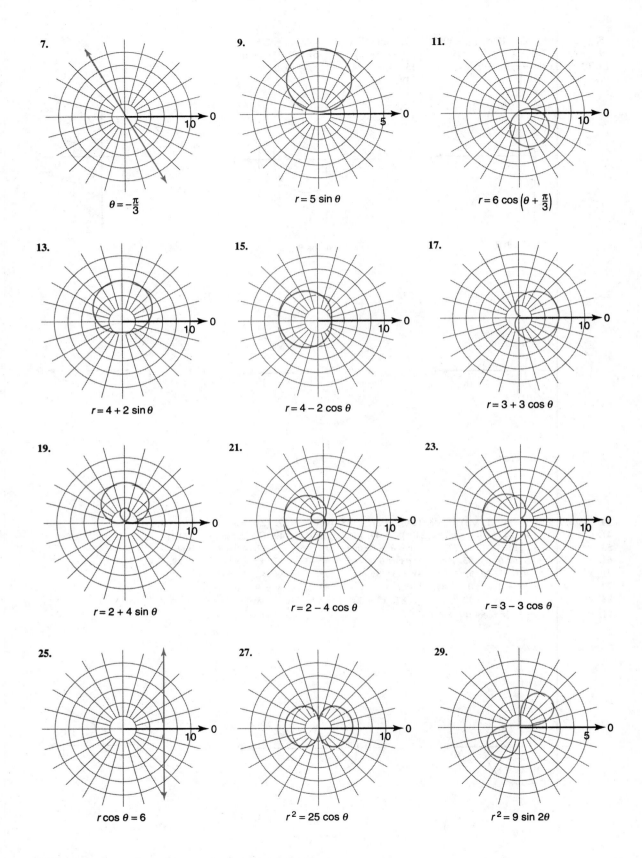

7.

$\theta = -\dfrac{\pi}{3}$

9.

$r = 5 \sin \theta$

11.

$r = 6 \cos \left(\theta + \dfrac{\pi}{3} \right)$

13.

$r = 4 + 2 \sin \theta$

15.

$r = 4 - 2 \cos \theta$

17.

$r = 3 + 3 \cos \theta$

19.

$r = 2 + 4 \sin \theta$

21.

$r = 2 - 4 \cos \theta$

23.

$r = 3 - 3 \cos \theta$

25.

$r \cos \theta = 6$

27.

$r^2 = 25 \cos \theta$

29.

$r^2 = 9 \sin 2\theta$

31.

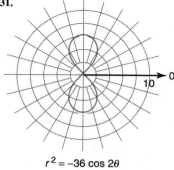

$r^2 = -36 \cos 2\theta$

33.

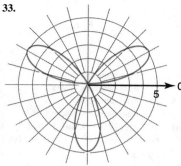

$r = 5 \sin 3\theta$

35.

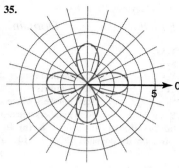

$r = 3 \cos 2\theta$

37.

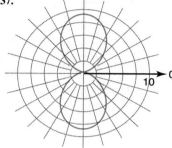

$r = 9 \sin^2 \theta$

39.

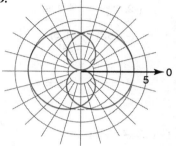

$r = 4 \cos \dfrac{\theta}{2}$

41.

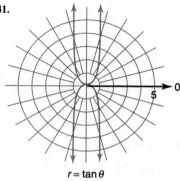

$r = \tan \theta$

43.

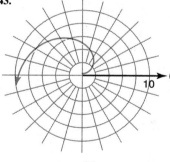

$r = 3\theta$

45.

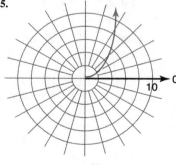

$r = 2^{3\theta}$

47.

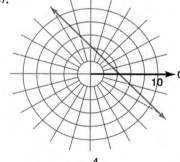

$r = \dfrac{4}{\sin \theta + \cos \theta}$

49.

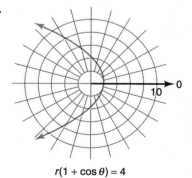

$r(1 + \cos \theta) = 4$

Function	Domain	Range
1. Yes	$\{2, 3, 4, 5\}$	$\{3, 4, 5, 6\}$
2. No	$\{2, 4, 6\}$	$\{1, 3, 4, 6\}$
3. Yes	Real numbers	Real numbers
4. Yes	Real numbers	Real numbers where $y \geq -5$
5. No	Real numbers where $x \geq 4$	Real numbers
6. Yes	Real numbers where $x \leq \frac{1}{2}$	Real numbers where $y \geq 0$

7. (a) 24 **(b)** 14 **(c)** -6 **8. (a)** 10 **(b)** -12 **(c)** 38 **9. (a)** 5 **(b)** $\frac{85}{4}$ **(c)** -15 is not in the domain of $h(x)$.
(d) 1 is not in the domain of $h(x)$. **10. (a)** $a^2 - 6a + 4$ **(b)** $4x^2 - 12x + 4$ **(c)** $z^2 - 10z + 20$

11.

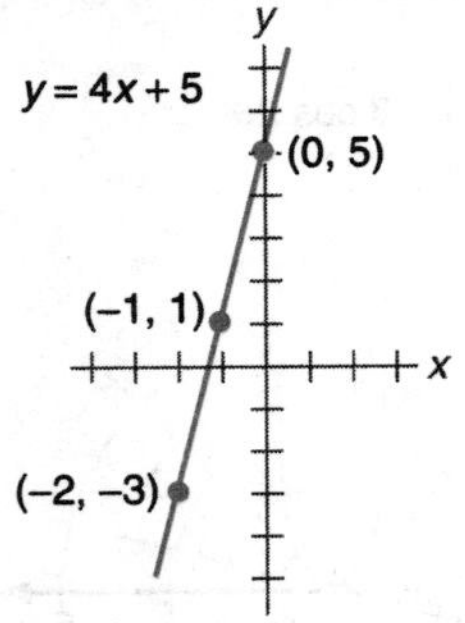

12.

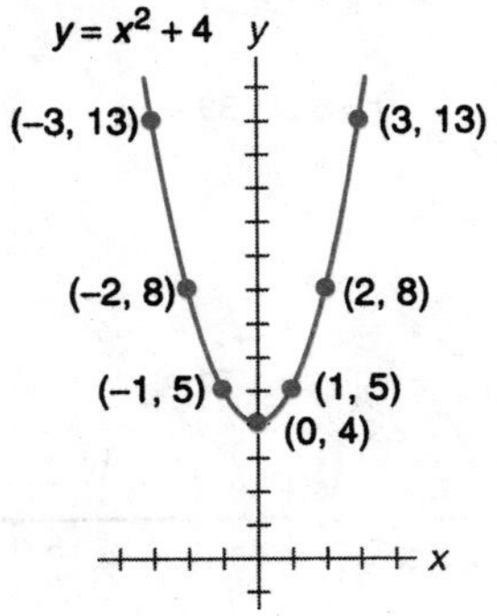

13.

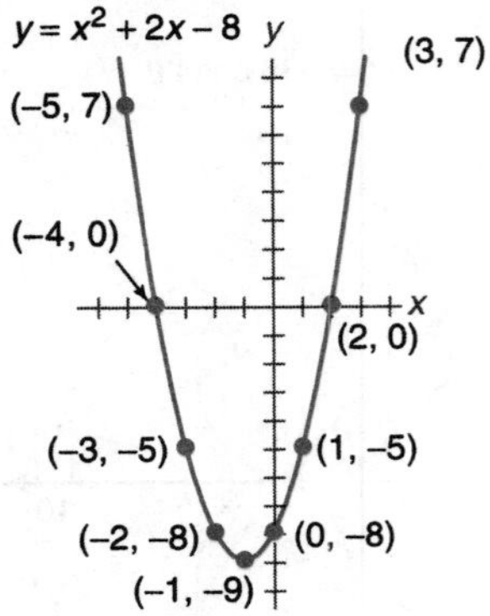

14. $y = 2x^2 + x - 6$

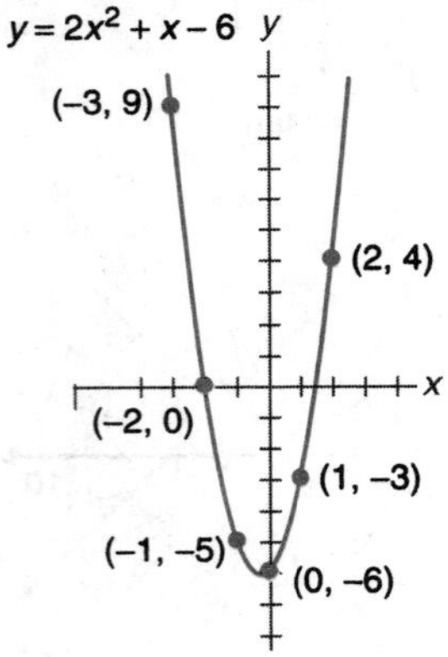

15. $y = -x^2 - x + 4$

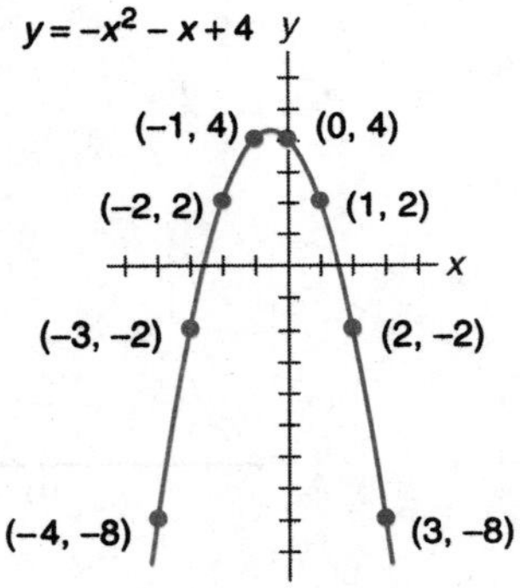

16.

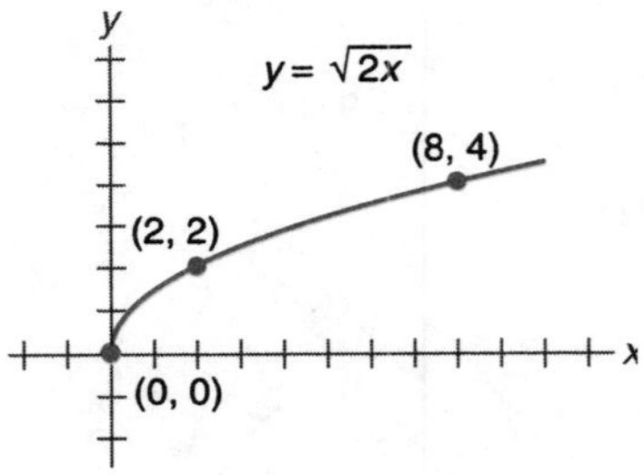

17. $y = \sqrt{-2 - 4x}$

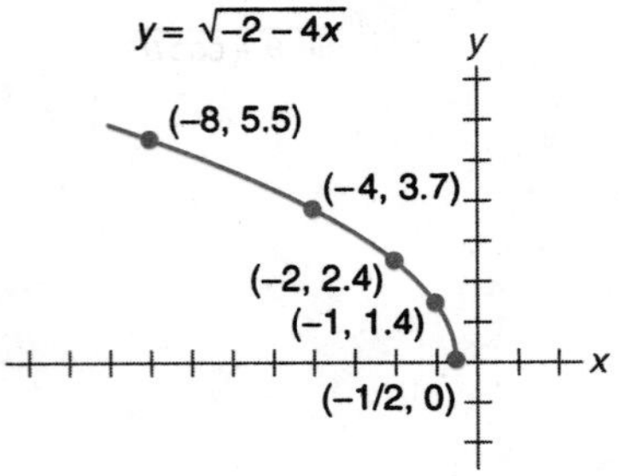

18. $y = x^3 - 6x$

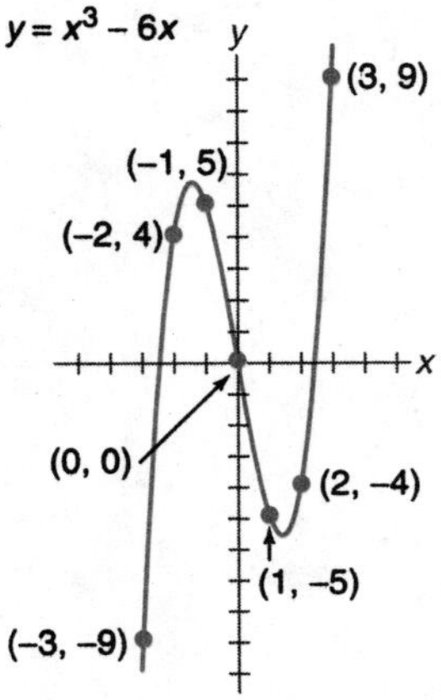

19. 1 and -1; 1.7 and -1.7; no solution   **20.** -4 and 2; 1.6 and -3.6; -4.5 and 2.5
21. -2 and 1; -2.6, and 1.6; -3 and 2   **22.** 0, 2.4, -2.4; 2.6, -2.3, -0.3; 2.1, -2.7, 0.5   **23.** 1, 1.7, 2
24. 2.1, 2.4   **25.** $-\frac{2}{9}$ **26.** $\sqrt{85}$ **27.** $(-\frac{3}{2}, -3)$ **28.** $11x + 2y - 58 = 0$ **29.** $2x - 3y + 9 = 0$
30. $x + 3y + 9 = 0$ **31.** $x = -3$ **32.** $m = \frac{3}{2}; b = -3$ **33.**

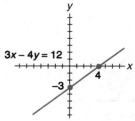

34. Perpendicular   **35.** Parallel   **36.** Neither   **37.** Perpendicular   **38.** Parallel   **39.** $2x - y - 8 = 0$
40. $5x - 3y + 20 = 0$ **41.** $(x - 5)^2 + (y + 7)^2 = 36$ or $x^2 + y^2 - 10x + 14y + 38 = 0$ **42.** $(4, -3); 7$
43. $(0, \frac{3}{2}); y = -\frac{3}{2}$

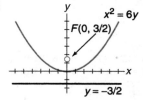

44. $y^2 = -16x$ **45.** $(y - 3)^2 = 8(x - 2)$ or $y^2 - 6y - 8x + 25 = 0$

46. $V(7, 0), (-7, 0); F(3\sqrt{5}, 0), (-3\sqrt{5}, 0)$ **47.** $\dfrac{x^2}{4} + \dfrac{y^2}{16} = 1$ or $4x^2 + y^2 = 16$

48. $V(6, 0), (-6, 0); F(2\sqrt{13}, 0), (-2\sqrt{13}, 0)$

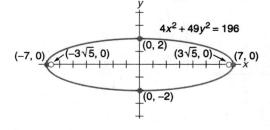

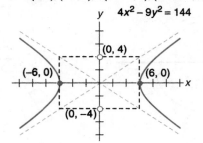

49. $\dfrac{y^2}{25} - \dfrac{x^2}{16} = 1$ or $16y^2 - 25x^2 = 400$ **50.** $\dfrac{(x - 3)^2}{9} + \dfrac{(y + 4)^2}{25} = 1$ **51.** $\dfrac{(x + 7)^2}{81} - \dfrac{(y - 4)^2}{9} = 1$

52. Hyperbola

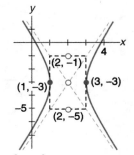

53. $(0, 0), (-12, -6)$ **54.** $(4, \sqrt{3}), (4, -\sqrt{3}), (-4, \sqrt{3}), (-4, -\sqrt{3})$

55.

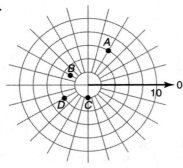

56.

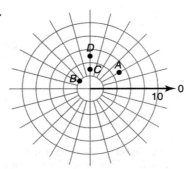

57. $(5, -225°), (-5, -45°), (-5, 315°)$ **58.** $(2, -11\pi/6), (-2, -5\pi/6), (2, \pi/6)$
59. (a) $(-2.6, -1.5)$ (b) $(-1, -1.7)$ (c) $(-4.3, 2.5)$ (d) $(0, 6)$ **60.** (a) $(4.2, 135°)$ (b) $(6, 270°)$ (c) $(2, 120°)$
61. (a) $(5, \pi)$ (b) $(12, 5\pi/6)$ (c) $(\sqrt{2}, 7\pi/4)$ **62.** $r = 7$ **63.** $r \sin^2 \theta = 9 \cos \theta$ **64.** $r = 8/(5 \cos \theta + 2 \sin \theta)$
65. $r^2 = 12/(1 - 5 \sin^2 \theta)$ **66.** $r = 6 \csc \theta \cot^2 \theta$ **67.** $r = \cos \theta \cot \theta$ **68.** $x = 12$ **69.** $x^2 + y^2 = 81$
70. $y = -\sqrt{3}x$ **71.** $x^2 + y^2 - 8x = 0$ **72.** $y^2 = 5x$ **73.** $xy = 4$ **74.** $x^4 + 2x^2y^2 + y^4 + 4y^2 - 4x^2 = 0$
75. $y = 1$ **76.** $x^4 + y^4 + 2x^2y^2 - 2x^2y - 2y^3 - x^2 = 0$ **77.** $x^2 = 4(y + 1)$

78.

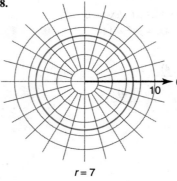

$r = 7$

79.

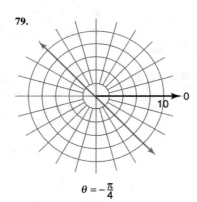

$\theta = -\dfrac{\pi}{4}$

80.

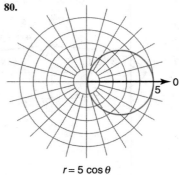

$r = 5 \cos \theta$

81.

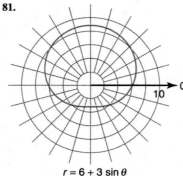

$r = 6 + 3 \sin \theta$

82.

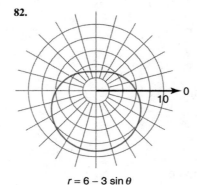

$r = 6 - 3 \sin \theta$

83.

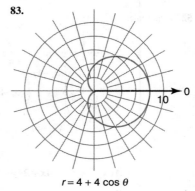

$r = 4 + 4 \cos \theta$

84.

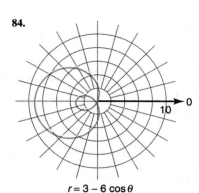

$r = 3 - 6 \cos \theta$

85.

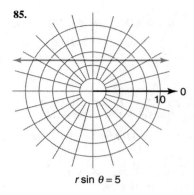

$r \sin \theta = 5$

86.

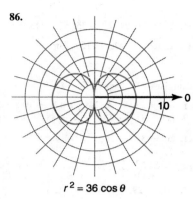

$r^2 = 36 \cos \theta$

87.

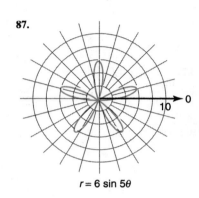

$r = 6 \sin 5\theta$

88.

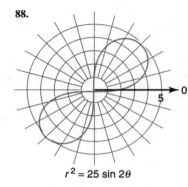

$r^2 = 25 \sin 2\theta$

89.

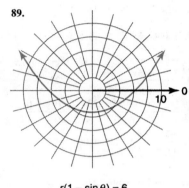

$r(1 - \sin \theta) = 6$

CHAPTER 2

Exercises 2.1, Pages 89–90

1. 9   **3.** -16 **5.** $\frac{1}{7}$ **7.** $2\sqrt{7}$ **9.** $3h + 7$ **11.** $3(\Delta t)^2 + 14(\Delta t) + 11$ **13.** $3(\Delta t)$; 3
15. $2(\Delta t)^2 + 4t(\Delta t)$; $2(\Delta t) + 4t$ **17.** $(\Delta t)^2 + 2t(\Delta t) - 2(\Delta t)$; $\Delta t + 2t - 2$ **19.** 50 m/s   **21.** 17 m/s
23. 6×10^5 m/s   **25.** 100 μA   **27.** 6 m/s   **29.** 10 m/s   **31.** $-\frac{1}{18}$ m/s   **33.** $-\frac{1}{4}$ m/s   **35.** 64 ft/s

Exercises 2.2, Pages 97–98

1. 4   **3.** 3   **5.** 1   **7.** -6 **9.** 1   **11.** 2   **13.** -6 **15.** 1   **17.** No limit   **19.** 0   **21.** $\frac{3}{4}$
23. 13   **25.** 11   **27.** 6   **29.** 102   **31.** -12 **33.** -11 **35.** $\frac{12}{5}$ **37.** -14 **39.** 10   **41.** 152
43. $2x$ **45.** $-1/x^2$ **47.** $1/(2\sqrt{a})$ **49.** Does not exist   **51.** b **53.** Does not exist   **55.** b **57.** No
59. No   **61.** No   **63.** No   **65.** Does not exist   **67.** 0   **69.** b **71.** Does not exist

Exercises 2.3, Pages 100–101

1. 6   **3.** -6 **5.** 9   **7.** -5 **9.** 12   **11.** $y = -4x - 4$ **13.** $y = -8x - 11$ **15.** $y = -13x - 3$
17. $y = -13x + 29$ **19.** $y = 4x - 3$ **21.** $(-\frac{1}{6}, \frac{1}{36})$ **23.** $(1, 2), (-1, -2)$

Exercises 2.4, Pages 104–105

1. 3   **3.** -2 **5.** $6x$ **7.** $2x - 2$ **9.** $6x - 4$ **11.** $-12x$ **13.** $3x^2 + 4$ **15.** $-1/x^2$ **17.** $-2/(x - 3)^2$
19. $-2/x^3$ **21.** $2x/(4 - x^2)^2$ **23.** $1/(2\sqrt{x + 1})$ **25.** $-1/\sqrt{1 - 2x}$ **27.** $-1/(2(x - 1)^{3/2})$ **29.** 6
31. $3/2$ **33.** $y = x - 4$ **35.** $x - 4y = 3$ **37.** $(4, 1), (2, -1)$ **39.** $(-3, 1)$

Exercises 2.5, Pages 110–111

1. 0   **3.** $5x^4$ **5.** 4   **7.** -3 **9.** $10x$ **11.** $2x - 3$ **13.** $8x - 3$ **15.** $-16x$ **17.** $9x^2 + 4x - 6$
19. $20x^4 - 6x^2 + 1$ **21.** $20x^7 - 6x^4 + 30x^3 - 3x^2$ **23.** $4\sqrt{7}x^3 - 3\sqrt{5}x^2 - \sqrt{3}$ **25.** -4 **27.** 92   **29.** 26

31. 2   **33.** 7107   **35.** $y = -5x + 2$ **37.** 120 W/A   **39.** 0.4 V/Ω **41.** $\frac{3}{2}x^{1/2}$ or $\frac{3\sqrt{x}}{2}$ **43.** $-4x^{-5}$ or $-\frac{4}{x^5}$

45. $120x^{19}$ **47.** $-112x^{-9}$ or $\frac{-112}{x^9}$ **49.** $-\frac{5}{3}x^{-4/3}$ or $\frac{-5}{3x\sqrt[3]{x}}$ **51.** 0.5 V/Ω

Exercises 2.6, Pages 113–114

1. $6x^2 + 2x$ **3.** $24x^2 + 12x - 10$ **5.** $20x + 7$ **7.** $12x^2 + 14x - 4$

9. $(x^2 + 3x + 4)(3x^2 - 4) + (x^3 - 4x)(2x + 3)$ or $5x^4 + 12x^3 - 24x - 16$

11. $(x^4 - 3x^2 - x)(6x^2 - 4) + (2x^3 - 4x)(4x^3 - 6x - 1)$ or $14x^6 - 50x^4 - 8x^3 + 36x^2 + 8x$ **13.** $\dfrac{5}{(2x + 5)^2}$

15. $\dfrac{-2x - 1}{(x^2 + x)^2}$ **17.** $\dfrac{7}{2(x + 2)^2}$ **19.** $\dfrac{2x^2 + 2x}{(2x + 1)^2}$ **21.** $\dfrac{-x^2 + 2x + 2}{(x^2 + x + 1)^2}$ **23.** $\dfrac{-12x^3 - 81x + 72}{x^3(3x - 4)^2}$ **25.** -7

27. 10   **29.** $-13/64$ **31.** $y = -5x + 21$ **33.** 10.4 V/s

Exercises 2.7, Page 118

1. $160(4x + 3)^{39}$ **3.** $5(3x^2 - 7x + 4)^4(6x - 7)$ **5.** $\dfrac{-12x^2}{(x^3 + 3)^5}$ **7.** $\dfrac{10x - 7}{2\sqrt{5x^2 - 7x + 2}}$ **9.** $\dfrac{16x^2 + 2}{\sqrt[3]{8x^3 + 3x}}$

11. $-\frac{3}{2}(2x + 3)^{-7/4}$ **13.** $15(4x + 1)(4x + 5)^3$ **15.** $6x^3(2x^2 - 1)(x^3 - x)^2$ **17.** $4(2x + 1)(x^2 + 1)(3x^2 + x + 1)$

19. $\dfrac{27x^3 - 5x^2 + 9x - 1}{\sqrt{9x^2 - 2x}}$ **21.** $\dfrac{33x^2 + 32x + 18}{(3x + 4)^{1/4}}$ **23.** $-\dfrac{4}{x^5} - 8(2x + 1)^3$ **25.** $\dfrac{-10x}{(3x - 1)^3}$

27. $\dfrac{(x^3 + 2)^3(40x^4 - 33x^3 - 16x + 6)}{(4x^2 - 3x)^2}$ **29.** $\dfrac{3(3x + 2)^4(4x - 9)}{(2x - 1)^4}$ **31.** $\dfrac{2x + 8}{(4x + 3)^{3/2}(3x - 1)^{1/3}}$

33. $\dfrac{8(1 + x)^3}{(1 - x)^5}$ **35.** 0.0632 m/s

Exercises 2.8, Page 121

1. $-4/3$ **3.** x/y **5.** $\dfrac{-x}{y + 2}$ **7.** $\dfrac{2x - y}{y^2 + x}$ **9.** $\dfrac{y^2 - 2x}{4y^3 - 2xy}$ **11.** $\dfrac{2xy^2 - 3x}{2y^3 - 2x^2y}$ **13.** $\dfrac{(9x^2 - 12)(x^3 - 4x)^2}{4y^3 + 8y}$

15. $\dfrac{2x - 2y + 8 - 3x^2 - 6xy - 3y^2}{3x^2 + 6xy + 3y^2 + 2x - 2y + 8}$ **17.** $\dfrac{y}{x - y(x - y)^2}$ **19.** $\frac{4}{5}$ **21.** $\frac{1}{3}$ **23.** $y = 4x + 9$

25. $12x + 5y = -8$ **27.** -1 **29.** $\frac{1}{6}$

Exercises 2.10, Page 127

1. $y' = 5x^4 + 6x,\ y'' = 20x^3 + 6,\ y''' = 60x^2,\ y^{(4)} = 120x$

3. $y' = 25x^4 + 6x^2 - 8,\ y'' = 100x^3 + 12x,\ y''' = 300x^2 + 12,\ y^{(4)} = 600x$ **5.** $-6/x^4$ **7.** 162

9. $-\frac{1215}{16}(3x + 2)^{-7/2}$ **11.** $\dfrac{6x^2 - 2}{(x^2 + 1)^3}$ **13.** $\dfrac{4}{(x - 1)^3}$ **15.** $y' = -x/y;\ y'' = -1/y^3$

17. $y' = \dfrac{2x - y}{x - 2y};\ y'' = \dfrac{6}{(x - 2y)^3}$ **19.** $y' = -y^{1/2}/x^{1/2};\ y'' = \dfrac{1}{2x^{3/2}}$ **21.** $y' = y^2/x^2;\ y'' = \dfrac{2y^3 - 2xy^2}{x^4}$ or $\dfrac{2y^3}{x^3}$

23. $y' = \dfrac{1}{2(1 + y)};\ y'' = \dfrac{-1}{4(1 + y)^3}$ **25.** $a = 6t^2 - 36t - 8$ **27.** $a = \dfrac{-9}{(6t - 4)^{3/2}}$ **29.** $x - 5y = -14;\ 4x - 5y = 14$

Chapter 2 Review, Pages 129–130

1. $6t(\Delta t) + 3(\Delta t)^2;\ 6t + 3(\Delta t)$ **2.** $10t(\Delta t) + 5(\Delta t)^2;\ 10t + 5(\Delta t)$ **3.** $2t(\Delta t) + (\Delta t)^2 - 3(\Delta t);\ 2t + \Delta t - 3$

4. $6t(\Delta t) + 3(\Delta t)^2 - 6(\Delta t);\ 6t + 3(\Delta t) - 6$ **5.** 27 m/s   **6.** 20 m/s   **7.** 10 m/s   **8.** 33 m/s   **9.** 12 m/s

10. 10 m/s   **11.** 4 m/s   **12.** 17 m/s   **13.** 4   **14.** -11 **15.** -4 **16.** 10   **17.** No limit   **18.** $\sqrt{15}$

19. $\frac{22}{9}$ **20.** $-\frac{37}{24}$ **21.** 168   **22.** 112   **23.** $-\frac{1}{4}$ **24.** $\frac{1}{2}$ **25.** $\frac{5}{2}$ **26.** $\frac{7}{10}$ **27.** Does not exist   **28.** c

29. c **30.** Does not exist   **31.** No   **32.** Yes   **33.** $-10;\ y = -10x + 2$ **34.** $-1;\ y = -x - 16$

35. $14;\ y = 14x - 11$ **36.** $-24;\ y = -24x - 13$ **37.** -0.048 cm/s   **38.** -64 ft/s   **39.** $20x^3 - 9x^2 + 4x + 5$

40. $100x^{99} + 400x^4$ **41.** $6x^5 - 4x^3 + 15x^2 - 4$ **42.** $21x^6 - 25x^4 + 12x^3 - 36x^2 - 10x + 20$

43. $\dfrac{3x^2 - 8x - 3}{(3x - 4)^2}$ **44.** $\dfrac{6x^5 - 18x^4 - 4x + 4}{(3x^4 + 2)^2}$ **45.** $30x(3x^2 - 8)^4$ **46.** $\frac{3}{4}(x^4 + 2x^3 + 7)^{-1/4}(4x^3 + 6x^2)$

47. $\dfrac{-12}{(3x + 5)^5}$ **48.** $\dfrac{(7x^2 + 21x)(7x^2 - 5)^{-1/2} - 2\sqrt{7x^2 - 5}}{(x + 3)^3}$ or $\dfrac{-7x^2 + 21x + 10}{(x + 3)^3\sqrt{7x^2 - 5}}$ **49.** $\dfrac{-3x^2 - 45x + 20}{2(x + 5)^2\sqrt{2 - 3x}}$

50. $\dfrac{2y^3 - x}{y - 6xy^2}$ **51.** $\dfrac{y}{2y^3 - y - x}$ **52.** $\dfrac{4x}{3y(y^2 + 1)^2}$ **53.** $\dfrac{9x^2(2x^3 - 3)^2}{2(y + 2)^3}$ **54.** 648   **55.** 0   **56.** -7

57. $\dfrac{4}{9\sqrt{2}}$ or $\dfrac{2\sqrt{2}}{9}$ **58.** $11x + y + 14 = 0$ **59.** $26x - y + 62 = 0$ **60.** $x - y + 10 = 0$

61. $13x + 4y - 55 = 0$ **62.** 4 m/s   **63.** 48 m/s   **64.** 2.75 m/s   **65.** 0.0788 m/s   **66.** $2x + y + 18 = 0$

67. 50.3 A   **68.** $\dfrac{dc}{dT} = 0.5 + 0.000012T$ **69.** $-\dfrac{1}{4\pi C\sqrt{LC}}$

70. $y' = 24x^5 - 32x^3 + 27x^2 - 6,\ y'' = 120x^4 - 96x^2 + 54x,\ y''' = 480x^3 - 192x + 54,\ y^{(4)} = 1440x^2 - 192$

71. $\dfrac{-1}{(2x - 3)^{3/2}}$ **72.** $\dfrac{72x^2 - 12}{(2x^2 + 1)^3}$ **73.** $y' = \dfrac{-y}{x + y},\ y'' = \dfrac{4}{(x + y)^3}$

74. $y' = \dfrac{y^{3/2}}{x^{3/2}},\ y'' = \dfrac{3y^2 - 3y^{3/2}x^{1/2}}{2x^3}$ or $\dfrac{3y^2}{2x^{5/2}}$ **75.** $a = -\tfrac{3}{4}(2t + 3)^{-7/4}$

CHAPTER 3

Exercises 3.1, Pages 140–141

1.

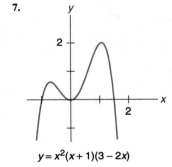

$y = 2x(x + 1)(x - 4)$

3.

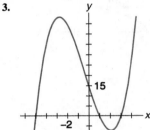

$y = (x - 1)(x - 3)(x + 5)$

5.

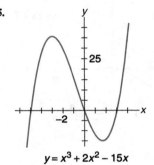

$y = x^3 + 2x^2 - 15x$

7.

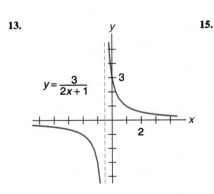

$y = x^2(x + 1)(3 - 2x)$

9.

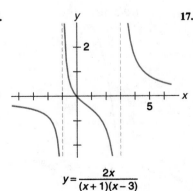

$y = x^4 - 13x^2 + 36$

11.

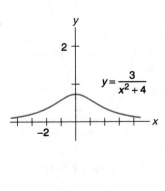

$y = x^2(x - 2)^2(x + 4)^2$

13.

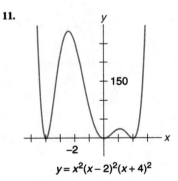

$y = \dfrac{3}{2x + 1}$

15.

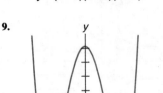

$y = \dfrac{2x}{(x + 1)(x - 3)}$

17.

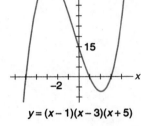

$y = \dfrac{3}{x^2 + 4}$

19.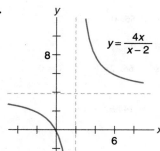

$$y = \frac{4x}{x-2}$$

21.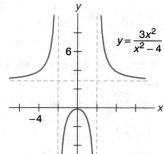

$$y = \frac{3x^2}{x^2-4}$$

23.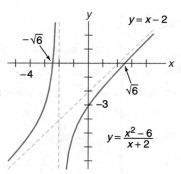

$y = x - 2$

$$y = \frac{x^2-6}{x+2}$$

25.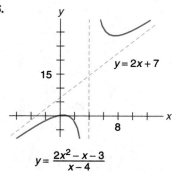

$y = 2x + 7$

$$y = \frac{2x^2 - x - 3}{x - 4}$$

27.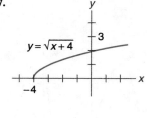

$y = \sqrt{x+4}$

29.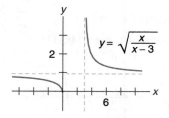

$$y = \sqrt{\frac{x}{x-3}}$$

31.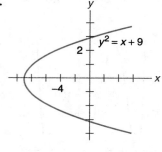

$y^2 = x + 9$

33.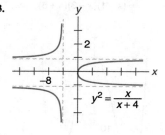

$$y^2 = \frac{x}{x+4}$$

35.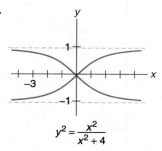

$$y^2 = \frac{x^2}{x^2+4}$$

Exercises 3.2, Page 145

1.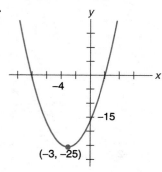

$(-3, -25)$

$y = x^2 + 6x - 16$

3.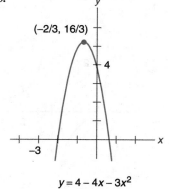

$(-2/3, 16/3)$

$y = 4 - 4x - 3x^2$

5.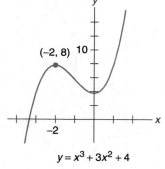

$(-2, 8)$

$y = x^3 + 3x^2 + 4$

7.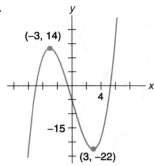

$(-3, 14)$

4

-15

$(3, -22)$

$y = \frac{1}{3}x^3 - 9x - 4$

9.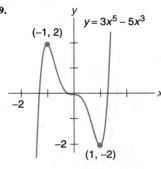

$y = 3x^5 - 5x^3$

$(-1, 2)$

-2

-2

$(1, -2)$

11.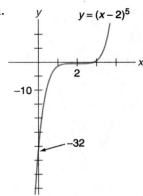

$y = (x - 2)^5$

2

-10

-32

13.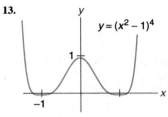

$y = (x^2 - 1)^4$

1

-1

15.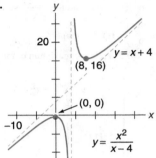

20

$y = x + 4$

$(8, 16)$

$(0, 0)$

-10

$y = \dfrac{x^2}{x - 4}$

17.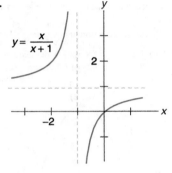

$y = \dfrac{x}{x + 1}$

2

-2

19.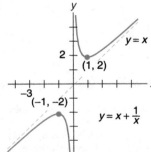

$y = x$

2

$(1, 2)$

-3

$(-1, -2)$

$y = x + \dfrac{1}{x}$

21.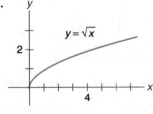

$y = \sqrt{x}$

2

4

23.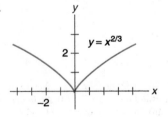

$y = x^{2/3}$

2

-2

Exercises 3.3, Page 152

1. (a) Increasing for $x > 2$, decreasing for $x < 2$ **(b)** Relative minimum at $(2, -4)$ **(c)** Concave upward for all values of x
(d) No points of inflection **(e)** See graph.
3. (a) Increasing for $x > 0$, decreasing for $x < 0$ **(b)** Relative minimum at $(0, 0)$ **(c)** Concave upward for all values of x
(d) No points of inflection **(e)** See graph.
5. (a) Increasing for $-1 < x < 1$, decreasing for $x < -1$ and $x > 1$ **(b)** Relative minimum at $(-1, -2)$, relative maximum at
$(1, 2)$ **(c)** Concave upward for $x < 0$, concave downward for $x > 0$ **(d)** Point of inflection at $(0, 0)$ **(e)** See graph.

1e.

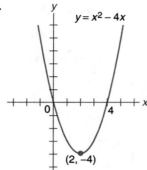

$y = x^2 - 4x$

$(2, -4)$

3e.

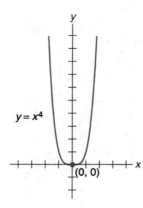

$y = x^4$

$(0, 0)$

5e.

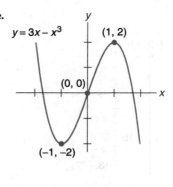

$y = 3x - x^3$

$(1, 2)$

$(0, 0)$

$(-1, -2)$

7. **(a)** Increasing for $x < 2$, decreasing for $x > 2$ **(b)** Relative maximum at $(2, 3)$ **(c)** Concave downward for all values of x
(d) No points of inflection **(e)** See graph.
9. **(a)** Increasing for $-2 < x < 0$ and $x > 2$, decreasing for $x < -2$ and $0 < x < 2$ **(b)** Relative maximum at $(0, 5)$, relative minimums at $(2, -11)$ and $(-2, -11)$

(c) Concave upward for $x < -\dfrac{2}{\sqrt{3}}$ and $x > \dfrac{2}{\sqrt{3}}$, concave downward for $-\dfrac{2}{\sqrt{3}} < x < \dfrac{2}{\sqrt{3}}$

(d) Points of inflection at $\left(\dfrac{-2}{\sqrt{3}}, \dfrac{-35}{9}\right)$ and $\left(\dfrac{2}{\sqrt{3}}, \dfrac{-35}{9}\right)$ **(e)** See graph.
11. **(a)** Increasing for $x < 0$, decreasing for $x > 0$ **(b)** No relative maximum or minimum **(c)** Concave upward for $x > 0$ and $x < 0$ **(d)** No points of inflection **(e)** See graph.

7e.

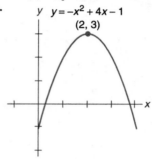

$y \quad y = -x^2 + 4x - 1$

$(2, 3)$

9e.

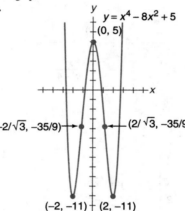

$y = x^4 - 8x^2 + 5$

$(0, 5)$

$(-2/\sqrt{3}, -35/9)$ $(2/\sqrt{3}, -35/9)$

$(-2, -11)$ $(2, -11)$

11e.

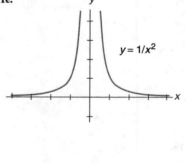

$y = 1/x^2$

13. **(a)** Increasing for $x < -2$ and $x > -2$ **(b)** No relative maximum or minimum **(c)** Concave upward for $x < -2$, concave downward for $x > -2$ **(d)** No points of inflection **(e)** See graph.
15. **(a)** Increasing for $x < -1$ and $x > -1$ **(b)** No relative maximum or minimum **(c)** Concave upward for $x < -1$, concave downward for $x > -1$ **(d)** No points of inflection **(e)** See graph.
17. **(a)** Increasing for $-1 < x < 1$, decreasing for $x < -1, x > 1$ **(b)** Relative maximum at $(1, \frac{1}{2})$, relative minimum at $(-1, -\frac{1}{2})$
(c) Concave upward for $-\sqrt{3} < x < 0, x > \sqrt{3}$, concave downward for $x < -\sqrt{3}, 0 < x < \sqrt{3}$ **(d)** Points of inflection at $(\sqrt{3}, \sqrt{3}/4), (0, 0), (-\sqrt{3}, -\sqrt{3}/4)$ **(e)** See graph.

13e.

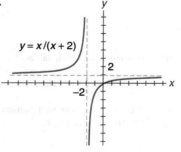

$y = x/(x+2)$

2

-2

15e.

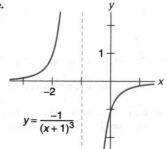

1

-2

$y = \dfrac{-1}{(x+1)^3}$

17e.

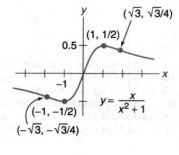

$(\sqrt{3}, \sqrt{3}/4)$

$(1, 1/2)$

0.5

-1

$(-1, -1/2)$

$y = \dfrac{x}{x^2+1}$

$(-\sqrt{3}, -\sqrt{3}/4)$

19. (a) Increasing for $x < -3$, $x > -3$ **(b)** No relative maximum or minimum   **(c)** Concave upward for $x < -3$, concave downward for $x > -3$ **(d)** No points of inflection   **(e)** See graph.

21. (a) Increasing for $x < 0$, decreasing for $x > 0$ **(b)** Relative maximum at $(0, 1)$ **(c)** Concave upward for $x < -2/\sqrt{3}$, $x > 2/\sqrt{3}$, concave downward for $-2/\sqrt{3} < x < 2/\sqrt{3}$ **(d)** Inflection points at $(2/\sqrt{3}, \frac{3}{4})$ and $(-2/\sqrt{3}, \frac{3}{4})$ **(e)** See graph.

23. (a) Increasing for $0 < x < 2$, decreasing for $x < 0$, $x > 2$ **(b)** Relative maximum at $(2, \frac{1}{4})$ **(c)** Concave upward for $x > 3$, concave downward for $x < 0$, $0 < x < 3$ **(d)** Point of inflection $(3, \frac{2}{9})$ **(e)** See graph.

19e.
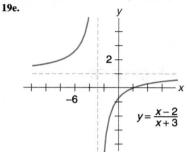

21e.
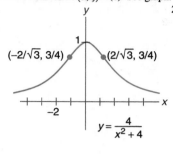

23e.
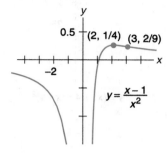

Exercises 3.4, Pages 158–159

1. 12.2474   **3.** 1.70998   **5.** 1.11944   **7.** Estimates $-3, 0.5, 1.5$; better $-2.93543, 0.462598, 1.47283$
9. Estimates $-0.3, 0.6, 2$; better $-0.340665, 0.678963, 2.16170$ **11.** Estimates $3, 4.4$; better $3.14159, 4.35715$
13. Estimates $1, 4.2$; better $1.10715, 4.24874$ **15.** 2.18994

Exercises 3.5, Pages 163–165

1. 28, 28   **3.** 2 cm × 2 cm × 0.5 cm   **5.** 200 m × 400 m   **7.** 81 cm^2 **9.** 1600 m   **11.** $96\sqrt{3}$ **13.** $\frac{32}{3}$
15. 4 Ω   **19.** $m = \frac{3}{2}$ at $x = \frac{1}{2}$ **21.** $i = -16$ A at $t = 2$ s   **23.** 20 cm × 20 cm × 10 cm   **25.** 20
27. $r = 2\sqrt{2}$ cm, $h = 4\sqrt{2}$ cm   **29.** $w = 2r/\sqrt{3}$, $d = 2r\sqrt{6}/3$ **31.** 4 km

Exercises 3.6, Pages 167–169

1. 36   **3.** -6 **5.** 0.06 Ω/s   **7.** 1.92 cm^2/min   **9.** 43.2 cm^3/min   **11.** -0.277 cm^2/min   **13.** $3/(80\pi)$ m/s
15. -160 W/s   **17.** 0.509 cm/s   **19.** $\frac{4}{3}$ m/s   **21.** 12 lb/in^2/min   **23.** -2.4 Ω/s   **25.** 240 ΩA   **27.** 8 V/s
29. (a) 8 m/min   **(b)** $\frac{8}{9}$ m/min

Exercises 3.7, Pages 171–172

1. $dy = (10x - 24x^2)\,dx$ **3.** $dy = \dfrac{-7\,dx}{(2x - 1)^2}$ **5.** $dy = 16t(2t^2 + 1)^3\,dt$

7. $ds = -2(t^4 - t^{-2})^{-3}(4t^3 + 2t^{-3})\,dt$ or $ds = \dfrac{-4t^3(2t^6 + 1)\,dt}{(t^6 - 1)^3}$ **9.** $dy = \dfrac{-x\,dx}{4y}$

11. $dy = \dfrac{x^{-1/2} - 6(x + y)^2}{6(x + y)^2 - y^{-1/2}}\,dx$ or $dy = \dfrac{y^{1/2} - 6x^{1/2}y^{1/2}(x + y)^2}{6x^{1/2}y^{1/2}(x + y)^2 - x^{1/2}}\,dx$ **13.** 43.2   **15.** 1.2   **17.** 282.7
19. (a) 1.20 cm^2 **(b)** 1.2025 cm^2 **(c)** 0.833%   **21. (a)** 84.9 m^3 **(b)** 662,000 kg   **23.** 0.3 hp   **25.** 4 V

Chapter 3 Review, Pages 175–176

1.
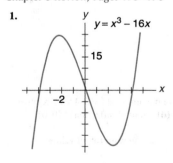

2.
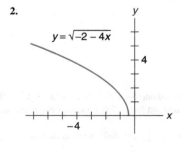

3.
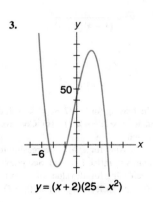

4.

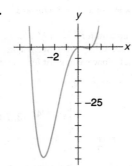

$y = (x^2 + 4x)(x-1)^2$

5.

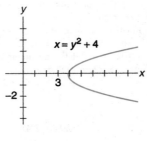

$x = y^2 + 4$

6.

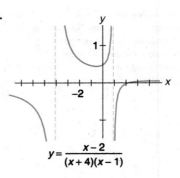

$y = \dfrac{x-2}{(x+4)(x-1)}$

7.

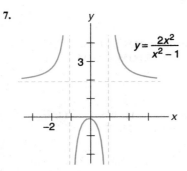

$y = \dfrac{2x^2}{x^2 - 1}$

8.

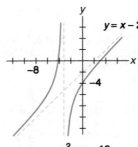

$y = x - 2$

$y = \dfrac{x^2 + x - 12}{x + 3}$

9.

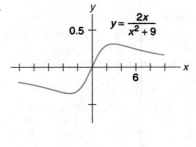

$y = \dfrac{2x}{x^2 + 9}$

10.

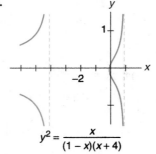

$y^2 = \dfrac{x}{(1-x)(x+4)}$

11. (a) Increasing for $-\sqrt{2} < x < \sqrt{2}$, decreasing for $x < -\sqrt{2}$ and $x > \sqrt{2}$ **(b)** Relative maximum at $(\sqrt{2}, 4\sqrt{2})$, relative minimum at $(-\sqrt{2}, -4\sqrt{2})$ **(c)** Concave upward for $x < 0$, concave downward for $x > 0$ **(d)** Point of inflection at $(0, 0)$
(e) See graph.
12. (a) Increasing for $x > \frac{3}{2}$, decreasing for $x < \frac{3}{2}$ **(b)** Relative minimum at $(\frac{3}{2}, -\frac{25}{4})$ **(c)** Concave upward for all values of x
(d) No points of inflection   **(e)** See graph.
13. (a) Increasing for all values of x **(b)** No relative maximum or minimum   **(c)** Concave upward for $x > 0$, concave downward
for $x < 0$ **(d)** Inflection point at $(0, -7)$ **(e)** See graph.

11e.

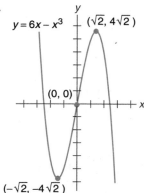

$y = 6x - x^3$

$(\sqrt{2}, 4\sqrt{2})$

$(0, 0)$

$(-\sqrt{2}, -4\sqrt{2})$

12e.

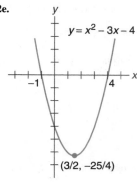

$y = x^2 - 3x - 4$

$(3/2, -25/4)$

13e.

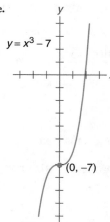

$y = x^3 - 7$

$(0, -7)$

14. (a) Increasing for $x < -1$, $x > 4$, decreasing for $-1 < x < 4$ **(b)** Relative maximum at $(-1, 11)$, relative minimum at $(4, -114)$ **(c)** Concave upward for $x > \frac{3}{2}$, concave downward for $x < \frac{3}{2}$ **(d)** Point of inflection $(1.5, -51.5)$ **(e)** See graph.
15. (a) Increasing for $x < -1$, decreasing for $x > -1$ **(b)** No relative maximum or minimum **(c)** Concave upward for $x < -1$, $x > -1$ **(d)** No points of inflection **(e)** See graph.
16. (a) Increasing for $x > 0$, decreasing for $x < 0$ **(b)** Relative minimum at $(0, -\frac{1}{4})$ **(c)** Concave upward for $-2/\sqrt{3} < x < 2/\sqrt{3}$, concave downward for $x < -2/\sqrt{3}$, $x > 2/\sqrt{3}$ **(d)** Points of inflection at $(2/\sqrt{3}, \frac{1}{16})$, $(-2/\sqrt{3}, \frac{1}{16})$
(e) See graph.

14e.

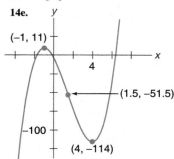

$(-1, 11)$

4

$(1.5, -51.5)$

-100

$(4, -114)$

$y = 2x^3 - 9x^2 - 24x - 2$

15e.

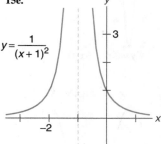

$y = \dfrac{1}{(x+1)^2}$

3

-2

16e.

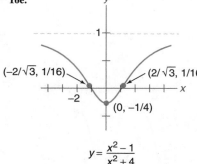

1

$(-2/\sqrt{3}, 1/16)$

$(2/\sqrt{3}, 1/16)$

-2

$(0, -1/4)$

$y = \dfrac{x^2 - 1}{x^2 + 4}$

17. (a) Increasing for $x < 0$, decreasing for $x > 0$ **(b)** Relative maximum at $(0, 10)$ **(c)** Concave upward for $x < -1/\sqrt{3}$, $x > 1/\sqrt{3}$, concave downward for $-1/\sqrt{3} < x < 1/\sqrt{3}$ **(d)** Points of inflection at $(-1/\sqrt{3}, \frac{15}{2})$, $(1/\sqrt{3}, \frac{15}{2})$
(e) See graph.
18. (a) Increasing for $-2 < x < 0$, decreasing for $x < -2$, $x > 0$ **(b)** Relative minimum at $(-2, -\frac{1}{4})$ **(c)** Concave upward for $-3 < x < 0$, $x > 0$, concave downward for $x < -3$ **(d)** Point of inflection $(-3, -\frac{2}{9})$ **(e)** See graph.

17e.

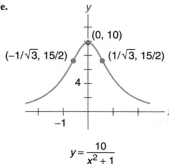

$(0, 10)$

$(-1/\sqrt{3}, 15/2)$

$(1/\sqrt{3}, 15/2)$

4

-1

$y = \dfrac{10}{x^2 + 1}$

18e.

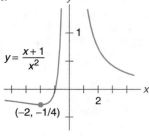

1

$y = \dfrac{x+1}{x^2}$

2

$(-2, -1/4)$

19. 9.74679 **20.** 4.93242 **21.** Estimates -0.8, 1, 4; better -0.791288, 1, 3.79129 **22.** Estimate 1, better 1.06366

23. 900 ft **24.** $b = h = 10\sqrt{2}$ **25.** 1 Ω **26.** 12 m^2 **27.** $3\sqrt{2}$ cm **28.** $(\frac{1}{2}, \sqrt{2}/2)$ **29.** $\dfrac{1}{288\pi}$ ft/s

30. 18 V/s   **31.** −0.0087 A/s   **32.** −0.8π cm²/min or −2.51 cm²/min   **33.** 0.255 km/day

34. 1.92 km/s   **35.** $dy = (20x^4 − 18x^2 + 2)\,dx$ **36.** $dy = −2(3x − 5)^{-5/3}\,dx$ **37.** $ds = \dfrac{(15t^2 + 6t + 20)\,dt}{(5t + 1)^2}$

38. $dy = \dfrac{2 − 4x(x^2 + y^2)}{4y(x^2 + y^2) − 1}\,dx$ **39.** 2.6   **40.** −0.000158   **41.** 45.2 in³   **42.** 0.3 m   **43.** 9.58 gal

44. 8.04 cm³   **45.** −74.1 kN

CHAPTER 4

Exercises 4.1, Pages 189–190

37. $\sin 4\theta$ **39.** $\cos \theta$ **41.** $\tan 5\theta$ **43.** $2 \sin \theta \cos \phi$ **45.** $\sin \dfrac{x}{2}$ **47.** $\cos 6x$ **49.** $\cos \dfrac{\theta}{8}$ **51.** $\cos \dfrac{x}{3}$

53. $10 \sin 8\theta$ **55.** $4 \cos 2\theta$

57.

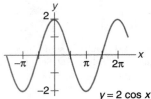

$y = 2 \cos x$

59.

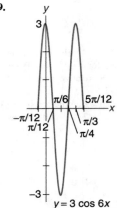

$y = 3 \cos 6x$

61.

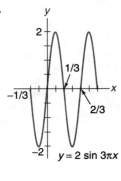

$y = 2 \sin 3\pi x$

63.

$y = −\sin\left(4x − \dfrac{2\pi}{3}\right)$

65.

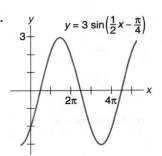

$y = 3 \sin\left(\dfrac{1}{2}x − \dfrac{\pi}{4}\right)$

67.

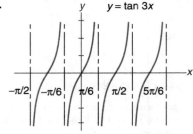

$y = \tan 3x$

Exercises 4.2, Pages 194–195

1. $7 \cos 7x$ **3.** $−10 \sin 5x$ **5.** $6x^2 \cos x^3$ **7.** $−24x \sin 4x^2$ **9.** $−4 \cos (1 − x)$ **11.** $6x \cos (x^2 + 4)$

13. $−4(10x + 1) \sin (5x^2 + x)$ **15.** $−4(x^3 − x) \sin (x^4 − 2x^2 + 3)$ **17.** $−6 \cos(3x − 1) \sin (3x − 1)$

19. $6 \sin^2 (2x + 3) \cos (2x + 3)$ **21.** $4(2x − 5) \cos (2x − 5)^2$ **23.** $−12x^2(x^3 − 4)^3 \sin (x^3 − 4)^4$

25. $\cos 3x \cos x − 3 \sin x \sin 3x$ **27.** $−6 \sin 5x \sin 6x + 5 \cos 6x \cos 5x$ **29.** $−7 \cos 4x \sin 7x − 4 \cos 7x \sin 4x$

31. $2(x + 1) \cos x^3 \cos (x^2 + 2x) − 3x^2 \sin (x^2 + 2x) \sin x^3$ **33.** $5(x^2 + 3x) \cos (5x − 2) + (2x + 3) \sin (5x − 2)$

35. $\dfrac{5x \cos 5x − \sin 5x}{x^2}$ **37.** $\dfrac{2x \cos 3x + 3(x^2 − 1) \sin 3x}{\cos^2 3x}$ **39.** $5 \cos 5x − 6 \sin 6x$

41. $(2x − 3) \cos (x^2 − 3x) − 4 \sin 4x$ **43.** $\sec^2 x$ **45.** $−\cos x$ **47.** $−\cos x$ **49.** $−25 \sin 5x − 36 \cos 6x$

51. $6\sqrt{3}$ **53.** $y = −10x + \pi$

Exercises 4.3, Page 199

1. $3 \sec^2 x$ **3.** $7 \sec 7x \tan 7x$ **5.** $−6x \csc^2 (3x^2 − 7)$ **7.** $−9 \csc (3x − 4) \cot (3x − 4)$

9. $10 \tan (5x − 2) \sec^2 (5x − 2)$ **11.** $−24 \cot^2 2x \csc^2 2x$ **13.** $\dfrac{2x + 1}{2\sqrt{x^2 + x}} \sec \sqrt{x^2 + x} \tan \sqrt{x^2 + x}$

15. $-\dfrac{\csc x(x \cot x + 1)}{3x^2}$ **17.** $3 \sec^2 3x - 2x \sec(x^2 + 1) \tan(x^2 + 1)$ **19.** $\sec x(2 \sec^2 x - 1)$ **21.** $\cos 2x$

23. $\sec x(x \tan x + 1)$ **25.** $2x \sec^2 x(x \tan x + 1)$ **27.** $-3 \csc 3x(2 \csc^2 3x - 1)$ **29.** $-3 \csc 3x \cot 3x$

31. $-2 \cos 2x$ **33.** $4(x + \sec^2 3x)^3(1 + 6 \sec^2 3x \tan 3x)$ **35.** $3 \sec x(\sec x + \tan x)^3$ **37.** $\cos(\tan x) \sec^2 x$

39. $-\sin x \sec^2(\cos x)$ **41.** $-2 \sin x \sin(\cos x) \cos(\cos x)$ or $-\sin x \sin(2 \cos x)$ **43.** $\dfrac{1 + \sin^2 x}{\cos^3 x}$

45. $-2 \sin x \cos x$ or $-\sin 2x$ **47.** $\dfrac{\cos x + \sin x - \sin x \sec^2 x}{(1 + \tan x)^2}$ **49.** $18 \sec^2 3x \tan 3x$

51. $2 \csc^2 x(x \cot x - 1)$ **53.** 2

Exercises 4.4, Page 206

1. $x = \frac{1}{3} \arcsin y$ **3.** $x = \arccos \dfrac{y}{4}$ **5.** $x = 2 \arctan \dfrac{y}{5}$ **7.** $x = 4 \operatorname{arccot} \dfrac{2y}{3}$ **9.** $x = 1 + \arcsin \dfrac{y}{3}$

11. $x = -\frac{1}{3} + \frac{1}{3} \arccos 2y$ **13.** $\dfrac{\pi}{3}$ **15.** $-\dfrac{\pi}{6}$ **17.** $\dfrac{5\pi}{6}$ **19.** $\dfrac{\pi}{4}$ **21.** $\dfrac{\pi}{3}$ **23.** $\dfrac{\pi}{4}$ **25.** $-\dfrac{\pi}{3}$ **27.** $\frac{1}{2}$

29. $\dfrac{1}{\sqrt{2}}$ **31.** 0 **33.** $\dfrac{\sqrt{3}}{2}$ **35.** 0.8 **37.** -0.1579 **39.** $\sqrt{1 - x^2}$ **41.** $\dfrac{\sqrt{x^2 - 1}}{x}$ **43.** $\dfrac{1}{x}$ **45.** x

47. $\sqrt{1 - 4x^2}$ **49.** $2x\sqrt{1 - x^2}$

Exercises 4.5, Page 209

1. $\dfrac{5}{\sqrt{1 - 25x^2}}$ **3.** $\dfrac{3}{1 + 9x^2}$ **5.** $\dfrac{1}{|1 - x|\sqrt{x^2 - 2x}}$ **7.** $\dfrac{-3}{\sqrt{2x - x^2}}$ **9.** $\dfrac{-12x}{1 + 9x^4}$ **11.** $\dfrac{15}{|x|\sqrt{x^6 - 1}}$

13. $\dfrac{3 \arcsin^2 x}{\sqrt{1 - x^2}}$ **15.** $\dfrac{-12 \arccos 3x}{\sqrt{1 - 9x^2}}$ **17.** $\dfrac{6 \arctan^3 \sqrt{x}}{\sqrt{x}(1 + x)}$ **19.** 0 **21.** $\dfrac{1 - x}{\sqrt{1 - x^2}}$

23. $\dfrac{3x}{\sqrt{1 - 9x^2}} + \arcsin 3x$ **25.** $\dfrac{x}{1 + x^2} + \arctan x$ **27.** $\arcsin x$ **29.** $\dfrac{\sqrt{1 - x^2} \arcsin x - x}{\sqrt{1 - x^2} \arcsin^2 x}$

31. $2/\sqrt{3}$ **33.** $\dfrac{-\pi - 2}{4}$

Exercises 4.6, Pages 215–216

1.

$y = 4^x$

3.

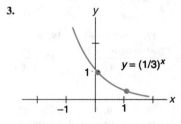

$y = (1/3)^x$

5.

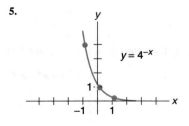

$y = 4^{-x}$

7.

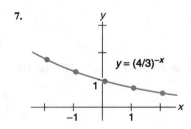

$y = (4/3)^{-x}$

9. $\log_3 9 = 2$ **11.** $\log_5 125 = 3$ **13.** $\log_9 3 = \frac{1}{2}$ **15.** $\log_{10} 0.00001 = -5$ **17.** $5^2 = 25$ **19.** $25^{1/2} = 5$

21. $2^{-2} = \frac{1}{4}$ **23.** $10^{-2} = 0.01$

25.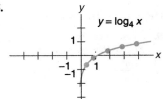

27.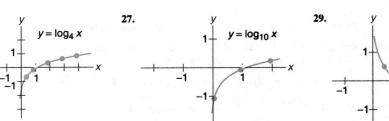

29.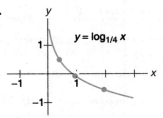

31. 64   **33.** $\frac{1}{2}$ **35.** 3   **37.** $\frac{1}{2}$ **39.** 5   **41.** 3   **43.** 144   **45.** 27   **47.** 4

49. $\log_2 5 + 3 \log_2 x + \log_2 y$ **51.** $3 \log_b y + \frac{1}{2} \log_b x - 2 \log_b z$ **53.** $\frac{2}{3} \log_b x - \frac{1}{3} \log_b y$

55. $\frac{1}{2} \log_2 y - \log_2 x - \frac{1}{2} \log_2 z$ **57.** $3 \log_b z + \frac{1}{2} \log_b x - \frac{1}{3} \log_b y$ **59.** $2 \log_b x + \log_b (x + 1) - \frac{1}{2} \log_b (x + 2)$

61. $\log_b xy^2$ **63.** $\log_b \dfrac{xy^2}{z^3}$ **65.** $\log_3 \dfrac{x\sqrt[3]{y}}{\sqrt{z}}$ **67.** $\log_{10} \dfrac{x^2}{(x + 1)\sqrt{x - 3}}$ **69.** $\log_b \dfrac{x^5 \sqrt[3]{x - 1}}{x + 2}$

71. $\log_{10} \dfrac{x(x - 1)^2}{\sqrt[3]{(x + 2)(x - 5)}}$ **73.** 3   **75.** 2   **77.** 3   **79.** -2 **81.** -3 **83.** 0   **85.** 5   **87.** 36   **89.** $\frac{1}{25}$

Exercises 4.7, Page 220

1. $\dfrac{4 \log e}{4x - 3}$ **3.** $\dfrac{\log_2 e}{x}$ **5.** $\dfrac{6x^2}{2x^3 - 3}$ **7.** $\dfrac{3 \sec^2 3x}{\tan 3x}$ or $3 \sec 3x \csc 3x$ **9.** $\dfrac{x \cos x + \sin x}{x \sin x}$ **11.** $\dfrac{3}{2(3x - 2)}$

13. $\dfrac{x^2 + 3}{x(x^2 + 1)}$ **15.** $\dfrac{\sec^2 (\ln x)}{x}$ **17.** $\dfrac{1}{x \ln x}$ **19.** $\dfrac{2}{x(1 + \ln^2 x^2)}$ **21.** $\dfrac{-2}{(\arccos x)\sqrt{1 - x^2}}$

23. $(3x + 2)(6x - 1)^2(x - 4)\left(\dfrac{3}{3x + 2} + \dfrac{12}{6x - 1} + \dfrac{1}{x - 4} \right)$

25. $\dfrac{(x + 1)(2x + 1)}{(3x - 4)(1 - 8x)}\left(\dfrac{1}{x + 1} + \dfrac{2}{2x + 1} - \dfrac{3}{3x - 4} + \dfrac{8}{1 - 8x} \right)$

27. $x^x(1 + \ln x)$ **29.** $2x^{2/x}\left(\dfrac{1 - \ln x}{x^2} \right)$ **31.** $(\sin x)^x[x \cot x + \ln (\sin x)]$ **33.** $(1 + x)\left[\dfrac{x^2}{1 + x} + 2x \ln (1 + x) \right]$

35. $y = x - 1$ **37.** $y = \sqrt{3}(x - \pi/6) - \ln 2$

Exercises 4.8, Page 222

1. $5e^{5x}$ **3.** $12x^2 e^{x^3}$ **5.** $\dfrac{3(10^{3x})}{\log_{10} e}$ **7.** $-\dfrac{6}{e^{6x}}$ **9.** $\dfrac{e^{\sqrt{x}}}{2\sqrt{x}}$ **11.** $(\cos x)e^{\sin x}$ **13.** $6e^{x^2 - 1}(2x^2 + 1)$

15. $e^{3x^2}(6x \cos x - \sin x)$ **17.** $-5e^{5x} \tan e^{5x}$ **19.** $e^x + e^{-x}$

21. $\dfrac{6xe^x(2 - x) - 2x^2}{(3e^x - x)^2}$ or $\dfrac{12xe^x - 6x^2 e^x - 2x^2}{(3e^x - x)^2}$ **23.** $\dfrac{6e^{3x}}{1 + e^{6x}}$ **25.** $\dfrac{6e^{-2x} \arccos^2 e^{-2x}}{\sqrt{1 - e^{-4x}}}$ **27.** xe^x **29.** $2x$

Exercises 4.9, Page 228

1. $\frac{1}{5}$ **3.** $-\frac{1}{3}$ **5.** $-\frac{1}{2}$ **7.** $\frac{1}{6}$ **9.** 1   **11.** $\frac{5}{2}$ **13.** 0   **15.** 0   **17.** Does not exist   **19.** 0

21. Two uses of l'Hospital's rule yields the original problem; 1

Exercises 4.10, Pages 231–232

1.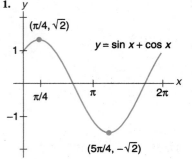

3.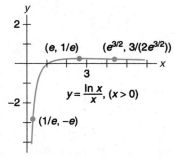

5.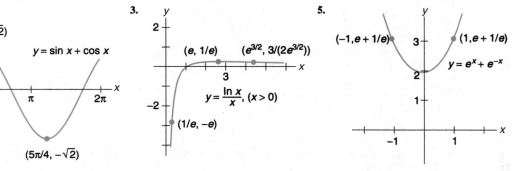

7.

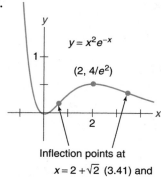

$y = x^2 e^{-x}$

$(2, 4/e^2)$

Inflection points at
$x = 2 + \sqrt{2}$ (3.41) and
$x = 2 - \sqrt{2}$ (0.586)

9.

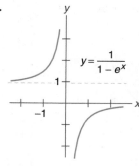

$y = \dfrac{1}{1 - e^x}$

11. $\left(\dfrac{1}{2}, \dfrac{1}{2e}\right)$ maximum   **13.** $(1, e^{-2})$ maximum; $(0, 0)$ minimum   **15.** $\left(e^{1/2}, \dfrac{1}{2e}\right)$ maximum   **17.** $y = -2x + \pi$

19. $y = 3x - 2$ **21.** $-4e^x \sin x$ **23.** $V_L = -300 \sin 2t$ **25.** 33.2 V   **27.** 2.12 W/s

29. $-0.1e^{-0.02t}(\sin 2t + 0.01 \cos 2t)$ **31.** $v = 6e^{3t} - 15e^{-3t}, a = 18e^{3t} + 45e^{-3t}$ **33.** $v = \dfrac{\pi}{2e^2}, a = -\dfrac{\pi}{2e^2}$

35. -0.0672

Chapter 4 Review, Pages 234–236

11. $\frac{1}{2} \sin 2\theta$ **12.** $\cos 6\theta$ **13.** $\cos^2 2\theta$ **14.** $\cos \dfrac{2\theta}{3}$ **15.** $\cos 5x$ **16.** $\sin x$

17.

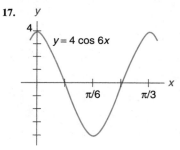

$y = 4 \cos 6x$

18.

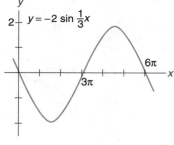

$y = -2 \sin \frac{1}{3}x$

19.

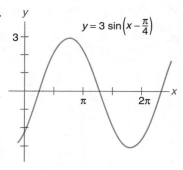

$y = 3 \sin\left(x - \dfrac{\pi}{4}\right)$

20.

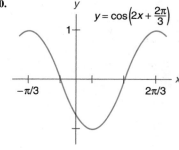

$y = \cos\left(2x + \dfrac{2\pi}{3}\right)$

21.

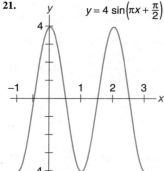

$y = 4 \sin\left(\pi x + \dfrac{\pi}{2}\right)$

22.

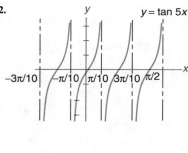

$y = \tan 5x$

23.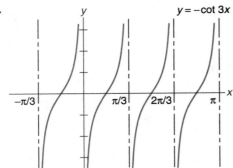
$y = -\cot 3x$

24.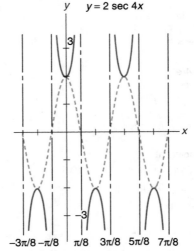
$y = 2 \sec 4x$

25. $2x \cos(x^2 + 3)$ **26.** $-8 \sin 8x$ **27.** $-15 \cos^2(5x - 1) \sin(5x - 1)$

28. $-2 \sin 2x \sin 3x + 3 \cos 2x \cos 3x$ **29.** $3 \sec^2(3x - 2)$ **30.** $4 \sec(4x + 3) \tan(4x + 3)$

31. $-12x \csc^2 6x^2$ **32.** $-2(16x + 1) \csc^2(8x^2 + x) \cot(8x^2 + x)$ **33.** $2 \sec^3 x - \sec x$ **34.** $2x + 2 \csc^2 x \cot x$

35. $\sec x \tan x \sec^2(\sec x)$ **36.** $\dfrac{-1}{1 + \sin x}$ **37.** $-3 \cos x(1 - \sin x)^2$ **38.** $8(1 + \sec 4x) \sec 4x \tan 4x$

39. $x = \frac{4}{3} \arcsin 2y$ **40.** $x = \dfrac{1}{2}\left(1 - \arctan \dfrac{y}{5}\right)$ **41.** $\dfrac{\pi}{4}$ **42.** $-\dfrac{\pi}{6}$

43. π **44.** $\dfrac{2\pi}{3}$ **45.** $\dfrac{\sqrt{3}}{2}$ **46.** $\sqrt{3}$ **47.** $\dfrac{\sqrt{x^2 + 1}}{x^2 + 1}$ **48.** $\dfrac{3x^2}{\sqrt{1 - x^6}}$ **49.** $\dfrac{3}{1 + 9x^2}$

50. $\dfrac{3}{|x|\sqrt{4x^2 - 1}}$ **51.** $\dfrac{2}{|x|\sqrt{16x^2 - 1}}$ **52.** $\dfrac{3 \arcsin 3\sqrt{x}}{\sqrt{x - 9x^2}}$ **53.** $\dfrac{x}{\sqrt{1 - x^2}} + \arcsin x$

54.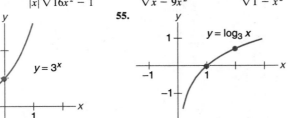
$y = 3^x$

55.
$y = \log_3 x$

56. 81 **57.** 2 **58.** 5 **59.** $\log_4 6 + 2 \log_4 x + \log_4 y$ **60.** $\log_3 5 + \log_3 x + \frac{1}{2}\log_3 y - 3 \log_3 z$

61. $2 \log x + 3 \log(x + 1) - \frac{1}{2}\log(x - 4)$ **62.** $3 \ln x + 3 \ln(x - 1) - \frac{1}{2}\ln(x + 1)$ **63.** $\log_2 \dfrac{xy^3}{z^2}$

64. $\log \dfrac{\sqrt{x + 1}}{(x - 2)^3}$ **65.** $\ln \dfrac{x^4}{(x + 1)^5(x + 2)}$ **66.** $\ln \dfrac{\sqrt{x}(x + 2)}{(x - 5)^2}$ **67.** 3 **68.** x^2 **69.** 2 **70.** x

71. $\dfrac{3x^2}{x^3 - 2}$ **72.** $\dfrac{4 \log_3 e}{4x + 1}$ **73.** $\dfrac{6}{x^3 + 3x}$ **74.** $-\dfrac{1}{x} \sin(\ln x)$

75. $\dfrac{\sqrt{x + 1}(3x - 4)}{x^2(x + 2)}\left[\dfrac{1}{2(x + 1)} + \dfrac{3}{3x - 4} - \dfrac{2}{x} - \dfrac{1}{x + 2}\right]$ **76.** $x^{1-x}\left[\dfrac{1 - x}{x} - \ln x\right]$ **77.** $2xe^{x^2 + 5}$

78. $\dfrac{3(8^{3x})}{\log_8 e}$ **79.** $-2e^{2x} \csc^2 e^{2x}$ **80.** $2x \, e^{\sin x^2} \cos x^2$ **81.** $\dfrac{-4e^{-4x}}{\sqrt{1 - e^{-8x}}}$ **82.** $x^2 e^{-4x}(3 - 4x)$

83.

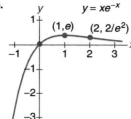

$y = xe^{-x}$

$(1, e)$ $(2, 2/e^2)$

84.

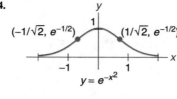

$(-1/\sqrt{2}, e^{-1/2})$ $(1/\sqrt{2}, e^{-1/2})$

$y = e^{-x^2}$

85. 0 **86.** 0 **87.** 2 **88.** −2 **89.** −1000 sin 5t **90.** $p = -360 \cos 3t \sin 3t$ or $-180 \sin 6t$ **91.** $y = 2x - 2$
92. $v = (\cos t)e^{\sin t}$ **93.** $-4e^{-1/2}$ or -2.43

CHAPTER 5

Exercises 5.1, Pages 243–244

1. $\frac{1}{8}x^8 + C$ **3.** $\frac{1}{3}x^9 + C$ **5.** $4x + C$ **7.** $\frac{54}{11}x^{11/6} + C$ **9.** $-\frac{3}{x^2} + C$ **11.** $\frac{5x^3}{3} - 6x^2 + 8x + C$

13. $x^3 - \frac{1}{2}x^2 - \frac{5}{2x^2} + C$ **15.** $\frac{4}{5}x^5 - 4x^3 + 9x + C$ **17.** $\frac{1}{9}(6x + 2)^{3/2} + C$ **19.** $(x^2 + 3)^4 + C$

21. $\frac{3}{40}(5x^2 - 1)^{4/3} + C$ **23.** $\frac{1}{10}(x^2 - 1)^5 + C$ **25.** $2\sqrt{x^2 + 1} + C$ **27.** $\frac{1}{4}(x^3 + 2x)^4 + C$ **29.** $\frac{-1}{3(x^3 - 4)} + C$

31. $\frac{2}{3}(5x^2 - x)^{3/2} + C$ **33.** $2\sqrt{x^2 + x} + C$ **35.** $\frac{1}{6}(2x + 3)^3 + C$ **37.** $\frac{1}{10}(2x - 1)^5 + C$

39. $\frac{x^7}{7} + \frac{3x^5}{5} + x^3 + x + C$ **41.** $\frac{1}{2}(x^2 + 1)^4 + C$ **43.** $\frac{2}{5}(5x^3 + 1)^5 + C$ **45.** $4\sqrt{x^3 + 1} + C$

47. $3(x^3 + 3x)^{2/3} + C$ **49.** $-1/x + 1/(2x^2) + C$

Exercises 5.2, Pages 247–248

1. $y = \frac{3}{2}x^2 + 1$ **3.** $y = x^3 + 3x + 6$ **5.** $y = \frac{1}{6}(x^2 - 3)^3 + 1$ **7.** $s = \frac{1}{2}t^3 + 16t + 50$
9. 64 ft (36 ft from the ground at $t = 2$); −80 ft/s **11.** 240 ft/s **13. (a)** 31.9 m **(b)** 5.10 s **(c)** 25 m/s

15. (a) $s = -16t^2 + 30t + 200$ **(b)** 4.59 s **17.** 213 rev **19.** 633 V **21.** $q = \frac{(t^2 + 1)^{3/2} - 1}{3}; \frac{2\sqrt{2} - 1}{3}$

Exercises 5.3, Pages 254–255

1. 2 **3.** $\frac{52}{3}$ **5.** 4 **7.** $\frac{3}{2}$ **9.** $\frac{14}{9}$ **11.** 4 **13.** $\frac{8}{5}$ **15.** $\frac{98}{3}$ **17.** $\frac{3}{4}$ **19.** $\frac{4}{5}$ **21.** $\frac{3}{7}$ **23.** 36
25. $\frac{4}{3}$ **27.** $\frac{1}{12}$ **29.** $\frac{4}{15}$

Exercises 5.4, Pages 258–259

1. $\frac{5}{2}$ **3.** $\frac{16}{3}$ **5.** −6 **7.** $\frac{14}{3}$ **9.** 40 **11.** $\frac{88}{3}$ **13.** 5546.2 **15.** $\frac{208}{3}$ **17.** $-\frac{15}{2}$ **19.** $-\frac{3}{10}$
21. $\frac{2\sqrt{2} - 1}{3}$ **23.** 12 **25.** $2\sqrt{10} - 2\sqrt{2}$

Chapter 5 Review, Page 260

1. $\frac{5}{3}x^3 - \frac{1}{2}x^2 + C$ **2.** $\frac{3}{8}x^8 + x^2 + 4x + C$ **3.** $\frac{4}{3}x^{9/2} + C$ **4.** $\frac{12}{5}x^{5/3} + C$ **5.** $\frac{-3}{4x^4} + C$ **6.** $\frac{-2}{\sqrt{x}} + C$

7. $\frac{1}{8}(3x^4 + 2x - 1)^4 + C$ **8.** $\frac{5}{16}(7x^2 + 8x + 2)^{8/5} + C$ **9.** $2\sqrt{x^2 + 5x} + C$ **10.** $3(5x^3 + 4x)^{1/3} + C$

11. $y = x^3 - 4$ **12.** $s = -16t^2 + 25t + 100$ **13.** 69.2 Ω **14.** 2.97 **15.** $\frac{14}{3}$ **16.** 6 **17.** $\frac{15}{64}$ **18.** 1

19. $\frac{144 - 4\sqrt{6}}{5}$ **20.** $\frac{16\sqrt{2} - 8}{3}$ **21.** $\frac{17}{12}$ **22.** $\frac{108}{5}$ **23.** $\frac{62}{3}$ **24.** $\frac{7}{18}$ **25.** $\frac{12\sqrt{6} - 4\sqrt{2}}{3}$

26. $\frac{4\sqrt{7} - 2}{3}$ **27.** −6 **28.** $\frac{6 - 3\sqrt{2}}{4}$

CHAPTER 6

1. $\frac{1}{3}$ **3.** $\frac{1}{2}$ **5.** $\frac{9}{2}$ **7.** $\frac{32}{3}$ **9.** $\frac{1}{6}$ **11.** $\frac{9}{2}$ **13.** $\frac{1}{2}$ **15.** $\frac{9}{2}$ **17.** 4   **19.** $\frac{44}{15}$ **21.** $\frac{343}{6}$ **23.** $\frac{22}{5}$ **25.** $\frac{37}{12}$

1. $\frac{26\pi}{3}$ **3.** $\frac{178\pi}{15}$ **5.** $\frac{8\pi}{3}$ **7.** 2π **9.** $\frac{\pi}{3}$ **11.** $\frac{\pi}{3}$ **13.** 2π **15.** 8π **17.** $\frac{4\pi}{15}$ **19.** $\frac{5\pi}{6}$
21. $\frac{8\pi}{3}$ **23.** $\frac{32\pi}{3}$ **25.** 60π **27.** $\frac{100\pi\sqrt{5}}{9}$

1. 2π **3.** 2π **5.** 4π **7.** $\frac{128\pi}{7}$ **9.** $\frac{8\pi}{3}$ **11.** $\frac{\pi}{3}$ **13.** $\frac{5\pi}{6}$ **15.** $\frac{4\pi}{21}$ **17.** $\frac{\pi}{2}$ **19.** $\frac{16\pi}{5}$

1. 15/7   **3.** -6.75 **5.** -6 **7.** $-\frac{11}{3}$ **9.** 15   **11.** 40   **13.** 11 mi north of Flatville   **15.** (20/7, 22/7)
17. $(-3.8, -7.2)$ **19.** $(2.1, -8.4)$ **21.** 100   **23.** 1.50 mi east and 2.56 mi south of A

1. 10 cm   **3.** $\frac{20}{3}$ cm   **5.** 8.77 cm   **7.** 4 cm from given end   **9.** $(4\frac{2}{3}, 4\frac{2}{3})$ **11.** (8, 2)   **13.** (0, 2.95)
15. $(\frac{27}{5}, \frac{9}{8})$ **17.** $(1, -0.4)$ **19.** (0, 1.6)   **21.** $(\frac{8}{15}, \frac{8}{21})$ **23.** $\left(0, \frac{4}{3\pi}\right)$ **25.** $(\frac{7}{8}, 0)$ **27.** $(\frac{3}{4}, 0)$ **29.** $(0, \frac{2}{3})$

1. 516; 3.79   **3.** 1965; 5.98   **5.** 963; 5.17   **7.** 759; 4.87   **9.** $\frac{64}{3}$; 0.894   **11.** $\frac{1}{7}$; 0.463   **13.** $\frac{64}{5}$; 0.894
15. 2; 1.41   **17.** 576π; 1.55   **19.** 2.29×10^4; 8.43   **21.** 1458π; 1.73   **23.** 4096π; 2.53

1. $\frac{63}{4}$ **3.** 25 in.-lb   **5.** 675 N cm or 6.75 J   **7.** 2.896×10^{-14} J   **9.** **(a)** 900 ft-lb   **(b)** 1875 ft-lb   **(c)** 2500 ft-lb
11. 225,800 ft-lb   **13.** 602,200 ft-lb   **15.** 58,810 ft-lb   **17.** 25,000 lb   **19.** 352,800 N   **21.** 710,500 N
23. 166.4 lb   **25.** 54,660 lb   **27.** 21,902 lb   **29.** $\frac{13}{3}$ **31.** $\frac{2}{5}$ **33.** 1.70 A

1. $\frac{16}{3}$ **2.** $\frac{2}{3}$ **3.** $\frac{1}{12}$ **4.** 8   **5.** $\frac{128}{15}$ **6.** 36   **7.** 8π **8.** 8π **9.** $\frac{\pi}{30}$ **10.** $\frac{8\pi}{3}$ **11.** $\frac{243\pi}{10}$
12. $\frac{99\pi}{2}$ **13.** $\frac{256\pi}{5}$ **14.** $\frac{63\pi}{2}$ **15.** 7.5   **16.** $(-1, -6.8)$ **17.** (9.6, 5.3)   **18.** $(2\frac{2}{3}, 6\frac{2}{3})$ **19.** $(\frac{3}{2}, \frac{27}{5})$
20. $(3, -3.6)$ **21.** $(0, \frac{3}{2})$ **22.** $(\frac{5}{6}, 0)$ **23.** (0, 2)   **24.** 462; 4.39   **25.** 192; 2.83   **26.** 576; 4.90
27. $\frac{8}{15}$; 0.447   **28.** $\frac{2\pi}{13}$; 0.519   **29.** $\frac{8\pi}{7}$; 0.845   **30.** 126π; 2.65   **31.** 200 in.-lb   **32.** 2.62×10^{-16} J
33. 130,000 ft-lb   **34.** 49,920 lb   **35.** 816,700 N   **36.** 9.5 V   **37.** 67.52 A   **38.** 20 W

Subject Index

Common Trigonometric Identities

1. $\sin \theta = \dfrac{1}{\csc \theta}$

2. $\cos \theta = \dfrac{1}{\sec \theta}$

3. $\tan \theta = \dfrac{1}{\cot \theta}$

4. $\cot \theta = \dfrac{1}{\tan \theta}$

5. $\sec \theta = \dfrac{1}{\cos \theta}$

6. $\csc \theta = \dfrac{1}{\sin \theta}$

7. $\tan \theta = \dfrac{\sin \theta}{\cos \theta}$

8. $\cot \theta = \dfrac{\cos \theta}{\sin \theta}$

9. $\sin^2 \theta + \cos^2 \theta = 1$

10. $1 + \tan^2 \theta = \sec^2 \theta$

11. $\cot^2 \theta + 1 = \csc^2 \theta$

12. $\sin (-\theta) = -\sin \theta$

13. $\cos (-\theta) = \cos \theta$

14. $\tan (-\theta) = -\tan \theta$

15. $\cot (-\theta) = -\cot \theta$

16. $\sec (-\theta) = \sec \theta$

17. $\csc (-\theta) = -\csc \theta$

18. $\sin (\theta + \phi) = \sin \theta \cos \phi + \cos \theta \sin \phi$

19. $\sin (\theta - \phi) = \sin \theta \cos \phi - \cos \theta \sin \phi$

20. $\cos (\theta + \phi) = \cos \theta \cos \phi - \sin \theta \sin \phi$

21. $\cos (\theta - \phi) = \cos \theta \cos \phi + \sin \theta \sin \phi$

22. $\tan (\theta + \phi) = \dfrac{\tan \theta + \tan \phi}{1 - \tan \theta \tan \phi}$

23. $\tan (\theta - \phi) = \dfrac{\tan \theta - \tan \phi}{1 + \tan \theta \tan \phi}$

24. $\sin 2\theta = 2 \sin \theta \cos \theta$

25. (a) $\cos 2\theta = \cos^2 \theta - \sin^2 \theta$

    (b) $\cos 2\theta = 2 \cos^2 \theta - 1$

    (c) $\cos 2\theta = 1 - 2 \sin^2 \theta$

26. $\tan 2\theta = \dfrac{2 \tan \theta}{1 - \tan^2 \theta}$

27. $\sin \dfrac{\theta}{2} = \pm \sqrt{\dfrac{1 - \cos \theta}{2}}$

28. $\cos \dfrac{\theta}{2} = \pm \sqrt{\dfrac{1 + \cos \theta}{2}}$

29. $\tan \dfrac{\theta}{2} = \dfrac{1 - \cos \theta}{\sin \theta}$

30. $\sin^2 \theta = \dfrac{1}{2}(1 - \cos 2\theta)$

31. $\cos^2 \theta = \dfrac{1}{2}(1 + \cos 2\theta)$

32. $\sin \theta + \sin \phi = 2 \sin \left(\dfrac{\theta + \phi}{2}\right) \cos \left(\dfrac{\theta - \phi}{2}\right)$

33. $\sin \theta - \sin \phi = 2 \cos \left(\dfrac{\theta + \phi}{2}\right) \sin \left(\dfrac{\theta - \phi}{2}\right)$

34. $\cos \theta + \cos \phi = 2 \cos \left(\dfrac{\theta + \phi}{2}\right) \cos \left(\dfrac{\theta - \phi}{2}\right)$

35. $\cos \theta - \cos \phi = -2 \sin \left(\dfrac{\theta + \phi}{2}\right) \sin \left(\dfrac{\theta - \phi}{2}\right)$

36. $\sin (\theta + \phi) + \sin (\theta - \phi) = 2 \sin \theta \cos \phi$

37. $\sin (\theta + \phi) - \sin (\theta - \phi) = 2 \cos \theta \sin \phi$

38. $\cos (\theta + \phi) + \cos (\theta - \phi) = 2 \cos \theta \cos \phi$

39. $\cos (\theta + \phi) - \cos (\theta - \phi) = -2 \sin \theta \sin \phi$